MW00331227

The Official BLUE BOOK®

HANDBOOK OF

UNITED STATES COINS

R.S. YEOMAN

EDITOR
KENNETH BRESSETT

63rd Edition
2006

Illustrated Catalog and Wholesale
Valuation List—1616 to Date

Containing mint records and wholesale prices for U.S. coins from 1616 to the present time, including colonials, regular issues, commemoratives, territorials, gold, Proof sets, and mint Sets. Information on collecting coins—how coins are produced—mints and mintmarks—grading of coins—location of mintmarks—preserving coins—starting a collection—history of mints—and interesting descriptions of all U.S. copper, nickel, silver, and gold coins. Illustrated.

Printed in U.S.A.

THE OFFICIAL BLUE BOOK OF UNITED STATES COINS™

www.whitmanbooks.com

The WCG™ pricing grid used throughout this publication is patent pending.

© 2005 Whitman Publishing, LLC
3101 Clairmont Road • Suite C • Atlanta GA 30329

For a complete listing of numismatic reference
books, supplies, and storage products, visit us at
www.whitmanbooks.com

About the Cover

The 1793 Flowing Hair, Chain Reverse large cent is a rarity from the early days of the United States Mint. An example in Mint State was auctioned for $431,250 in 2005. The 1933 Saint-Gaudens double eagle holds the all-time record for highest price paid for a coin: $7.59 million in 2002. Five 1913 Liberty Head nickels are known to exist. One was auctioned in 2001 for $1.84 million; others have traded hands recently for $3–4 million and more.

TABLE OF CONTENTS

CONTRIBUTORS TO THE SIXTY-THIRD EDITION

Special Consultants: Philip Bressett, Tom Hallenbeck

Whitman Publishing extends its thanks to these members of the coin buying community who have contributed pricing for this year's *Handbook of United States Coins*. Their data were compiled and then reviewed by editor Kenneth Bressett and the special consultants listed above. This process ensures input from a broad range of dealers and auctioneers from across the country—experts who buy, sell, and trade coins every day and know the market inside and out.

Michael Aron	Stuart Levine
Fonda Chase	Denis W. Loring
J.H. Cline	Jack McNamara
Gary Cohen	Dwight N. Manley
Silvano DiGenova	Michael C. Moline
Jeff Garrett	Mike Orlando
Dennis Gillio	William S. Panitch
Ira M. Goldberg	William P. Paul
Lawrence S. Goldberg	Joel Rettew, Jr.
Kenneth M. Goldman	Joel Rettew, Sr.
J.R. Grellman, Jr.	Maurice Rosen
Gene L. Henry	William J. Spencer
Karl D. Hirtzinger	David M. Sundman
Jesse Iskowitz	Jerry Treglia
Bradley S. Karoleff	Frank E. Van Valen
Mike Kliman	Mark S. Yaffe
Julian M. Leidman	

Special credit is due to the following for service in past editions of the *Handbook*:

Gary Adkins, David Akers, John Albanese, Buddy Alleva, Dr. Richard S. Appel, Richard M. August, Dr. Richard Bagg, Mitchell A. Battino, Lee J. Bellisario, Jack Beymer, Mark R. Borckardt, Q. David Bowers, Elizabeth W. Coggan, Alan R. Cohen, Marc Crane, John Dannreuther, Tom DeLorey, Kenneth Duncan, Sheridan Downey, Col. Steven Ellsworth, John Feigenbaum, Ronald Gillio, Ron Guth, James Halperin, John Hamrick, Steve Ivy, James J. Jelinski, A.M. Kagin, Donald H. Kagin, John J. Kraljevich, Jr., Richard A. Lecce, Robert B. Lecce, David Leventhal, Kevin Lipton, Andy Lustig, Chris McCawley, Robert T. McIntire, Harry Miller, Lee S. Minshull, Robert Mish, Scott P. Mitchell, Paul Montgomery, Charles Moore, Richard Nachbar, Chris Napolitano, Paul Nugget, John M. Pack, Robert M. Paul, Robert J. Rhue, Tom Rinaldo, Greg Rohan, Leonard R. Saunders, Mary Sauvain, Cherie Schoeps, Richard J. Schwary, James A. Simek, Richard E. Snow, Lawrence Stack, Anthony J. Swiatek, Anthony Terranova, Fred Weinberg, and Douglas Winter.

Special photo credits are due to the following:

American Numismatic Rarities, Douglas F. Bird, Steve Contursi, Bill Fivaz, Ira & Larry Goldberg Coins & Collectibles, Tom Mulvaney, the Museum of the American Numismatic Association, Noyes–Lusk DVD Photo Project, Numismatic Guaranty Corporation of America (NGC), Brent Pogue, Sarasota Rare Coin Gallery, the Smithsonian Institution, heritagecoins.com, Rick Snow, Spectrum, Stack's Rare Coins of New York, Superior Galleries, Anthony Swiatek, and the United States Mint.

Since 1941, annually revised editions of this *Handbook* have aided thousands of people who have coins to sell or are actively engaged in collecting United States coins. The popular coin-folder method of collecting by date has created ever-changing premium values, based on the supply and demand of each date and mint. Through its panel of contributors, the *Handbook* has, over the years, reported these changing values. It also serves as a source of general numismatic information to all levels of interest in the hobby.

The values shown are representative prices paid by dealers for various United States coins. These are averages of prices assembled from many widely separated sources. On some issues slight differences in price among dealers may result from proximity to the various mints or heavily populated centers. Other factors, such as local supply and demand or dealers' stock conditions, may also cause deviations from the prices listed. While many coins bring no premium in circulated grades, they usually bring premium prices in Mint State and Proof. Extremely rare and valuable coins are usually sold at public auction, and prices vary according to current demand.

THIS BOOK IS NOT A RETAIL PRICE LIST

Premium prices are the average amount dealers will pay for coins (according to condition) if required for their stock.

IF YOU HAVE COINS TO SELL

Whitman Publishing, LLC is not in the rare coin business; however, chances are that the dealer from whom you purchased this book is engaged in the buying and selling of rare coins—contact him first. In the event that you purchased this book from a source other than a numismatic establishment, consult your local telephone directory for the names of coin dealers (they will be found sometimes under the heading of "Stamp and Coin Dealers"). If you live in a city or town that does not have any coin dealers, obtain a copy of one of the trade publications (such as *Coin World* or *Numismatic News*) or check the Internet in order to obtain the names and addresses of many of the country's leading dealers. Information or sample copies may be obtained by writing to the individual publisher.

Current average *retail* valuations of all U.S. coins are listed in Whitman's *A Guide Book of United States Coins*™ by R.S. Yeoman, edited by Kenneth Bressett, Whitman Publishing, LLC, Atlanta, GA ($16.95 hardcover; $14.95 coilbound).

HOW TO USE THIS BOOK

A dash in a price column indicates that coins in that grade exist even though there are no current sales or auction records from them (The dash does *not* necessarily mean that such coins are excessively rare.) Italicized prices indicate unsettled or speculative values. A number of listings of rare coins do not have prices or dashes in certain grades. This indicates that they are not available or not believed to exist in those grades.

Mintages of Proof coins are listed in parentheses.

Italicized mintages are estimates.

Numismatics or coin collecting is one of the world's oldest hobbies, dating back several centuries. Coin collecting in America did not develop to any extent until about 1840, as our pioneer forefathers were too busy carving a country out of wilderness to afford the luxury of a hobby. The discontinuance of the large-sized cent in 1857 caused many people to attempt to accumulate a complete set of the pieces while they were still in circulation. One of the first groups of collectors to band together for the study of numismatics was the Numismatic and Antiquarian Society of Philadelphia, organized on January 1, 1858. Lack of an economical method to house a collection held the number of devotees of coin collecting to a few thousand until Whitman Publishing and other manufacturers placed low-priced coin boards and folders on the market in the 1930s. Since that time, the number of Americans collecting coins has increased many-fold.

THE PRODUCTION OF COINS

To collect coins intelligently it is necessary to have some knowledge of the manner in which they are produced. Coins are made in factories called "mints." The Mint of the United States was established at Philadelphia by a resolution of Congress dated April 2, 1792. The Act also provided for the coinage of gold eagles ($10), half eagles, and quarter eagles; silver dollars, half dollars, quarter dollars, dimes (originally spelled "disme"), and half dismes or half dimes; and copper cents and half cents. The first coins struck were one-cent and half-cent pieces, in March of 1793 on a hand-operated press. Most numismatic authorities consider the half disme of 1792 the first United States coinage, quoting the words of George Washington as their authority. Washington, in his annual address, November 6, 1792, said, "There has been a small beginning in the coining of the half dimes, the want of small coins in circulation calling the first attention to them." Though the half disme is considered America's first coinage, it was not the first coinage produced at the Mint, these coins were produced off premises in July of 1792 before the Mint was completed. In the new Philadelphia Mint are a number of implements from the original mint, and some coins discovered when the old building was wrecked. These coins included half dismes, and the placard identifying them states that Washington furnished the silver and gave the coined pieces to his friends as souvenirs.

Prior to the adoption of the Constitution, the Continental Congress arranged for the issuance of copper coins under private contract. These are known as the *Fugio cents* from their design, which shows a sundial and the Latin word "fugio"—"I Fly" or, in connection with the sundial, "Time Flies." The ever-appropriate motto "Mind Your Business" is also on the coin.

In the manufacture of a given coin, the first step is the cutting of the die. Prior to the latter part of the 19th century, dies for United States coins were "cut by hand." Briefly, this method is as follows: the design having been determined, a drawing the exact size of the coin is made. A tracing is made from this drawing. A piece of steel is smoothed and coated with transfer wax, and the tracing impressed into the wax. The engraver then tools out the steel where the relief or raised effect is required. If the design is such that it can all be produced by cutting away steel, the die is hardened and ready for use. Some dies are not brought to a finished state, as some part of the design can perhaps be done better in relief. In that case, when all that can be accomplished to advantage in the die is completed, it is hardened, a soft-steel impression is taken from it, and the unfinished parts are then completed. This piece of steel is in turn hardened and, by a press, driven into another piece of soft steel, thus making a die which, when hardened, is ready for the making of coins.

This hand method of cutting dies accounts for the many die varieties of early United States coins. Where the amount of coinage of a given year was large enough to wear out many dies, each new die placed in the coining press created another die variety of that year. The dies being cut by hand, no two were exactly alike in every detail, even though some of the major elements such as the head or wreath, were sunk into the die by individual master punches. Of the cents dated 1794, more than sixty different die varieties have been discovered.

Thousands of dies are now used by the mints of the United States each year, but they are all made from one master die, which is produced in the following manner:

COLLECTING COINS

After the design is settled upon, the plaster of paris or wax model is prepared several times the actual size of the coin. When this model is finished an electrotype (an exact duplicate in metal) is made and prepared for the reducing lathe. The reducing lathe is a machine that works on the principle of the pantograph, only in this case the one point traces or follows the form of the model while another much smaller point in the form of a drill cuts away the steel and produces a reduced size die of the model. The die is finished and details are sharpened or worked over by an engraver with chisel and graver. The master die is used to make duplicates in soft steel which are then hardened and ready for the coining press. To harden dies, they are placed in cast-iron boxes packed with carbon to exclude the air, and when heated to a bright red are cooled suddenly with water.

In the coinage operations the first step is to prepare the metal. Among the alloys that have been used are the following: silver coins, 90% silver and 10% copper; five-cent pieces, 75% copper and 25% nickel; one-cent pieces, 95% copper and 5% zinc. (The 1943 cent consists of steel coated with zinc; and the five-cent piece of 1942–1945 contains 35% silver, 56% copper, and 9% manganese.) Under the Coinage Act of 1965, the composition of dimes, quarters, and half dollars was changed to eliminate or reduce the silver content of these coins. The copper-nickel "clad" dimes, quarters, half dollars, and dollars are composed of an outer layer of copper-nickel (75% copper and 25% nickel) bonded to an inner core of pure copper. The silver clad half dollar and dollar have an outer layer of 80% silver bonded to an inner core of 21% silver, with a total content of 40% silver. Current cents are made from a core of 99.2% zinc, 0.8% copper, with a plating of pure copper.

Alloys are melted in crucibles and poured into molds to form ingots. The ingots are in the form of thin bars and vary in size according to the denomination of the coin. The width is sufficient to allow three or more coins to be cut from the strips.

The ingots are next put through rolling mills to reduce the thickness to required limits. The strips are then fed into cutting presses which cut circular blanks *(planchets)* of the approximate size of the finished coin. The blanks are run through annealing furnaces to soften them; next they move through tumbling barrels, rotating cylinders containing cleaning solutions which clean and burnish the metal; and finally into centrifugal drying machines.

The blanks are next fed into a milling machine which produces the raised or upset rim. The blank is now ready for the coining press.

The blank is held firmly by a collar, as it is struck under heavy pressure varying from 40 tons for the one-cent pieces and dimes to 170 tons for silver dollars. Upper and lower dies impress the design on both sides of the coin. The pressure is sufficient to produce a raised surface level with that of the milled rim. The collar holding the blank for silver or clad coins is grooved. The pressure forces the metal into the grooves of the collar, producing the "reeding" on the finished coin.

HOW A PROOF COIN IS MADE

Selected dies are inspected for perfection and are highly polished and cleaned. They are again wiped clean or polished after every 15 to 25 impressions and are replaced frequently to avoid imperfections from wear. Coinage blanks are polished and cleaned to assure high quality in striking. They are then hand fed into the coinage press one at a time, each blank receiving two blows from the dies to bring up sharp, high-relief details. The coinage operation is done at slow speed. Finished proofs are individually inspected and are handled by gloves or tongs. They also receive a final inspection by packers before being sonically sealed in special plastic cases.

Certain coins, including Lincoln cents, Buffalo nickels, quarter eagles, half eagles, eagles, and double eagles, between the years 1908 and 1916, were made with Matte Proof (nickel and silver) and Sand Blast and Satin Proof (gold) finishes. These later Proofs have a dull frosted surface which was either applied to the dies, or produced by special treatment after striking.

MINTS AND MINTMARKS

In addition to the Philadelphia Mint, the U.S. government has from time to time established branch mints in various parts of the country. At present a branch mint operates in Denver and another in San Francisco. Starting in 1968, Proof sets and some of the regular coins were produced at the San Francisco Mint and Assay Office. The Denver Mint has operated since 1906. A mint was operated at New Orleans from 1838 to 1861 and again from 1879 to 1909. Mints were also in service at Carson City, Nevada, from 1870 to 1893; at Charlotte, North Carolina, from 1838 to 1861; at Dahlonega, Georgia, from 1838 to 1861; and at San Francisco since 1854. The U.S. government also operated a mint in the Philippines in the early 1900s.

Coins struck at Philadelphia before 1979 (except 1942 to 1945 five-cent pieces) do not bear a mintmark. Historically the mintmark was used only for branch mints. Recent exceptions include the Lincoln cent and the Kennedy half dollar, which both use the P for Philadelphia. All coins struck after 1967 have the mintmark on the obverse. The letters signifying the various mints are as follows:

C—Charlotte, North Carolina (gold coins only; 1838–1861)
CC—Carson City, Nevada (1870–1893)
D—Dahlonega, Georgia (gold coins only; 1838–1861)
D—Denver, Colorado (1906 to date)
O—New Orleans, Louisiana (1838–1861; 1879–1909)
P—Philadelphia, Pennsylvania (1793 to date; P not used in early years)
S—San Francisco, California (1854 to date)
W—West Point, New York (1984 to date)

The mintmark is of utmost importance to collectors because, historically, coinage of the branch mints has often been much smaller than quantities struck at Philadelphia. Many early coins of the branch mints are very scarce.

DISTINGUISHING MARKS

The illustrations and explanations in this section will help the collector identify certain well-known varieties.

Half Cents of 1795–1796
Showing Location of Pole to Cap

The end of the pole lies parallel with the lines of the bust, which is pointed. On some coins, the pole is missing due either to engraver error (while cutting the die) or to an error in "relapping" (when the die is ground to remove wear, clash marks, etc.).

Pole to Cap   **No Pole to Cap**

Stemless Wreath Variety of Half Cents and Large Cents

For this variety, the obverse is actually the reverse side. Illustrations below show both Stemless and Stems to Wreath types for each comparison—stemless wreath found on the 1804, 1805, and 1806 half cents; and on the 1797, 1802, and 1803 large cents.

Stemless Wreath   **Stems to Wreath**

1804 Half Cent Spiked Chin Variety;
Plain 4 versus Crosslet 4 Variety

Details showing differences in 1804 Plain 4 and Crosslet 4. Note serif on horizontal bar of numeral 4 as shown at right.

Plain 4   **Crosslet 4**

The 1856 Flying Eagle Cent

Collectors are advised to inspect any 1856 Flying Eagle cent carefully. A few observations will aid in establishing genuineness of this cent, as follows:

The Date

The 6 in the date should be as illustrated. If the lower half is thick, it is probably an altered 1858. A magnifying glass will often reveal poor workmanship.

The figure 5 slants slightly to the right on a genuine 1856. The vertical bar points to the center of the ball just beneath. On the 1858, this bar points outside the ball. (Compare the two illustrations.)

The Legend

The center of the O in OF is crude and almost squared on the genuine 1856, but on the large letter 1858 it is rounded.

The letters A and M in AMERICA are joined in both the 1856 and 1858 Large Letters cents, but they join at a slight angle on the 1856, while the bottom of the letters form a smooth curve on the 1858 Large Letters cent.

1858 Flying Eagle Cent

The letters A and M in the word AMERICA are joined on the Large Letters variety. They are separated on the Small Letters variety.

Large Letters   **Small Letters**

1864 Bronze Liberty Head Cent With "L" on Ribbon

A small "L," the initial of the designer Longacre, was added to the Indian design late in 1864 and was continued through 1909. For coins in less than Fine condition, this small letter will often be worn away. The point of the bust is rounded on the 1864 variety without "L"; the bust is pointed on the variety with "L." The initial must be visible, however, for the 1864 variety to bring the higher premium. If the coin is turned slightly so that the portrait faces the observer, the highlighted details will usually appear to better advantage.

During 1909, initials appeared on the reverse. Starting in 1918, they appear below the shoulder.

1918-S, 8 Over 7
*A variety of the kind
on this quarter dollar
is rarely found in coinage
of the 20th century.*

**1938-D, D Over S
Buffalo Nickel**

**1942, 2 Over 1
Mercury Dime**

**1955, Doubled-
Die Obverse
Lincoln Cent**

**Large Date Cent
(1960)**

**Small Date Cent
(1960)**

**Large Date Cent
(1982)**

**Small Date Cent
(1982)**

CONDITIONS OF COINS
Essential Elements of the ANA Grading System

PROOF—A specially made coin distinguished by sharpness of detail and usually with a brilliant, mirrorlike surface. *Proof* refers to the method of manufacture and is not a condition, but normally the term implies perfect condition unless otherwise noted.

> **GEM PROOF (PF-65)**—Brilliant surfaces with no noticeable blemishes or flaws. A few scattered, barely noticeable marks or hairlines.

> **CHOICE PROOF (PF-63)**—Reflective surfaces with only a few blemishes in secondary focal places. No major flaws.

> **PROOF (PF-60)**—Surface may have several contact marks, hairlines, or light rubs. Luster may be dull and eye appeal lacking.

MINT STATE—The terms *Mint State (MS)* and *Uncirculated (Unc.)* are used interchangeably to describe coins showing no trace of wear. Such coins may vary to some degree because of blemishes, toning, or slight imperfections, as described in the following subdivisions:

> **PERFECT UNCIRCULATED (MS-70)**—Perfect new condition, showing no trace of wear. The finest quality possible, with no evidence of scratches, handling, or contact with other coins. Very few regular-issue coins are ever found in this condition.

> **GEM UNCIRCULATED (MS-65)**—An above average Uncirculated coin that may be brilliant or lightly toned and that has very few contact marks on the surface or rim. MS-67 through MS-62 indicate slightly higher or lower grades of preservation.

> **CHOICE UNCIRCULATED (MS-63)**—Has some distracting contact marks or blemishes in prime focal areas. Luster may be impaired.

> **UNCIRCULATED (MS-60)**—Has no trace of wear but may show a number of contact marks, and surface may be spotted or lack some luster.

CHOICE ABOUT UNCIRCULATED (AU-55)—Evidence of friction on high points of design. Most of the mint luster remains.

ABOUT UNCIRCULATED (AU-50)—Traces of light wear on many of the high points. At least half of the mint luster is still present.

CHOICE EXTREMELY FINE (EF-45)—Light overall wear on highest points. All design details are very sharp. Some of the mint luster is evident.

EXTREMELY FINE (EF-40)—Light wear on design throughout, but all features sharp and well defined. Traces of luster may show.

CHOICE VERY FINE (VF-30)—Light, even wear on the surface and highest parts of the design. All lettering and major features are sharp.

VERY FINE (VF-20)—Moderate wear on high points of design. All major details are clear.

FINE (F-12)—Moderate to considerable even wear. Entire design is bold with overall pleasing appearance.

VERY GOOD (VG-8)—Well worn with main features clear and bold, although rather flat.
GOOD (G-4)—Heavily worn, with design visible but faint in areas. Many details are flat.
ABOUT GOOD (AG-3)—Very heavily worn with portions of lettering, date, and legend worn smooth. The date may be barely readable.

Important: Damaged coins, such as those that are bent, corroded, scratched, holed, nicked, stained, or mutilated, are worth less than those without defects. Flawless uncirculated coins are generally worth more than values quoted in this book. Slightly worn coins ("sliders") that have been cleaned and conditioned ("whizzed") to simulate uncirculated luster are worth considerably less than perfect pieces.

Unlike damage inflicted after striking, manufacturing defects do not always lessen values. Examples include colonial coins with planchet flaws and weakly struck designs; early silver and gold with weight-adjustment "file marks" (parallel cuts made prior to striking); and coins with "lint marks" (surface marks due to the presence of dust or other foreign matter during striking).

Brief guides to grading are placed before each major coin type in this book.

PRESERVING AND CLEANING COINS

Most numismatists will tell you to "never clean a coin" and it is good advice! Cleaning coins will almost always reduce their value. Collectors prefer coins in their original condition.

Some effort should be made to protect Uncirculated and Proof coins so they won't need cleaning. Tarnish on a coin is purely a chemical process caused by oxygen in the air acting on the metal, or by chemicals with which the coin comes in contact. One of the most common chemicals causing tarnish is sulphur; most paper, with the exception of specially manufactured "sulphur-free" kinds, contains sulphur due to the sulphuric acid that is used in paper manufacture; therefore do not wrap coins in ordinary paper. Also keep Uncirculated and Proof coins away from rubber bands (a rubber band placed on a silver coin for a few days will produce a black stripe on the coin where the band touched). The utmost in protection is obtained by storing the coin in an airtight box, away from moisture and humidity, and by using holders made of inert materials.

Many coins become marred by careless handling. Always hold the coin by the edge. The accompanying illustration shows the right and wrong way to handle numismatic specimens. It is a breach of numismatic etiquette to handle another collector's coin except by the edge, even if it is not an Uncirculated or Proof piece.

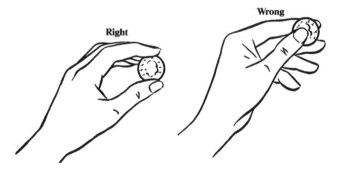

Right

Wrong

STARTING A COLLECTION

One may start a collection of United States coins with very little expense by systematically assembling the various dates and mintmarks of all the types and denominations that are now in general circulation. Whitman's many different coin folders make this possible.

With the exception of the price paid for the coin folder, collecting coins received in everyday business transactions entails no expense whatsoever; a Jefferson nickel taken out of circulation, for example, can always be spent for five cents if the occasion arises. Filling an album or two out of circulation is probably the best method of determining whether coin collecting appeals to you. Not everyone can be a successful coin collector. It requires patience, intelligence of a high order, and a certain desire to know the meaning behind a lot of things that at first glance appear meaningless. You may not be cut out to be a collector but you'll never know until you look further into the subject, and if by the time an album or two of coins are collected you have no burning desire to acquire many more different coins, you will probably never be a collector. However, chances are that you will be, because if you have read this far in this book, it shows that you are interested in the subject.

Perfection is the goal of every endeavor and coin collecting is no exception. After an album has been filled with circulated specimens, the next step will be to replace them with coins in Uncirculated condition, or perhaps to start collecting an obsolete series; in either case, it will be necessary to purchase some coins from dealers or other collectors. The most logical way to keep abreast with the market, or obtain the addresses of the country's leading dealers, is to subscribe to one or more of the trade publications. These magazines carry advertisements of various dealers listing coins for sale. Moreover, through this source the beginner may obtain price lists and catalogs from the dealers.

There are several good reference books available at reasonable prices which will be helpful to the collector who wishes to know more about U.S. coins and paper money. R.S. Yeoman's *A Guide Book Of United States Coins*™ (Red Book) lists retail values of all regular U. S. coins and also lists all coins of the U.S. colonial period and private and territorial gold coins.

Most coin, book, and hobby dealers can supply the following titles:

The Official Red Book®: A Guide Book of United States Coins™—R.S. Yeoman, edited by Kenneth Bressett

A Guide Book of Morgan Silver Dollars: A Complete History and Price Guide—Q. David Bowers

A Guide Book of Double Eagle Gold Coins—Q. David Bowers

Coin Collecting: A Beginner's Guide to the World of Coins—Kenneth Bressett

United States Pattern Coins: Experimental and Trial Pieces—J. Hewitt Judd, edited by Q. David Bowers

The Official ANA Grading Standards for United States Coins—Kenneth Bressett, et al.

A Guide Book of United States Type Coins—Q. David Bowers

Join a Coin Club

A beginner should join a "coin club" if he or she is fortunate enough to live in a city which has one. The association with more experienced collectors will be of great benefit. Practically all the larger cities have one or more clubs and they are being rapidly organized in the smaller towns. Trade publications carry information about coin clubs and special events such as coin shows and conventions.

The American Numismatic Association is a national organization that collectors can join. The ANA web site (www.money.org) has a list of member coin clubs throughout the United States. Contact the ANA by mail at 818 North Cascade Avenue, Colorado Springs, CO 80903, or by phone at 719-632-2646.

Early American coins are rare in conditions better than those listed and are consequently valued much higher.

BRITISH NEW WORLD ISSUES
Sommer Islands (Bermuda)

This coinage, issued around 1616, was the first struck for England's colonies in the New World. The coins were known as "Hogge Money" or "Hoggies."

The pieces were made of copper lightly silvered, in four denominations: shilling, sixpence, threepence, and twopence, indicated by Roman numerals. The hog is the main device and appears on the obverse side of each. SOMMER ISLANDS is inscribed within beaded circles. The reverse shows a full-rigged galleon with the flag of St. George on each of four masts.

Shilling

	G	VG	F	VF	EF
Twopence	$2,200.	$3,600.	$5,000.	$8,750.	$15,000.
Threepence *(very rare)*					
Sixpence	1,900.	3,000.	4,500.	8,500.	15,000.
Shilling	2,750.	3,800.	5,250.	10,000.	22,500.

Massachusetts
"New England" Coinage (1652)

In 1652 the General Court of Massachusetts ordered the first metallic currency to be struck in the English Americas, the New England silver threepence, sixpence, and shilling. These coins were made from silver bullion procured principally from the West Indies. Joseph Jenks made the punches for the first coins at his Iron Works in Saugus, Massachusetts, close to Boston where the mint was located. John Hull was appointed mintmaster; his assistant was Robert Sanderson.

NE Shilling (1652)

	G	VG	F	VF
NE Threepence *(unique)*	—	—	—	—
NE Sixpence *(8 known)*	—	—	—	$70,000.
NE Shilling	$7,000.	$17,000.	$35,000.	60,000.

Willow Tree Coinage (1653–1660)

The simplicity of the design on the N.E. coins invited counterfeiting and clipping of the edges. Therefore, they were soon replaced by the Willow Tree, Oak Tree, and Pine Tree series. The Willow Tree coins were struck from 1653 to 1660, the Oak Trees 1660 to 1667, and the Pine Trees 1667 to 1682. All of them (with the exception of the Oak Tree twopence) bore the date 1652. Many varieties of all of these coins exist. Values shown are for the most common types.

Sixpence

	Fair	G	VG	F	VF
1652 Willow Tree Threepence *(3 known)*.......	—	—	—	—	—
1652 Willow Tree Sixpence *(14 known)*........	—	$7,000.	$12,000.	$24,000.	$60,000.
1652 Willow Tree Shilling..................	$3,000.	6,500.	12,000.	25,000.	60,000.

Oak Tree Coinage (1660–1667)

Twopence

Threepence

	G	VG	F	VF	EF	AU
1662 Oak Tree Twopence..................	$200.	$325.	$500.	$1,200.	$2,300.	$5,000.
1652 Oak Tree Threepence.................	225.	350.	600.	1,250.	2,750.	5,750.
1652 Oak Tree Sixpence...................	200.	350.	650.	1,250.	3,200.	6,800.
1652 Oak Tree Shilling....................	250.	415.	675.	1,675.	3,800.	7,000.

Pine Tree Coinage (1667–1682)

The first Pine Tree coins were minted on the same size planchets as the Oak Tree pieces. Subsequent issues of the shilling were narrower and thicker, to conform to the size of English coins.

Shilling, Large Planchet (1667–1674)   **Shilling, Small Planchet (1675–1682)**

COLONIAL ISSUES

	G	VG	F	VF	EF	AU
1652 Pine Tree Threepence	$240.	$425.	$650.	$1,550.	$2,050.	$3,700.
1652 Pine Tree Sixpence	275.	450.	700.	1,900.	2,200.	4,000.
1652 Pine Tree Shilling, Large Planchet	350.	625.	1,200.	2,350.	3,200.	4,650.
1652 Pine Tree Shilling, Small Planchet	300.	525.	900.	2,100.	2,350.	4,250.

Maryland
Lord Baltimore Coinage

In 1659, Cecil Calvert, the Lord Proprietor of Maryland, had coinage struck in England for use in Maryland. There were four denominations: shillings, sixpence, fourpence (groat) in silver, and copper penny (denarium). The silver coins have the bust of Lord Baltimore on the obverse, and the Baltimore family arms with the denomination in Roman numerals on the reverse.

Lord Baltimore Shilling

Fourpence (groat)

	G	VG	F	VF	EF	AU
Penny (copper) *(6 known)*	—	—	—	—	—	—
Fourpence	$650.	$1,300.	$3,000.	$6,100.	$8,250.	$13,000.
Sixpence	575.	1,000.	2,200.	4,200.	6,250.	7,500.
Shilling................................	925.	1,700.	3,000.	6,000.	8,000.	12,000.

New Jersey
St. Patrick or Mark Newby Coinage

Mark Newby, who came to America from Dublin, Ireland, in November 1681, brought copper pieces believed by numismatists to have been struck in England circa 1663 to 1672. These are called St. Patrick coppers. The coin received wide circulation in the New Jersey Province, having been authorized to pass as legal tender by the General Assembly in May 1682. The smaller piece, known as a farthing, was never specifically authorized for circulation in the colonies.

St. Patrick Farthing

	G	VG	F	VF	EF	AU
St. Patrick "Farthing".......................	$40.	$90.	$250.	$750.	$1,600.	$3,250.
St. Patrick "Halfpenny"	85.	170.	450.	1,150.	2,200.	

COINAGE AUTHORIZED BY BRITISH ROYAL PATENT
American Plantations Tokens

These tokens struck in nearly pure tin were the first authorized coinage for the British colonies in America. They were made under a franchise granted in 1688 to Richard Holt. Restrikes were made circa 1828 from original dies.

	G	F	EF	AU	Unc.
(1688) James II Plantation Token Farthing,					
1/24 Part Real, tin.	$75.	$210.	$500.	$850.	$1,500.
1/24 Part Real, Restrike	35.	120.	300.	450.	700.

Coinage of William Wood
Rosa Americana Coins

William Wood, an Englishman, obtained a patent from George I to make tokens for Ireland and the American colonies. The Rosa Americana pieces were issued in three denominations—halfpenny, penny, and twopence—and were intended for use in America.

Penny

	VG	F	VF	EF	AU	Unc.
(No date) Twopence, Motto in Ribbon	$60.	$120.	$250.	$500.	$900.	$1,900.
1722 Halfpenny, DEI GRATIA REX UTILE DULCI	35.	90.	165.	350.	700.	1,600.
1722 Penny	35.	90.	165.	350.	700.	1,600.
1722 Twopence	55.	120.	210.	450.	850.	1,800.

Halfpenny

Twopence

	VG	F	VF	EF	AU	Unc.
1723 Halfpenny	$35.	$80.	$150.	$325.	$650.	$1,400.
1723 Penny	35.	90.	175.	300.	550.	1,300.
1723 Twopence *(illustrated)*	60.	110.	225.	450.	750.	1,700.

Wood's Hibernia Coinage

The type intended for Ireland had a seated figure with a harp on the reverse side and the word HIBERNIA. Denominations struck were the halfpenny and the farthing with dates 1722, 1723, and 1724. Although these have no association with the Americas, because of the connection with William Wood many American collectors desire to obtain them.

1722, Hibernia Halfpenny	**First Type**	**Second Type**

	VG	F	VF	EF	AU	Unc.
1722 Farthing, second type		$110.	$200.	$435.	$725.	$1,250.
1722 Halfpenny (first or second type)	$25.	35.	60.	175.	225.	450.

1723, Hibernia Farthing	**1724, Hibernia Halfpenny**

	VG	F	VF	EF	AU	Unc.
1723 Farthing	$18.	$29.	$57.	$135.	$180.	$350.
1723 Halfpenny	18.	29.	50.	130.	180.	350.
1724 Farthing	25.	65.	135.	300.	400.	750.
1724 Halfpenny	24.	55.	125.	250.	375.	700.

Virginia Halfpennies

In 1773, coinage of a copper halfpenny was authorized for Virginia by the British Crown. The style is similar to the regular English coinage. These pieces did not arrive in Virginia until 1775, but after then they did circulate on a limited basis. Most examples know today are Uncirculated, by virtue of a hoard of several thousand pieces that came to light in the 19th century and was distributed in numismatic channels.

	VG	F	VF	EF	AU	Unc.
1773 Halfpenny	$30.	$45.	$85.	$180.	$275.	$475.

EARLY AMERICAN AND RELATED TOKENS
Elephant Tokens
London Elephant Tokens

The London Elephant tokens were struck circa 1672 to 1694. Although they were undated, two examples are known to have been struck over 1672 British halfpennies. Most are struck in copper, but one is made of brass. The legend on this piece, GOD PRESERVE LONDON, is probably just a general plea for divine aid and not a specific reference to the outbreak of plague in 1665 or the great fire of 1666.

These pieces were not struck for the colonies, and probably did not circulate widely in America, although a few may have been carried there by colonists. They are associated with the 1694 Carolina and New England Elephant tokens, through a shared obverse die.

	VG	F	VF	EF	AU	Unc.
(1694) Halfpenny, GOD PRESERVE LONDON, Thick or Thin Planchet	$125.	$210.	$360.	$775.	$1,000.	$1,700.

Carolina Elephant Tokens

Although no law is known authorizing coinage for Carolina, very interesting pieces known as Elephant Tokens were made with the date 1694. These copper tokens were of halfpenny denomination. The reverse reads GOD PRESERVE CAROLINA AND THE LORDS PROPRIETERS. 1694.

The Carolina pieces were probably struck in England and perhaps intended only as tokens, or possibly as advertising to heighten interest in the Carolina Plantation.

	VG	F	VF	EF
1694 CAROLINA.	$2,000.	$3,500.	$5,250.	$9,000.

New England Elephant Tokens

Like the Carolina Tokens, the New England Elephant Tokens were believed to have been struck in England as promotional pieces to increase interest in the American colonies.

	VG	F	VF	EF
1694 NEW ENGLAND	$1,300.	$1,500.	$20,000.	$29,000.

New Yorke in America Token

Little is known about the origin of this token. The design of a heraldic eagle on a regulated staff with oak leaf finials is identical to the crest found on the arms of William Lovelace, governor of New York, 1663 to 1673. It seems likely that this piece is a token farthing struck by Lovelace for use in New York.

	VG	F
(Undated) Brass	$2,200.	$4,500.

Gloucester Tokens

This token appears to have been a private coinage by a merchant of Gloucester (county), Virginia. The only specimens known are struck in brass. The exact origin and use of these pieces are unknown.

	F
1714 Shilling, brass *(2 known)*	$20,000.

Higley or Granby Coppers

The Higley coppers were private issues. All the tokens were made of pure copper. There were seven obverse and four reverse dies. The first issue, in 1737, bore the legend the value of threepence. After a time the quantity exceeded the local demand, and a protest arose against the value of the piece. The inscription was changed to value me as you please.

	G	VG	F	VF
1737 THE VALVE OF THREE PENCE, CONNECTICVT, 3 Hammers	$4,000.	$6,000.	$12,000.	$25,000.
1737 THE VALVE OF THREE PENCE, I AM A GOOD COPPER, 3 Hammers	4,250.	6,250.	12,500.	26,000.
1737 VALUE ME AS YOU PLEASE, I AM GOOD COPPER, 3 Hammers	4,250.	6,250.	12,500.	26,000.
(1737) VALUE ME AS YOU PLEASE, J CUT MY WAY THROUGH, Broad Axe	4,250.	6,250.	12,500.	26,000.
1739 VALUE ME AS YOU PLEASE, J CUT MY WAY THROUGH, Broad Axe	5,000.	7,750.	14,000.	32,000.

Hibernia-Voce Populi Coins

These coins, struck in the year 1760, were made in Dublin. Although these have no connection with America, they have been listed in numismatic publications in the United States for a long time and are collected by tradition.

Farthing (1760)

Halfpenny (1760)

	G	VG	F	VF	EF	AU	Unc.
1760 Farthing	$110.	$160.	$225.	$500.	$1,000.	$1,500.	$3,000.
1760 Halfpenny....................	40.	50.	100.	175.	250.	450.	800.

Pitt Tokens

William Pitt is the subject of these pieces, probably intended as commemorative medalets. He was a friend to the interests of America.The halfpenny served as currency during a shortage of regular coinage.

	VG	F	VF	EF	AU	Unc.
1766 Farthing			$5,000.			
1766 Halfpenny..........................	$160.	$300.	425.	$1,100.	$1,600.	$2,400.

Rhode Island Ship Medals

Although this medal has a Dutch inscription, the spelling and design indicate an English or Anglo-American origin. It is believed that this token was struck in England circa 1779–1780 as propaganda to persuade the Dutch to sign the Treaty of Armed Neutrality. Specimens are known in brass, copper, tin, and pewter. As with many colonial issues, modern copies exist.

1778–1779, Rhode Island Ship Medal

Values shown are for brass or copper pieces. Those struck in pewter are rare and valued higher.

	VF	EF	AU	Unc.
Rhode Island Ship Token	$425.	$800.	$1,000.	$1,600.

John Chalmers Issues

John Chalmers, a silversmith, struck a series of silver tokens at Annapolis in 1783. Certain of the dies were by Thomas Sparro, who also engraved bank note plates. As most examples show wear today, these pieces seem to have served well in commerce.

	VG	F	VF	EF	AU
1783 Threepence	$500.	$1,000.	$2,000.	$3,250.	$4,300.
1783 Sixpence	850.	1,500.	3,000.	5,750.	7,500.
1783 Shilling	500.	1,000.	1,800.	3,000.	4,500.

FRENCH NEW WORLD ISSUES

None of the coins of the French regime is strictly American. They were all general issues for the French colonies of the New World. The copper of 1717 to 1722 was authorized by edicts of 1716 and 1721 for use in New France, Louisiana, and the French West Indies.

Copper Sou or Nine Deniers

	VG	F	VF
1721B (Rouen)	$55.	$110.	$250.
1721H (La Rochelle)	40.	65.	100.
1722H	30.	55.	90.

French Colonies in General

Coined for use in the French colonies, these circulated only unofficially in Louisiana, along with other foreign coins and tokens. Most were counterstamped RF (République Française) for use in the West Indies. The mintmark A signifies the Paris Mint.

	VG	VF	EF	AU
1767 French Colonies, Sou	$28	$85	$210	$360
1767 French Colonies, Sou, counterstamped RF	25	65	125	200

SPECULATIVE ISSUES, TOKENS, AND PATTERNS
Nova Constellatio Coppers

The Nova Constellatio pieces were struck supposedly by order of Gouverneur Morris. Evidence indicates that they were all struck in Birmingham, England and imported for American circulation as a private business venture.

1783, CONSTELLATIO, Pointed Rays

1783, CONSTELATIO, Blunt Rays

1785, CONSTELLATIO, Blunt Rays

1785, CONSTELLATIO, Pointed Rays

	VG	F	VF	EF	AU	Unc.
1783, CONSTELLATIO, Pointed Rays	$45.	$100.	$175.	$350.	$600.	$1,300.
1783, CONSTELLATIO, Blunt Rays	45.	110.	200.	375.	750.	1,600.
1785, CONSTELLATIO, Blunt Rays	55.	120.	250.	450.	800.	1,800.
1785, CONSTELLATIO, Pointed Rays	45.	110.	200.	400.	700.	1,300.

Immune Columbia Pieces

Nearly all of these are very rare. Many if not most seem to be unofficial, including pieces produced at the private Machin's Mills Mint in Newburgh, New York.

1785, Copper, Star Reverse

1785, George III Obverse

1787, IMMUNIS COLUMBIA, Eagle Reverse

	G	VG	F	VF	EF	AU
1785 Copper, Star Reverse				$7,500.	$8,000.	
1785, George III Obverse	$1,400.	$2,000.	$3,000.			
1785, VERMON AUCTORI Obverse, IMMUNE COLUMBIA.	1,650.	2,250.	3,000.	6,500.		
1787, IMMUNIS COLUMBIA, Eagle Reverse. . .	110.	225.	475.	1,300.	2,500.	$3,750.

Confederatio Coppers

Some Confederatio Coppers may have been patterns, but others seem to have been made in limited numbers for general circulation. This will explain why the die with the CONFEDERATIO legend was combined with other designs such as a bust of George Washington, Libertas et Justitia of 1785, Immunis Columbia of 1786, the New York "Excelsiors," Inimica Tyrannis Americana, and others. In all there were thirteen dies struck in fourteen combinations. There are two types of the Confederatio reverse. In one instance the stars are contained in a small circle; in the other, larger stars are in a larger circle.

Typical Obverse　　　　**Small Circle Reverse**　　　　**Large Circle Reverse**

	VF
1785, Stars in Small Circle, various obverses	$7,500.
1785, Stars in Large Circle, various obverses	7,000.

Speculative Patterns

1786, IMMUNIS COLUMBIA　　　**Eagle Reverse**　　　**Shield Reverse**

	VF
1786, IMMUNIS COLUMBIA, Eagle Reverse	$16,000.
1786, IMMUNIS COLUMBIA, Shield Reverse	11,000.
(No date) (1786) Washington Obverse, Shield Reverse	27,000.
1786, Eagle Obverse, Shield Reverse	19,000.
1786, Washington Obverse, Eagle Reverse *(unique)*	—

COINAGE OF THE STATES
New Hampshire

New Hampshire was the first of the states to consider the subject of coinage following the Declaration of Independence.

William Moulton was empowered to make a limited quantity of coins of pure copper, authorized by the State House of Representatives in 1776.

	VG
1776 New Hampshire Copper	$10,000.

Massachusetts

The coinage of Massachusetts copper cents and half cents in 1787 and 1788 was under the direction of Joshua Witherle. These were the first coins bearing the denomination "cent" as established by Congress. Many varieties exist, the most valuable being that with arrows in the eagle's right talon.

1787 Half Cent

1787 Cent

1788 Half Cent

1788 Cent

	G	F	VF	EF	AU	Unc.
1787 Half Cent	$35.	$75.	$225.	$475.	$850.	$1,650.
1787 Cent, Arrows in Right Talon	2,500.	6,500.				
1787 Cent, Arrows in Left Talon *(illustrated)*	30.	70.	210.	450.	825.	1,600.
1788 Half Cent	35.	75.	225.	475.	850.	1,600.
1788 Cent	35.	75.	225.	475.	850.	1,800.

Connecticut

Authority for establishing a mint near New Haven was granted by the state to Samuel Bishop, Joseph Hopkins, James Hillhouse, and John Goodrich in 1785. Today, well over 300 different die varieties are known of Connecticut coppers dated from 1785 to 1788. These pieces circulated widely and effectively; most are seen with significant evidence of circulation.

1785, Bust Facing Right

**1785, Bust
Facing Left**

**1786–1787, Mailed
Bust Facing Right**

**1786–1787, Mailed
Bust Facing Left**

**1787, Draped
Bust Facing Left**

**1788, Mailed
Bust Facing Right**

**1788, Mailed
Bust Facing Left**

1788, Draped Bust Facing Left

See next page for chart.

	G	VG	F	VF	EF
1785, Bust Facing Right	$25.	$35.	$70.	$200.	$550.
1785, Bust Facing Left	80.	150.	250.	400.	700.
1786, Mailed Bust Facing Right	35.	45.	75.	190.	525.
1786, Mailed Bust Facing Left	25.	35.	75.	150.	375.
1787, Mailed Bust Facing Right	40.	60.	150.	400.	650.
1787, Mailed Bust Facing Left	20.	30.	60.	135.	350.
1787, Draped Bust Facing Left	20.	30.	60.	145.	375.
1788, Mailed Bust Facing Right	18.	30.	70.	190.	430.
1788, Mailed Bust Facing Left	18.	28.	65.	165.	400.
1788, Draped Bust Facing Left	20.	30.	85.	200.	450.

New York and Related Issues
Brasher Doubloons

Perhaps the most famous pieces coined before the establishment of the U.S. Mint at Philadelphia were those produced by a well-known goldsmith and jeweler, Ephraim Brasher.

Brasher produced a gold piece weighing about 408 grains, approximately equal in value to a Spanish doubloon (about $15.00).

The punch-mark EB appears in either of two positions as illustrated. This mark is found on some foreign gold coins as well, and probably was so used by Brasher as evidence of his testing of their value. Many modern forgeries exist.

	EF
1787 New York gold doubloon, EB on Breast	—
1787 New York gold doubloon, EB on Wing	—

Copper Coinage

No coinage was authorized for New York following the Revolutionary War, although several propositions were considered. The only coinage laws passed were those regulating coins already in use.

	G	VG	F	VF
1786, NON VI VIRTUTE VICI	$1,900.	$2,300.	$4,000.	$8,500.

	G	VG	F	VF	EF
1787 EXCELSIOR Copper, Eagle on Globe Facing Right	$750.	$1,200.	$2,500.	$5,000.	$11,000.
1787 EXCELSIOR Copper, Eagle on Globe Facing Left.......	750.	1,100.	2,200.	4,500.	10,000.

1787, George Clinton **1787, Indian and NY Arms** **1787, Indian and Eagle on Globe**

	G	VG	F	VF	EF
1787, George Clinton	$3,250.	$4,500.	$6,750.	$14,000.	—
1787, Indian and New York Arms...........	2,200.	3,400.	4,500.	9,000.	$15,000.
1787, Indian and Eagle on Globe	3,250.	4,500.	6,750.	13,000.	27,500.

Nova Eborac Coinage for New York

1787, NOVA EBORAC Reverse, Seated Figure Facing Right **1787, NOVA EBORAC Reverse, Seated Figure Facing Left**

See next page for chart.

	Fair	G	F	VF	EF	AU
1787, NOVA EBORAC, Seated Figure Facing Right	$20.	$40.	$150.	$425.	$850.	$1,400.
1787, NOVA EBORAC, Seated Figure Facing Left	20.	40.	130.	400.	800.	1,300.

New Jersey

On June 1, 1786, the New Jersey Colonial legislature granted to Thomas Goadsby, Albion Cox, and Walter Mould authority to coin some three million coppers no later than June 1788, on condition that they delivered to the Treasurer of the State "one-tenth part of the full sum they shall strike and coin," in quarterly installments. These coppers were to pass current at 15 to the shilling. Produced in significant quantities, these coins are often seen in the market today and are widely collectible, although certain varieties can be rare and especially valuable.

Narrow Shield   **Wide Shield**

	G	F	VF	EF	AU
1786, Narrow Shield	$20.	$80.	$210.	$600.	$1,000.
1786, Wide Shield	25.	100.	225.	625.	1,100.

Small Planchet

	G	F	VF	EF	AU
1787, Small Planchet, Plain Shield	$25.	$85.	$210.	$600.	$1,000.
1787, Large Planchet, Plain Shield	25.	100.	235.	650.	1,100.

Fox Before Legend

	G	F	VF	EF	AU
1788, Horse's Head Facing Right	$20.	$90.	$200.	$550.	$950.
1788, Similar, Indistinct Coulter	25.	120.	250.	700.	1,200.
1788, Horse's Head Facing Left	125.	400.	1,100.	2,750.	

Vermont

Reuben Harmon, Jr. was granted permission to coin copper pieces beginning July 1, 1785. The franchise was extended for eight years in 1786. However, in 1787 production was shifted to Machin's Mills, Newburgh, New York, in which Harmon had a proprietary interest. Although the Vermont coins were legally issued there, most other products of Machin's Mills were counterfeits, some dies for which were combined with Vermont pieces, creating several illogical pieces below, including the 1785 Immune Columbia and the 1788 Georgivs III Rex.

| 1785, IMMUNE COLUMBIA | 1785–1786, Plow Type | | 1786, Baby Head | |

	G	VG	F	VF	EF
1785, IMMUNE COLUMBIA	$1,650.	$2,250.	$3,000.	$6,500.	—
1785, Plow Type, VERMONTS	150.	250.	450.	900.	$2,750.
1786, Plow Type, VERMONTENSIUM	125.	225.	400.	850.	1,500.
1786, Baby Head	150.	300.	600.	1,600.	2,500.

| 1786–1787, Bust Left | 1787, BRITTANIA | | 1787, Bust Right | |

	G	VG	F	VF	EF
1786, Bust Left	$70.	$200.	$320.	$750.	$1,300.
1787, Bust Left	1,800.	3,200.	4,750.	12,000.	—
1787, BRITANNIA	40.	85.	135.	210.	625.
1787, Bust Right *(several varieties)*	50.	100.	175.	270.	750.

1788, Bust Right

1788, GEORGIVS III REX

	G	VG	F	VF	EF
1788, Bust Right..........................	$50.	$100.	$175.	$270.	$750.
1788, GEORGIVS III REX	175.	275.	900.	1,600.	3,250.

Note: This piece should not be confused with the common English halfpence with similar design and reverse legend BRITANNIA.

PRIVATE TOKENS AFTER CONFEDERATION
North American Tokens

This piece was struck in Dublin, Ireland. The obverse shows the seated figure of Hibernia facing left. Although dated 1781, it is believed to have been struck early in the next century.

	VG	F	VF	EF
1781 Copper or Brass	$20.	$50.	$125.	$220.

Bar Coppers

The Bar "Copper" is undated and of uncertain origin. It has 13 parallel and unconnected bars on one side. On the other side is the large Roman letter USA monogram. The design was supposedly copied from a Continental button.

	VG	F	VF	EF	AU
(Undated) (Circa 1785) Bar Copper	$450.	$800.	$1,400.	$2,000.	$2,650.

Auctori Plebis Tokens

This token is sometimes included with the coins of Connecticut as it greatly resembles issues of that state. It was struck in England by an unknown maker, possibly for use in America.

	G	VG	F	VF	EF	AU	Unc.
1787, AUCTORI PLEBIS	$30.	$50.	$100.	$225.	$400.	$1,250.	$2,100.

Mott Store Cards

This item has long been considered an early token because of its date (1789). Some scholars believe it was most likely produced circa 1809 as a commemorative of the founding of the Mott Company, and probably served as a business card.

	VG	F	VF	EF	AU	Unc.
1789, Mott Token.	$50.	$100.	$200.	$400.	$600.	$1,250.

Standish Barry Threepence

Standish Barry, a Baltimore silversmith, circulated a silver threepence in 1790. The tokens were believed to have been an advertising venture at a time when small change was scarce.

	VG	F	VF
1790 Threepence	$1,200.	$3,000.	$6,000.

Kentucky Tokens

These tokens were struck in England about 1792 to 1794. Each star in the triangle represents a state, identified by its initial letter. These pieces are usually called Kentucky Cents because the letter K (for Kentucky) happens to be at the top. In the 19th century these were often called "triangle tokens," from the arrangement of the stars. Values are for the normal issue with plain edge; lettered edge varieties exist and are scarcer.

	VG	VF	EF	AU	Unc.
(1792–1794) Copper, Plain Edge	$40.	$100.	$175.	$275.	$525.

Franklin Press Tokens

This piece is an English tradesman's token but, being associated with Benjamin Franklin, has accordingly been included in American collections.

	VG	VF	EF	AU	Unc.
1794, Franklin Press Token	$45.	$110.	$185.	$275.	$525.

Talbot, Allum & Lee Cents

Talbot, Allum & Lee, engaged in the India trade and located in New York, placed a large quantity of English-made coppers in circulation during 1794 and 1795. ONE CENT appears on the 1794 issue.

1794 Cent, With NEW YORK

1795 Cent

	G	VG	VF	EF	AU	Unc.
1794 Cent, With NEW YORK		$35.	$85.	$150.	$225.	$475.
1794 Cent, Without NEW YORK	$100.	200.	350.	550.	1,000.	2,100.
1795 Cent		35.	70.	175.	245.	525.

WASHINGTON PORTRAIT PIECES

An interesting series of coins and tokens dated from 1783 to 1795 bear the portrait of George Washington. The likenesses in most instances were faithfully reproduced and were designed to honor Washington. Many of these pieces were of English origin and made later than the dates indicate.

	F	VF	EF	AU	Unc.
1783, Military Bust	$35.	$70.	$170.	$450.	$950.

	F	VF	EF	AU	Unc.
1783, Draped Bust	$40.	$75.	$200.	$425.	$900.

1783, UNITY STATES		**Undated Double-Head Cent**			

	VG	F	VF	EF	AU	Unc.
1783, UNITY STATES	$40.		$125.	$200.	$475.	$1,100.
(Undated) Double-Head Cent		$40.	125.	200.	475.	1,100.

Obverse | **Large Eagle Reverse** | **Small Eagle Reverse**

	F	EF	AU	Unc.
1791 Cent, Large Eagle (Date on Obverse)	$175.	$425.	$625.	$1,200.
1791 Cent, Small Eagle (Date on Reverse)	175.	425.	625.	1,200.

	F	EF	AU
1791 Liverpool Halfpenny, Lettered Edge	$425.	$1,000.	$2,400.

1792 Eagle With Stars, Copper	—
1792 Eagle With Stars, Silver	—
1792 Eagle With Stars, Gold *(unique)*	—

(1792) Undated Cent,
WASHINGTON BORN VIRGINIA

1792 Cent,
WASHINGTON PRESIDENT

	VG	F	VF
(1792) Undated Cent, WASHINGTON BORN VIRGINIA, copper	$750.	$1,500.	$2,400.
1792 Cent, WASHINGTON PRESIDENT, Plain Edge	850.	2,400.	3,250.

1792 Getz Pattern

1793 Ship Halfpenny

1795 Halfpenny, Grate Token

	VG	F	VF	EF	AU	Unc.
1792, Getz Pattern, Copper	$2,200.	$3,750.	—	—		
1793 Ship Halfpenny, Lettered Edge		100.	$200.	$325.	$475.	$1,100.
1795, Grate Token, Lettered Edge		145.	350.	425.	750.	
1795, Grate Token, Reeded Edge.		85.	175.	250.	350.	

	F	VF	EF	AU	Unc.
1795, LIBERTY AND SECURITY Halfpenny, Plain Edge	$75.	$150.	$275.	$525.	—
1795, LIBERTY AND SECURITY Halfpenny, Lettered Edge	65.	125.	250.	500.	—
Undated (1795) LIBERTY AND SECURITY Penny	125.	200.	375.	525.	$1,300.

	G	F	VF	EF
1795, NORTH WALES Halfpenny	$50.	$150.	$225.	$425.

	F	VF	EF	AU	Unc.
SUCCESS Medal, Large, Plain or Reeded Edge	$80.	$175.	$350.	$725.	$1,000.
SUCCESS Medal, Small, Plain or Reeded Edge	100.	220.	375.	800.	1,100.

CONTINENTAL CURRENCY

The Continental Currency pieces probably had some assigned value at their time of issue. The exact nature of their monetary role is uncertain; they might have been patterns, or they might have seen circulation. At any rate, this was the first dollar-sized coin proposed for the United States. They were probably struck in Philadelphia. As with many early pieces, modern replicas exist.

	G	F	VF	EF	AU	Unc.
1776, CURENCY, pewter *(2 varieties)*	$1,500.	$3,000.	$3,750.	$6,500.	$8,500.	$16,000.
1776, CURENCY, silver *(2 known)*.		70,000.				
1776, CURRENCY, pewter	1,700.	3,300.	4,000.	7,000.	10,000.	20,000.
1776, CURRENCY, EG FECIT, pewter	1,500.	3,000.	3,750.	6,500.	8,500.	18,000.

FUGIO CENTS

The first coins issued by authority of the United States were the "Fugio" cents. The legends have been credited to Benjamin Franklin by many, and the coins, as a consequence, have been referred to as Franklin cents.

1787, With Pointed Rays   **1787, With Club Rays**

	VG	F	VF	EF	AU	Unc.
Pointed Rays, STATES UNITED						
at Side of Circle *(illustrated)*	$100.	$190.	$300.	$500.	$650.	$1,100.
Pointed Rays, UNITED STATES at Side of Circle . . .	100.	190.	300.	500.	650.	1,100.
Club Rays, Rounded Ends	150.	300.	625.	1,400.		

The half cent was authorized to be coined April 2, 1792. Originally the weight was to have been 132 grains, but this was changed to 104 grains by the Act of January 14, 1793, before coinage commenced. The weight was again changed to 84 grains January 26, 1796 by presidential proclamation in conformity with the Act of March 3, 1795. Coinage was discontinued by the Act of February 21, 1857. All were coined at the Philadelphia Mint.

LIBERTY CAP (1793–1797)

AG-3 ABOUT GOOD—Clear enough to identify.
G-4 GOOD—Outline of bust of Liberty clear, no details. Date readable. Reverse lettering incomplete.
VG-8 VERY GOOD—Some hair details. Reverse lettering complete.
F-12 FINE—Most of hair detail visible. Leaves worn, but all visible.
VF-20 VERY FINE—Hair near ear and forehead worn, other areas distinct. Some details in leaves visible.
EF-40 EXTREMELY FINE—Light wear on highest parts of head and wreath.
AU-50 ABOUT UNCIRCULATED—Only a trace of wear on Liberty's face.

Head Facing Left (1793)

	Mintage	AG-3	G-4	VG-8	F-12	VF-20	EF-40	AU-50
1793	35,334	$600.	$1,100.	$1,700.	$2,500.	$4,000.	$7,250.	$10,500.

Head Facing Right (1794–1797)

	Mintage	AG-3	G-4	VG-8	F-12	VF-20	EF-40	AU-50
1794	81,600	$75.	$160.	$235.	$450.	$800.	$2,000.	$3,000.

Pole to Cap   **Punctuated Date**   **No Pole to Cap**

	Mintage	AG-3	G-4	VG-8	F-12	VF-20	EF-40	AU-50
1795, All kinds	139,690							
1795, Lettered Edge, With Pole		$50.	$150.	$225.	$425.	$850.	$1,850.	$2,300.
1795, Lettered Edge, Punctuated Date		50.	150.	225.	425.	850.	1,850.	2,300.
1795, Plain Edge, Punctuated Date		45.	135.	190.	400.	750.	1,800.	2,300.
1795, Plain Edge, No Pole		45.	135.	190.	400.	750.	1,800.	2,300.
1796, With Pole	1,390	2,700.	4,500.	6,500.	9,000.	16,000.	24,000.	
1796, No Pole	*	6,750.	10,000.	14,000.	24,000.	35,000.	48,000.	

* Included in number above.

HALF CENTS

1797, Plain Edge

1797, 1 Above 1, Plain Edge

	Mintage	AG-3	G-4	VG-8	F-12	VF-20	EF-40	AU-50
1797, All kinds	12,7840							
1797, Lettered Edge		$130.	$450.	$775.	$1,600.	$3,200.	$3,750.	
1797, Plain Edge		75.	150.	225.	475.	850.	1,900.	$3,200.
1797, Gripped Edge		2,700.	6,000.	15,000.				
1797, 1 Above 1, Plain Edge		50.	140.	200.	375.	625.	1,700.	

DRAPED BUST (1800–1808)

AG-3 ABOUT GOOD—Clear enough to identify.
G-4 GOOD—Outline of bust of Liberty clear, few details, date readable. Reverse lettering worn and incomplete.
VG-8 VERY GOOD—Some drapery visible. Date and legends complete.
F-12 FINE—Shoulder drapery and hair over brow worn smooth.
VF-20 VERY FINE—Only slight wear in previously mentioned areas. Slight wear on reverse.
EF-40 EXTREMELY FINE—Light wear on highest parts of head and wreath.
AU-50 ABOUT UNCIRCULATED—Wear slight on hair above forehead.

1st Reverse

2nd Reverse

	Mintage	AG-3	G-4	VG-8	F-12	VF-20	EF-40	AU-50
1800	202,908	$12.	$25.	$30.	$45.	$90.	$175.	$325.
1802, 2 Over 0	20,266	100.	300.	550.	1,300.	3,500.	8,000.	
1803	92,000	12.	25.	30.	45.	100.	325.	500.

| **Plain 4** | **Crosslet 4** | **Stemless Wreath** | **Stems to Wreath** |

	Mintage	AG-3	G-4	VG-8	F-12	VF-20	EF-40	AU-50
1804, All kinds	1,055,312							
1804, Plain 4, Stems to Wreath		$14.	$28.	$35.	$70.	$120.	$350.	$500.
1804, Plain 4, Stemless Wreath		12.	25.	30.	42.	55.	120.	240.
1804, Crosslet 4, Stemless Wreath		12.	25.	30.	42.	55.	120.	240.
1804, Crosslet 4, Stems to Wreath		12.	25.	30.	42.	55.	120.	240.

| | 1804, "Spiked Chin" | Small 5 | Large 5 |

	Mintage	AG-3	G-4	VG-8	F-12	VF-20	EF-40	AU-50
1804, "Spiked Chin"	*	$13.	$25.	$30.	$45.	$75.	$165.	$275.
1805, All kinds	814,464							
1805, Medium 5, Stemless Wreath		12.	25.	30.	45.	60.	120.	240.
1805, Small 5, Stems to Wreath		75.	250.	550.	1,000.	2,000.		
1805, Large 5, Stems to Wreath		10.	22.	27.	40.	60.	120.	240.

* Included in "1804, All kinds" mintage (previous page).

| Small 6 | Large 6 | 1808, 8 Over 7 | Normal Date |

	Mintage	AG-3	G-4	VG-8	F-12	VF-20	EF-40	AU-50
1806, All kinds	356,000							
1806, Small 6, Stems to Wreath		$25.	$90.	$160.	$275.	$425.	$1,000.	$2,100.
1806, Small 6, Stemless Wreath		10.	22.	26.	35.	50.	115.	240.
1806, Large 6, Stems to Wreath		10.	22.	26.	35.	50.	115.	240.
1807	476,000	10.	22.	26.	40.	65.	185.	325.
1808, 8 Over 7	400,000	25.	50.	100.	250.	475.	1,200.	2,750.
1808, Normal Date	*	10.	22.	26.	35.	60.	200.	325.

* Included in number above.

CLASSIC HEAD (1809–1836)

G-4 GOOD—LIBERTY only partly visible on hair band. Lettering, date, stars, worn but visible.
VG-8 VERY GOOD—LIBERTY entirely visible on hair band. Lower curls worn.
F-12 FINE—Only partial wear on LIBERTY, and hair at top worn in spots.
VF-20 VERY FINE—Lettering clear-cut. Hair only slightly worn.
EF-40 EXTREMELY FINE—Light wear on highest points of hair and leaves.
AU-50 ABOUT UNCIRCULATED—Sharp hair detail with only a trace of wear on higher points.
MS-60 UNCIRCULATED—Typical brown to red surface. No trace of wear.
MS-63 CHOICE UNCIRCULATED—Well-defined color, brown to red. No traces of wear.

Brilliant or red Uncirculated coins are worth more than prices shown. Spotted, cleaned, or discolored pieces are worth less.

	Mintage	AG-3	G-4	VG-8	F-12	VG-20	EF-40	MS-60	MS-63
1809, All kinds	1,154,572	$15.	$20.	$26.	$35.	$55.	$110.	$225.	$325.
1810	215,000	17.	25.	45.	75.	200.	275.	700.	1,250.
1811	63,140	60.	120.	260.	575.	1,400.	1,750.	3,200.	4,000.
1825	63,000	16.	22.	26.	35.	65.	100.	325.	475.
1826	234,000	16.	22.	26.	35.	65.	95.	225.	350.

13 Stars **12 Stars**

	Mintage	AG-3	G-4	VG-8	F-12	VG-20	EF-40	MS-60	MS-63	PF-63
1828, 13 Stars	606,000	$15.	$20.	$26.	$35.	$45.	$75.	$135.	$200.	
1828, 12 Stars	*	16.	21.	29.	40.	95.	135.	425.	650.	
1829	487,000	15.	20.	26.	35.	55.	85.	150.	200.	
1831	2,200									$4,500.
1832		15.	20.	24.	32.	45.	70.	150.	200.	2,200.
1833		15.	20.	24.	32.	45.	70.	150.	200.	2,200.
1834		15.	20.	24.	32.	45.	70.	150.	200.	2,000.
1835		15.	20.	24.	32.	45.	70.	150.	200.	2,000.
1836										3,400.

* Included in number above.

BRAIDED HAIR (1840–1857)

VG-8 VERY GOOD—Beads in hair uniformly distinct. Hair lines visible in spots.
F-12 FINE—Hair lines above ear worn. Beads sharp.
VF-20 VERY FINE—Lowest curl worn; hair otherwise distinct.
EF-40 EXTREMELY FINE—Light wear on highest points of hair and on leaves.
AU-50 ABOUT UNCIRCULATED—Very slight trace of wear on hair above Liberty's ear.
MS-60 UNCIRCULATED—No trace of wear. Clear luster.
MS-63 CHOICE UNCIRCULATED—No trace of wear.
PF-63 CHOICE PROOF—Nearly perfect.
Brilliant or red Uncirculated coins are worth more than prices shown. Spotted, cleaned, or discolored pieces are worth less.

	PF-63		PF-63
1840, Original	$2,500.	1845, Original	$3,500.
1840, Restrike	2,250.	1845, Restrike	3,250.
1841, Original	2,600.	1846, Original	3,250.
1841, Restrike	2,500.	1846, Restrike	2,600.
1842, Original	2,750.	1847, Original	2,600.
1842, Restrike	2,500.	1847, Restrike	2,600.
1843, Original	2,500.	1848, Original	2,600.
1843, Restrike	2,500.	1848, Restrike	2,600.
1844, Original	3,500.	1849, Original, Small Date	2,900.
1844, Restrike	2,600.	1849, Restrike, Small Date	2,900.

Small Date **Large Date**

	Mintage	G-4	VG-8	F-12	VF-20	EF-40	AU-50	MS-60	MS-63	PF-63
1849, Large Date	39,864	$17.	$23.	$27.	$32.	$60.	$80.	$165.	$250.	
1850	39,812	17.	23.	27.	32.	60.	80.	165.	275.	
1851	147,672	14.	20.	25.	30.	45.	70.	120.	225.	
1852										$3,000.
1853	129,694	14.	20.	25.	30.	45.	70.	120.	225.	
1854	55,358	14.	20.	25.	30.	45.	70.	120.	225.	2,700.
1855	56,500	14.	20.	25.	30.	45.	70.	120.	225.	2,700.
1856	40,430	16.	21.	26.	32.	50.	80.	125.	250.	2,600.
1857	35,180	17.	23.	28.	40.	65.	110.	160.	275.	2,600.

Cents and half cents were the first coins struck under the authority of the United States government. Coinage began in 1793 with laws specifying that the cent should weigh exactly twice as much as the half cent. Large cents were coined every year from 1793 to 1857 with the exception of 1815, when a lack of copper prevented production. All were coined at the Philadelphia Mint. Varieties listed are those most significant to collectors. Numerous other die varieties may be found because each of the early dies was individually made.

FLOWING HAIR (1793)

AG-3 ABOUT GOOD—Date and devices clear enough to identify.
G-4 GOOD—Lettering worn but readable. No detail on bust.
VG-8 VERY GOOD—Date and lettering distinct, some details of head visible.
F-12 FINE—About half of hair and other details visible.
VF-20 VERY FINE—Ear visible, most details visible.
EF-40 EXTREMELY FINE—Wear evident on highest points of hair and back of temple.

Chain Reverse (1793)

| | | Obverse | AMERI. Reverse | | AMERICA Reverse | |

	Mintage	AG-3	G-4	VG-8	F-12	VF-20	EF-40
1793, Chain, All kinds 36,103							
1793, AMERI. in Legend		$1,000.	$2,500.	$3,400.	$7,000.	$12,500.	$24,000.
1793, AMERICA		950.	2,500.	3,400.	7,000.	12,500.	24,000.

Wreath Reverse (1793)

| | | Obverse | Wreath Reverse | | Strawberry Leaf Variety | |

	Mintage	AG-3	G-4	VG-8	F-12	VF-20	EF-40
1793, Wreath, All kinds 63,353							
1793, Vine/Bars Edge		$225.	$750.	$950.	$2,000.	$3,400.	$6,000.
1793, Lettered Edge		300.	800.	1,000.	2,100.	3,600.	6,100.
1793, Strawberry Leaf . . . . *(4 known)*							

LIBERTY CAP (1793–1796)

1793, Vine and Bar Edge
Chain and wreath type only.

Lettered Edge (1793–1795)
ONE HUNDRED FOR A DOLLAR

Beaded Border (1793)

Head of 1793 (1793–1794)
Head in high, rounded relief.

Head of 1794 (1794)
Well-defined hair;
hook on lowest curl.

Head of 1795 (1794–1796)
Head in low relief;
no hook on lowest curl.

	Mintage	AG-3	G-4	VG-8	F-12	VF-20	EF-40
1793, Liberty Cap	11,056	$650.	$1,200.	$2,000.	$4,000.	$10,000.	$24,000.
1794, All kinds	918,521						
1794, "Head of 1793"		175.	425.	800.	1,500.	3,500.	7,000.
1794, "Head of 1794"		30.	85.	150.	350.	600.	1,500.
1794, "Head of 1795"		30.	85.	150.	350.	550.	1,300.
1795, Lettered Edge	37,000	30.	85.	150.	350.	575.	1,800.
1795, Plain Edge	501,500	25.	70.	110.	300.	450.	1,200.
1796, Liberty Cap	109,825	40.	125.	175.	350.	700.	1,875.

DRAPED BUST (1796–1807)

AG-3 ABOUT GOOD—Clear enough to identify.
G-4 GOOD—Lettering worn, but clear; date clear. Bust lacking in detail.
VG-8 VERY GOOD—Drapery on Liberty partly visible. Less wear in date and lettering.
F-12 FINE—Hair over brow smooth; some detail showing in other parts of hair.
VF-20 VERY FINE—Hair lines slightly worn. Hair over brow better defined.
EF-40 EXTREMELY FINE—Hair above forehead and left of eye outlined and detailed. Only slight wear on olive leaves.

LIHERTY Error

	Mintage	AG-3	G-4	VG-8	F-12	VF-20	EF-40
1796, Draped Bust	363,375	$25.	$55.	$100.	$225.	$550.	$1,325.
1796, LIHERTY Error	*	55.	100.	250.	425.	1,500.	3,500.

* Included in number above.

Gripped Edge	With Stems	Stemless

	Mintage	AG-3	G-4	VG-8	F-12	VF-20	EF-40
1797, All kinds	897,510						
1797, Gripped Edge, 1796 Reverse		$20.	$42.	$90.	$200.	$325.	$1,200.
1797, Plain Edge, 1796 Reverse		25.	45.	95.	225.	350.	1,300.
1797, 1797 Reverse, With Stems		15.	25.	65.	150.	225.	550.
1797, 1797 Reverse, Stemless		20.	45.	100.	200.	425.	1,500.

1798, 8 Over 7	1799, 9 Over 8	1800 Over 1798	1800, 80 Over 79

	Mintage	AG-3	G-4	VG-8	F-12	VF-20	EF-40
1798, All kinds	1,841,745						
1798, 8 Over 7		$20.	$45.	$100.	$175.	$650.	$1,850.
1798		10.	25.	40.	100.	200.	700.
1799, 9 Over 8	*	450.	950.	1,650.	3,500.	11,000.	
1799, Normal Date		400.	850.	1,500.	3,500.	10,000.	
1800, All kinds	2,822,175						
1800 Over 1798		10.	22.	33.	90.	275.	1,100.
1800, 80 Over 79		10.	20.	27.	80.	200.	700.
1800, Normal Date		9.	17.	25.	65.	175.	550.
* Included in 1798 mintage.							

Fraction 1/000	Corrected Fraction	1801 Reverse, 3 Errors

	Mintage	AG-3	G-4	VG-8	F-12	VF-20	EF-40
1801, All kinds	1,362,837						
1801, Normal Reverse		$8.	$15.	$27.	$55.	$150.	$425.
1801, 3 Errors: 1/000, One Stem, and IINITED		25.	50.	85.	300.	700.	2,500.
1801, Fraction 1/000		9.	17.	30.	80.	170.	625.
1801, 1/100 Over 1/000		10.	22.	33.	85.	225.	675.
1802, All kinds	3,435,100						
1802, Normal Reverse		8.	20.	28.	60.	120.	425.
1802, Fraction 1/000		10.	25.	40.	85.	200.	600.
1802, Stemless Wreath		8.	20.	28.	60.	120.	400.

1803, Small Date, Blunt 1	1803, Large Date, Pointed 1	Small Fraction	Large Fraction

LARGE CENTS

	Mintage	AG-3	G-4	VG-8	F-12	VF-20	EF-40
1803, All kinds	3,131,691						
1803, Small Date, Small Fraction		$8.	$20.	$27.	$55.	$125.	$400.
1803, Small Date, Large Fraction		8.	20.	27.	55.	125.	400.
1803, Large Date, Small Fraction		900.	2,100.	3,500.	6,500.	10,000.	
1803, Large Date, Large Fraction		15.	25.	50.	100.	325.	1,100.
1803, 1/100 Over 1/000		10.	22.	35.	75.	175.	625.
1803, Stemless Wreath		10.	22.	35.	75.	175.	625.

Broken Dies

*All genuine 1804 cents have crosslet 4 in date and a large fraction.
The 0 in date is in line with O in OF on reverse.*

	Mintage	AG-3	G-4	VG-8	F-12	VF-20	EF-40
1804 **(a)**	96,500	$185.	$400.	$750.	$1,600.	$2,100.	$4,200.
1805	941,116	8.	20.	30.	70.	150.	400.
1806	348,000	10.	25.	35.	75.	190.	650.

a. Values shown are for coins with normal or broken dies.

Small 1807, 7 Over 6	**Large 1807, 7 Over 6**
(Blunt 1)	**(Pointed 1)**

	Mintage	AG-3	G-4	VG-8	F-12	VF-20	EF-40
1807, All kinds	829,221						
1807, Small 7 Over 6, Blunt 1		$350.	$1,000.	$2,000.	$4,100.	$7,250.	$15,000.
1807, Large 7 Over 6		8.	20.	28.	60.	150.	425.
1807, Small Fraction		8.	20.	28.	60.	190.	500.
1807, Large Fraction		8.	20.	28.	60.	170.	475.

CLASSIC HEAD (1808–1814)

AG-3 ABOUT GOOD—Details clear enough to identify.
G-4 GOOD—Legends, stars, and date worn, but plain.
VG-8 VERY GOOD—LIBERTY all readable. Liberty's ear visible. Details worn but plain.
F-12 FINE—Hair on forehead and before ear nearly smooth. Ear and hair under ear sharp.
VF-20 VERY FINE—Some detail in all hair lines. Slight wear on leaves on reverse.
EF-40 EXTREMELY FINE—All hair lines sharp. Very slight wear on high points.

See next page for chart.

	Mintage	AG-3	G-4	VG-8	F-12	VF-20	EF-40
1808	1,007,000	$10.	$22.	$45.	$110.	$250.	$625.
1809	222,867	22.	45.	90.	175.	450.	1,300.

1810, 10 Over 09	**1810, Normal Date**	**1811, Last 1 Over 0**	**1811, Normal Date**

	Mintage	AG-3	G-4	VG-8	F-12	VF-20	EF-40
1810, All kinds	1,458,500						
1810, 10 Over 09		$8.	$20.	$35.	$110.	$300.	$650.
1810, Normal Date		8.	20.	32.	100.	250.	525.
1811, All kinds	218,025						
1811, Last 1 Over 0		15.	30.	55.	200.	500.	1,700.
1811, Normal Date		14.	28.	45.	125.	375.	775.
1812	1,075,500	8.	18.	32.	100.	250.	525.
1813	418,000	11.	22.	40.	125.	275.	650.
1814	357,830	8.	18.	32.	110.	250.	575.

LIBERTY HEAD (1816–1857)

G-4 GOOD—Details on Liberty's head partly visible. Even wear in date and legends.
VG-8 VERY GOOD—LIBERTY, date, stars, and legends clear. Part of hair cord visible.
F-12 FINE—All hair lines visible. Hair cords uniformly visible.
VF-20 VERY FINE—Hair cords only slightly worn. Hair lines only partly worn, all well defined.
EF-40 EXTREMELY FINE—Both hair cords stand out sharply. All hair lines sharp.
AU-50 ABOUT UNCIRCULATED—Only traces of wear on hair and highest points on leaves and bow.
MS-60 UNCIRCULATED—Typical brown surface. No trace of wear.
MS-63 CHOICE UNCIRCULATED—Some distracting contact marks or blemishes in prime focal areas. Impaired luster possible.

Matron Head (1816–1836)

13 Stars		**15 Stars**

Brilliant or red Uncirculated coins are worth more than prices shown. Spotted, cleaned, or discolored pieces are worth less.

	Mintage	G-4	VG-8	F-12	VF-20	EF-40	AU-50	MS-60	MS-63
1816	2,820,982	$8.	$10.	$15.	$30.	$65.	$100.	$200.	$375.
1817, 13 Stars	3,948,400	8.	9.	13.	25.	45.	85.	175.	350.
1817, 15 Stars	*	9.	11.	15.	50.	225.	325.	850.	—
1818	3,167,000	8.	9.	13.	25.	45.	85.	175.	350.

* Included in number above.

1819, 9 Over 8 **1820, 20 Over 19**

	Mintage	G-4	VG-8	F-12	VF-20	EF-40	AU-50	MS-60	MS-63
1819, All kinds............	2,671,00	$8.	$10.	$14.	$25.	$50.	$100.	$175.	$350.
1819, 9 Over 8.................	*	9.	12.	17.	35.	150.	175.	300.	450.
1820, All kinds...........	4,407,550	6.	8.	12.	30.	50.	85.	175.	350.
1820, 20 Over 19..............	*	9.	12.	17.	35.	150.	200.	400.	650.
1821...................	389,000	15.	25.	60.	185.	425.	1,000.	3,500.	—
1822...................	2,072,339	8.	10.	21.	50.	100.	275.	450.	710.

* Included in number above.

1823, 3 Over 2 **1824, 4 Over 2** **1826, 6 Over 5**

	Mintage	G-4	VG-8	F-12	VF-20	EF-40	AU-50	MS-60	MS-63
1823, 3 Over 2.................	*	$25.	$45.	$150.	$300.	$1,000.	$1,750.	$2,800.	—
1823, Normal Date	*	28.	50.	175.	350.	1,300.	2,000.	3,000.	—
1824, 4 Over 2.................	*	9.	15.	40.	150.	500.	1,000.	2,000.	—
1824, Normal Date	1,262,000	6.	8.	15.	75.	200.	300.	750.	$1,200.
1825	1,461,100	6.	8.	12.	45.	150.	250.	675.	1,100.
1826, 6 Over 5..........	1,517,425	10.	16.	35.	100.	400.	575.	1,000.	2,000.
1826, Normal Date	**	6.	8.	10.	40.	100.	175.	375.	625.
1827	2,357,732	6.	8.	10.	35.	65.	125.	250.	475.

* Included in number below. ** Included in number above.

Date Size, Through 1828 **Date Size, 1828 and Later**

	Mintage	G-4	VG-8	F-12	VF-20	EF-40	AU-50	MS-60	MS-63
1828, Large Narrow Date....	2,260,624	$6.	$8.	$13.	$40.	$70.	$150.	$350.	$600.
1828, Small Wide Date.............	*	7.	9.	15.	50.	100.	200.	500.	—
1829...................	1,414,500	6.	8.	12.	30.	60.	100.	250.	500.
1830...................	1,711,500	6.	8.	12.	30.	60.	100.	250.	500.
1831...................	3,359,260	6.	8.	10.	20.	50.	90.	200.	350.
1832...................	2,362,000	6.	8.	10.	20.	50.	80.	175.	325.
1833...................	2,739,000	6.	8.	10.	20.	50.	80.	175.	325.
1834...................	1,855,100	6.	8.	10.	20.	70.	100.	200.	350.
1835...................	3,878,400	6.	8.	10.	20.	65.	90.	200.	350.
1836...................	2,111,000	6.	8.	10.	20.	55.	85.	160.	300.

* Included in number above.

Matron Head Modified (1837–1839)

G-4 GOOD—Considerably worn. LIBERTY readable.
VG-8 VERY GOOD—Hairlines smooth but visible; outline of ear clearly defined.
F-12 FINE—Hairlines at top of head and behind ear worn but visible. Braid over brow plain; ear clear.
VF-20 VERY FINE—All details sharper than for F-12. Only slight wear on hair over brow.
EF-40 EXTREMELY FINE—Hair above ear detailed, but slightly worn.
AU-50 ABOUT UNCIRCULATED—Trace of wear on high points of hair above ear and eye and on highest points on leaves and bow.
MS-60 UNCIRCULATED—Typical brown surface. No trace of wear.
MS-63 CHOICE UNCIRCULATED—Some distracting contact marks or blemishes in prime focal areas. Impaired luster possible.

1839 Over 1836

Brilliant or red Uncirculated coins are worth more than prices shown. Cleaned or discolored pieces are worth less.

	Mintage	G-4	VG-8	F-12	VF-20	EF-40	AU-50	MS-60	MS-63
1837	5,558,300	$6.	$8.	$10.	$20.	$65.	$90.	$160.	$240.
1838	6,370,200	6.	8.	10.	20.	30.	85.	150.	210.
1839	3,128,661	6.	8.	10.	20.	40.	80.	150.	210.
1839, 9 Over 6, Plain Cords	*	110.	275.	500.	1,100.	2,500.	4,500.	—	—
1840	2,462,700	6.	8.	10.	20.	50.	80.	150.	275.
1841	1,597,367	6.	8.	10.	16.	40.	75.	150.	275.
1842	2,383,390	6.	8.	10.	16.	40.	75.	150.	250.

* Included in number above.

Small Letters

| "Head of 1840" Petite Head (1839–1843) | "Head of 1844" Mature Head (1843–1857) | **Large Letters** |

	Mintage	G-4	VG-8	F-12	VF-20	EF-40	AU-50	MS-60	MS-63
1843, Petite, Small Letters	2,425,342	$6.	$8.	$12.	$20.	$30.	$60.	$145.	$175.
1843, Petite, Large Letters		8.	10.	20.	35.	70.	125.	325.	575.
1843, Mature, Large Letters		7.	9.	15.	25.	50.	90.	160.	400.
1844, Normal Date	2,398,752	6.	8.	10.	18.	32.	65.	120.	175.
1844, 44 Over 81	*	7.	10.	16.	35.	110.	225.	475.	950.
1845	3,894,804	6.	8.	12.	20.	30	70.	125.	175.
1846	4,120,800	6.	8.	12	20.	30.	70.	125.	175.
1847	6,183,669	6.	8.	12.	20.	30.	70.	125.	175.
1847, 7 Over Small 7	*	7.	10.	15.	30.	65.	125.	300.	800.

* Included in number above.

	Mintage	G-4	VG-8	F-12	VF-20	EF-40	AU-50	MS-60	MS-63
1848	6,415,799	$6.	$8.	$12.	$18.	$30.	$70.	$110.	$150.
1849	4,178,500	6.	8.	12.	18.	30.	70.	125.	170.
1850	4,426,844	6.	8.	12.	18.	30.	70.	125.	170.

1844, 44 Over 81 **1851, 51 Over 81** **1847, 7 Over "Small" 7**

Brilliant or red Uncirculated coins are worth more than prices shown. Spotted, cleaned, or discolored pieces are worth less.

	Mintage	G-4	VG-8	F-12	VF-20	EF-40	AU-50	MS-60	MS-63
1851, Normal Date	9,889,707	$6.	$8.	$12.	$18.	$30.	$70.	$125.	$170.
1851, 51 Over 81	*	8.	10.	16.	28.	70.	110.	250.	425.
1852	5,063,094	6.	8.	12.	18.	30.	70.	125.	170.
1853	6,641,131	6.	8.	12.	18.	30.	70.	125.	170.
1854	4,236,156	6.	8.	12.	18.	30.	70.	125.	170.

* Included in number above.

1855, Upright 5's **1855, Slanting 5's** **1855, Knob on Ear**

	Mintage	G-4	VG-8	F-12	VF-20	EF-40	AU-50	MS-60	MS-63
1855, All kinds	1,574,829								
1855, Upright 5's		$6.	$8.	$12.	$18.	$30.	$70.	$125.	$170.
1855, Slanting 5's.		6.	8.	12.	18.	30.	70.	140.	175.
1855, Slanting 5's, Knob on Ear		6.	9.	13.	20.	35.	85.	150.	250.
1856, Upright 5	2,690,463	6.	8.	12.	18.	30.	70.	140.	170.
1856, Slanting 5	*	6.	8.	12.	18.	30.	70.	140.	170.

* Included in number above.

1857, Large Date **1857, Small Date**

	Mintage	G-4	VG-8	F-12	VF-20	EF-40	AU-50	MS-60	MS-63
1857, Large Date	333,546	$15.	$25.	$30.	$35.	$50.	$100.	$175.	$275.
1857, Small Date	*	16.	27.	32.	40.	55.	115.	200.	300.

* Included in number above.

FLYING EAGLE (1856–1858)

The Act of February 21, 1857 provided for the coinage of the small cent. The 1856 Flying Eagle cent was not an authorized Mint issue, as the law governing the new size coin was enacted after the date of issue. It is believed that nearly 1,000 original strikings and 1,500 or more restrikes were made of the 1856. They are properly referred to as patterns.

G-4 GOOD—All details worn, but readable.
VG-8 VERY GOOD—Details in eagle's feathers and eye evident, but worn.
F-12 FINE—Eagle-head details and feather tips sharp.
VF-20 VERY FINE—Considerable detail visible in feathers in right wing and tail.
EF-40 EXTREMELY FINE—Slight wear, all details sharp.
AU-50 ABOUT UNCIRCULATED—Slight wear on eagle's left wing and breast.
MS-60 UNCIRCULATED—No trace of wear. Light blemishes.
MS-63 CHOICE UNCIRCULATED—Some distracting contact marks or blemishes in prime focal areas. Some impairment of luster possible.
PF-63 CHOICE PROOF—Nearly perfect.

| **1858, 8 Over 7** | **1856–1858, Large Letters** | **1858, Small Letters** |

Brilliant Uncirculated and Proof coins are worth more than prices shown. Spotted, cleaned, or discolored pieces are worth less.

	Mintage	G-4	VG-8	F-12	VF-20	EF-40	AU-50	MS-60	MS-63	PF-63
1856	2,000	$3,750.	$4,250.	$4,750.	$5,500.	$6,000.	$6,500.	$7,000.	$9,500.	$10,000.
1857 . . . (485) . . 17,450,000		10.	12.	16.	27.	75.	95.	185.	340.	3,750.
1858, Large Letters (80) . . 24,600,000		10.	12.	16.	27.	75.	95.	185.	340.	3,750.
1858, Small Letters (200) . . . . *		10.	12.	16.	27.	75.	95.	185.	340.	3,750.
1858, 8 Over 7		45.	95.	200.	400.	700.	1,200.	4,200.		

* Included in number above.

INDIAN HEAD (1859–1909)

The small cent was redesigned in 1859, and a representation of an Indian princess was adopted as the obverse device. The 1859 reverse was also changed to represent a laurel wreath. In 1860 the reverse was modified to display an oak wreath with a small shield at the top. From 1859 to 1863, cents were struck in copper-nickel. In 1864 the composition was changed to bronze, although copper-nickel cents were also struck during that year.

SMALL CENTS

G-4 GOOD—No LIBERTY visible.
VG-8 VERY GOOD—At least some letters of LIBERTY readable on head band.
F-12 FINE—LIBERTY mostly visible.
VF-20 VERY FINE—Slight but even wear on LIBERTY.
EF-40 EXTREMELY FINE—LIBERTY sharp. All other details sharp. Only slight wear on ribbon end.
AU-50 ABOUT UNCIRCULATED—Very slight trace of wear above the ear and the lowest curl of hair.
MS-60 UNCIRCULATED—No trace of wear. Light blemishes.
MS-63 CHOICE UNCIRCULATED—Some distracting contact marks or blemishes in prime focal areas. Impaired luster possible.
PF-63 CHOICE PROOF—Nearly perfect.

**Without Shield at Top of Wreath
(1859 Only)**

**With Shield on Reverse
(1860–1909)**

Variety 1 – Copper-Nickel, Laurel Wreath Reverse (1859)

Brilliant or red Uncirculated coins are worth more than prices shown. Spotted, cleaned, or discolored pieces are worth less.

	Mintage	G-4	VG-8	F-12	VF-20	EF-40	AU-50	MS-60	MS-63	PF-63
1859 . . . . .(800). . . 36,400,000		$6.	$7.	$9.	$26.	$52.	$95.	$125.	$250.	$725.

Variety 2 – Copper-Nickel, Oak Wreath With Shield (1860–1864)

	Mintage	G-4	VG-8	F-12	VF-20	EF-40	AU-50	MS-60	MS-63	PF-63
1860 . . .(1,000). . . 20,566,000		$5.00	$6.00	$7.	$9.	$30.	$60.	$100.	$160.	$475.
1861 . . .(1,000). . . 10,100,000		10.00	12.00	16.	30.	60.	80.	125.	175.	550.
1862 . . . . .(550). . . 28,075,000		5.00	5.50	6.	8.	20.	35.	60.	90.	425.
1863 . . . . .(460). . . 49,840,000		5.00	5.50	6.	8.	20.	35.	60.	90.	425.
1864 . . . . .(370). . . 13,740,000		7.00	9.00	13.	22.	35.	60.	100.	125.	450.

Variety 3 – Bronze (1864–1909)

1864, Indian Head Cent With "L"

	Mintage	G-4	VG-8	F-12	VF-20	EF-40	AU-50	MS-60	MS-63	PF-63
1864, All kinds . . . 39,233,714										
1864, No L										
. . . . . .(150).		$3.50	$5.50	$8.	$20.	$30.	$38.	$50.	$75.	$450.
1864, w/L (20).		20.00	35.00	50.	85.	140.	175.	200.	325.	—
1865 . . . .(500). . . 35,429,286		3.50	4.50	8.	10.	18.	30.	45.	75.	300.
1866 . . . .(725). . . . 9,826,500		19.00	22.00	30.	55.	85.	130.	150.	240.	300.
1867 . . . .(625). . . . 9,821,000		19.00	22.00	30.	55.	85.	130.	150.	240.	300.
1868 . . . .(600). . . 10,266,500		19.00	22.00	30.	55.	85.	130.	150.	240.	300.
1869 . . . .(600). . . . 6,420,000		30.00	35.00	85.	135.	200.	245.	275.	400.	300.
1870 . .(1,000). . . . 5,275,000		25.00	30.00	80.	120.	175.	245.	275.	425.	300.
1871 . . . .(960). . . . 3,929,500		30.00	40.00	115.	165.	200.	270.	325.	460.	330.
1872 . . . .(950). . . . 4,042,000		35.00	50.00	150.	200.	250.	350.	400.	600.	375.
1873 . .(1,100). . . 11,676,500		10.00	13.00	22.	35.	75.	90.	110.	200.	225.
1874 . . . .(700). . . 14,187,500		8.00	10.00	13.	25.	50.	80.	100.	150.	200.
1875 . . . .(700). . . 13,528,000		9.00	12.00	18.	30.	45.	70.	100.	150.	200.
1876 . .(1,150). . . . 7,944,000		14.00	17.00	18.	55.	90.	130.	170.	250.	200.
1877 . . . .(900). 852,500		350.00	420.00	525.	800.	1,000.	1,350.	1,750.	2,300.	1,750.

Brilliant or red Uncirculated coins are worth more than prices shown. Spotted, cleaned, or discolored pieces are worth less.

	Mintage	G-4	VG-8	F-12	VF-20	EF-40	AU-50	MS-60	MS-63	PF-63
1878	(2,350)....5,797,500	$13.00	$16.00	$22.00	$60.00	$90.	$130.	$165.	$225.	$185.
1879	(3,200)...16,228,000	3.50	5.00	7.00	15.00	35.	40.	50.	80.	150.
1880	(3,955)...38,961,000	1.50	1.75	2.75	5.00	13.	22.	30.	60.	125.
1881	(3,575)...39,208,000	1.50	1.75	2.75	3.75	9.	14.	26.	40.	125.
1882	(3,100)...38,578,000	1.50	1.75	2.75	3.75	9.	14.	26.	40.	125.
1883	(6,609)...45,591,500	1.50	1.75	2.75	3.75	9.	14.	26.	40.	125.
1884	(3,942)...23,257,800	1.75	2.00	3.00	5.50	12.	18.	30.	50.	125.
1885	(3,790)...11,761,594	2.75	3.00	5.00	12.00	30.	40.	60.	85.	125.
1886	(4,290)...17,650,000	1.50	2.50	7.00	20.00	60.	75.	100.	125.	135.
1887	(2,960)...45,223,523	1.00	1.25	1.50	2.00	7.	12.	25.	40.	125.
1888	(4,582)...37,489,832	.70	1.00	1.70	2.50	7.	12.	25.	40.	125.
1889	(3,336)...48,866,025	.70	1.00	1.70	2.50	5.	11.	22.	40.	125.
1890	(2,740)...57,180,114	.70	1.00	1.70	2.50	5.	11.	22.	40.	125.
1891	(2,350)...47,070,000	.70	1.00	1.70	2.50	5.	11.	22.	40.	125.
1892	(2,745)...37,647,087	.70	1.00	1.70	2.50	5.	11.	22.	40.	125.
1893	(2,195)...46,640,000	.70	1.00	1.70	2.50	5.	11.	22.	40.	125.
1894	(2,632)...16,749,500	1.75	2.00	3.75	6.00	20.	25.	30.	50.	150.
1895	(2,062)...38,341,574	.75	1.00	1.20	1.75	5.	10.	22.	40.	125.
1896	(1,862)...39,055,431	.75	1.00	1.20	1.75	5.	10.	22.	40.	125.
1897	(1,938)...50,464,392	.75	1.00	1.20	1.75	5.	10.	22.	40.	125.
1898	(1,795)...49,821,284	.75	1.00	1.20	1.75	5.	10.	22.	40.	125.
1899	(2,031)...53,598,000	.75	1.00	1.20	1.75	5.	10.	22.	40.	125.
1900	(2,262)...66,831,502	.70	.90	1.00	1.25	4.	9.	18.	37.	100.
1901	(1,985)...79,609,158	.70	.90	1.00	1.25	4.	9.	18.	37.	100.
1902	(2,018)...87,374,704	.70	.90	1.00	1.25	4.	9.	18.	37.	100.
1903	(1,790)...85,092,703	.70	.90	1.00	1.25	4.	9.	18.	37.	100.
1904	(1,817)...61,326,198	.70	.90	1.00	1.25	4.	9.	18.	37.	100.
1905	(2,152)...80,717,011	.70	.90	1.00	1.25	4.	9.	18.	37.	100.
1906	(1,725)...96,020,530	.70	.90	1.00	1.25	4.	9.	18.	37.	100.
1907	(1,475)..108,137,143	.70	.90	1.00	1.25	4.	9.	18.	37.	100.

Location of Mintmark S on Reverse of Indian Cent (1908 and 1909 Only)

	Mintage	G-4	VG-8	F-12	VF-20	EF-40	AU-50	MS-60	MS-63	PF-63
1908	(1,620)...32,326,367	$.70	$.90	$1.00	$1.25	$4.00	$9.	$18.	$37.	$100.
1908S	1,115,000	30.00	40.00	45.00	50.00	75.00	95.	150.	250.	
1909	(2,175)...14,368,470	1.50	2.00	1.75	2.50	7.50	12.	20.	35.	100.
1909S	309,000	170.00	200.00	210.00	250.00	300.00	350.	450.	575.	

LINCOLN, WHEAT EARS REVERSE (1909–1958)

Victor D. Brenner designed this cent which was issued to commemorate the 100th anniversary of Lincoln's birth. The designer's initials V.D.B. appear on the reverse of a limited quantity of cents of 1909. Later in the year they were removed from the dies but restored in 1918 as very small incuse letters beneath the shoulder. The Lincoln type was the first cent to have the motto IN GOD WE TRUST.

G-4 GOOD—Date worn but apparent. Lines in wheat heads missing. Full rims.
VG-8 VERY GOOD—Half of lines visible in upper wheat heads.
F-12 FINE—Wheat lines worn but visible.
VF-20 VERY FINE—Lincoln's cheekbone and jawbone worn but separated. No worn spots on wheat heads.
EF-40 EXTREMELY FINE—Slight wear. All details sharp.
AU-50 ABOUT UNCIRCULATED—Slight wear on cheek and jaw and on wheat stalks.
MS-60 UNCIRCULATED—No trace of wear. Light blemishes or discoloration.
MS-63 CHOICE UNCIRCULATED—No trace of wear. Slight blemishes. Red-brown color.
MS-65 GEM UNCIRCULATED—No trace of wear. Barely noticeable blemishes. Nearly full red color.
PF-63 CHOICE PROOF—Reflective surfaces with only a few blemishes in secondary focal places. No major flaws.

Location of mintmark S or D on obverse of Lincoln cent.

**Designer's Initials
V.D.B. (1909 Only)**

**No V.D.B. on Reverse
(1909–1958)**

Brilliant Uncirculated coins are worth more than prices shown. Spotted, cleaned, or discolored pieces are worth less.

	Mintage	G-4	VG-8	F-12	VF-20	EF-40	AU-50	MS-60	MS-63
1909, V.D.B.	27,995,000	$2.00	$2.25	$2.50	$2.75	$3.00	$4.25	$6.	$8.
1909, V.D.B., Proof **(a)**	(1,194)								800.
1909S, V.D.B.	484,000	300.00	350.00	375.00	475.00	600.00	675.00	750.	900.
1909	72,702,618	.50	.70	.75	1.25	1.75	3.00	8.	12.
1909 **(a)**	(2,352)								180.
1909S	1,825,000	35.00	40.00	50.00	70.00	90.00	100.00	125.	200.
1910	146,801,218	.05	.10	.15	.20	.75	2.50	9.	13.
1910 **(a)**	(4,083)								150.
1910S	6,045,000	4.00	5.00	6.00	7.00	15.00	30.00	40.	50.
1911	101,177,787	.05	.10	.25	.40	1.00	3.00	10.	25.
1911 **(a)**	(2,411)								175.
1911D	12,672,000	1.75	2.25	3.75	8.00	17.00	30.00	45.	65.
1911S	4,026,000	9.00	10.00	11.00	15.00	25.00	40.00	80.	130.
1912	68,153,060	.10	.25	.50	1.50	2.50	8.00	17.	25.
1912 **(a)**	(2,145)								150.
1912D	10,411,000	2.50	2.75	3.50	7.50	23.00	35.00	70.	115.
1912S	4,431,000	5.00	6.50	7.50	10.00	23.00	35.00	70.	100.
1913	76,532,352	.10	.20	.40	1.25	6.00	10.00	15.	25.
1913 **(a)**	(2,848)								150.
1913D	15,804,000	.75	1.00	1.50	3.50	12.00	20.00	50.	90.
1913S	6,101,000	3.00	4.00	5.00	6.00	17.00	35.00	75.	125.
1914	75,238,432	.10	.25	.50	1.50	5.00	15.00	25.	35.
1914 **(a)**	(1,365)								180.
1914D **(b)**	1,193,000	75.00	90.00	110.00	175.00	325.00	600.00	800.	1,500.
1914S	4,137,000	5.00	6.00	8.00	12.00	30.00	70.00	135.	230.
1915	29,092,120	.30	.50	1.35	3.50	20.00	30.00	45.	60.
1915 **(a)**	(1,150)								275.
1915D	22,050,000	.35	.50	.65	2.00	8.00	20.00	40.	55.
1915S	4,833,000	3.50	4.00	5.00	10.00	22.00	55.00	90.	140.
1916	131,833,677	.03	.05	.10	.30	1.00	5.00	10.	15.
1916 **(a)**	(1,050)								
1916D	35,956,000	.08	.13	.40	.75	5.00	10.00	35.	50.
1916S	22,510,000	.30	.40	.75	1.50	6.00	15.00	38.	70.
1917	196,429,785	.03	.05	.10	.25	.60	3.00	10.	15.
1917D	55,120,000	.08	.10	.25	1.00	6.00	14.00	35.	45.
1917S	32,620,000	.08	.10	.25	.50	2.75	12.00	35.	60.

a. Matte Proof. **b.** Beware of altered date or mintmark. No V.D.B. on shoulder of genuine 1914-D cent.

Designer's initials placed on Lincoln's shoulder next to rim, starting 1918.

Brilliant Uncirculated coins before 1934 are worth more than prices shown. Spotted, cleaned, or discolored pieces are worth less.

	Mintage	G-4	VG-8	F-12	VF-20	EF-40	AU-50	MS-60	MS-63
1918	288,104,634	$.03	$.05	$.10	$.20	$1.00	$3.00	$6.00	$15.00
1918D	47,830,000	.08	.13	.35	1.00	6.00	9.00	32.00	65.00
1918S	34,680,000	.08	.13	.35	.80	3.00	15.00	35.00	75.00
1919	392,021,000	.03	.04	.05	.15	.75	1.50	5.00	14.00
1919D	57,154,000	.04	.06	.10	.40	2.00	15.00	28.00	50.00
1919S	139,760,000	.04	.06	.10	.30	1.35	7.00	18.00	42.00
1920	310,165,000	.03	.04	.05	.15	.50	1.50	6.00	12.00
1920D	49,280,000	.04	.06	.10	.30	3.00	12.00	33.00	50.00
1920S	46,220,000	.04	.06	.10	.30	2.00	15.00	42.00	100.00
1921	39,157,000	.05	.08	.15	.35	1.50	6.00	22.00	38.00
1921S	15,274,000	.35	.50	.70	1.50	12.00	35.00	50.00	100.00
1922D	7,160,000	3.50	4.50	5.00	8.00	14.00	25.00	42.00	60.00
1922, No D (c)	*	220.00	275.00	300.00	450.00	950.00	1,750.00	3,500.00	9,500.00
1923	74,723,000	.03	.04	.05	.15	1.00	2.50	7.00	14.00
1923S	8,700,000	.50	.60	.75	2.00	14.00	35.00	100.00	175.00
1924	75,178,000	.03	.04	.06	.15	1.50	3.50	15.00	25.00
1924D	2,520,000	7.00	10.00	12.00	19.00	40.00	80.00	140.00	175.00
1924S	11,696,000	.35	.45	.70	1.00	6.00	28.00	55.00	100.00
1925	139,949,000	.03	.04	.05	.15	.50	2.00	5.00	10.00
1925D	22,580,000	.04	.06	.10	.30	3.00	11.00	27.00	38.00
1925S	26,380,000	.04	.06	.10	.25	3.00	14.00	40.00	75.00
1926	157,088,000	.03	.04	.05	.15	.50	2.00	5.00	8.00
1926D	28,020,000	.04	.06	.10	.30	2.50	9.00	35.00	50.00
1926S	4,550,000	.85	1.25	2.00	2.50	7.00	20.00	60.00	115.00
1927	144,440,000	.03	.04	.05	.20	.50	1.00	5.00	10.00
1927D	27,170,000	.04	.06	.10	.25	1.00	4.00	25.00	40.00
1927S	14,276,000	.25	.30	.50	1.00	4.00	11.00	35.00	70.00
1928	134,116,000	.03	.04	.05	.15	.50	1.00	4.50	10.00
1928D	31,170,000	.04	.06	.10	.25	.85	4.00	15.00	34.00
1928S	17,266,000	.06	.10	.25	.50	1.50	5.00	34.00	55.00
1929	185,262,000	.03	.04	.05	.15	.35	1.50	4.00	6.00
1929D	41,730,000	.04	.06	.10	.25	1.00	2.00	12.00	15.00
1929S	50,148,000	.03	.05	.10	.15	.60	1.75	7.00	11.00
1930	157,415,000	.03	.04	.05	.15	.25	.75	2.00	3.50
1930D	40,100,000	.04	.06	.10	.25	.60	1.00	5.00	10.00
1930S	24,286,000	.03	.05	.10	.15	.40	2.00	3.50	5.00
1931	19,396,000	.15	.20	.30	.40	.60	2.00	10.00	15.00
1931D	4,480,000	1.00	1.25	1.50	2.00	4.00	10.00	30.00	40.00
1931S	866,000	30.00	35.00	37.00	40.00	45.00	50.00	60.00	70.00
1932	9,062,000	.40	.50	.60	1.00	1.25	3.50	10.00	13.00
1932D	10,500,000	.25	.35	.40	.50	.85	3.00	10.00	15.00
1933	14,360,000	.25	.35	.45	.60	1.10	3.50	10.00	15.00
1933D	6,200,000	.60	.75	1.00	1.25	1.75	4.00	12.00	15.00
1934	219,080,000	.03	.03	.03	.03	.10	1.00	3.00	4.00
1934D	28,446,000	.04	.06	.08	.10	.25	1.25	7.50	14.00
1935	245,388,000	.03	.03	.03	.04	.06	.20	2.00	3.00
1935D	47,000,000	.03	.03	.03	.04	.20	.50	3.00	4.00
1935S	38,702,000	.03	.04	.04	.04	.12	1.25	4.00	6.00
1936	309,632,000	.03	.03	.03	.04	.06	.25	1.00	3.00
1936, PF-63	(5,569)								85.00
1936D	40,620,000	.03	.03	.03	.04	.08	.20	1.00	3.00
1936S	29,130,000	.03	.03	.03	.04	.10	.20	1.00	3.00

* Included in number above. **c.** 1922 cents with a weak or missing mintmark were made from extremely worn dies that originally struck normal 1922-D cents. Three different die pairs were involved; two of them produced "Weak D" coins. One die pair (no. 2, identified by a "strong reverse") is acknowledged as striking "No D" coins. Weak D cents are worth considerably less. Beware of removed mintmark.

SMALL CENTS

	Mintage	G-4	VG-8	F-12	VF-20	EF-40	MS-60	MS-63	MS-65	PF-63
1937 (9,320)..309,170,000		$.02	$.02	$.02	$.03	$.05	$.20	$.50	$3.00	
1937, Proof										$34.00
1937D..........50,430,000		.02	.02	.02	.03	.06	.30	.75	4.00	
1937S..........34,500,000		.03	.03	.03	.04	.06	.30	.80	4.00	
1938 (14,734)..156,682,000		.02	.02	.02	.03	.05	.30	.75	2.00	
1938, Proof										25.00
1938D..........20,010,000		.02	.03	.04	.06	.15	.50	1.00	5.00	
1938S..........15,180,000		.06	.08	.10	.12	.15	.30	1.00	4.00	
1939 (13,520)..316,466,000		.02	.02	.02	.03	.05	.20	.30	2.50	
1939, Proof										23.00
1939D..........15,160,000		.06	.08	.10	.12	.15	.35	1.00	4.00	
1939S..........52,070,000		.03	.03	.03	.04	.10	.30	.70	4.00	
1940 (15,872)..586,810,000		.02	.02	.02	.03	.03	.20	.30	2.00	
1940, Proof										16.00
1940D..........81,390,000		.02	.02	.02	.03	.03	.20	.40	2.00	
1940S..........112,940,000		.02	.02	.02	.03	.04	.20	.40	2.75	
1941 (21,100)..887,018,000		.02	.02	.02	.03	.03	.20	.30	2.00	
1941, Proof										15.00
1941D..........128,700,000		.02	.02	.02	.03	.03	.40	.80	3.00	
1941S..........92,360,000		.02	.02	.02	.03	.04	.35	.80	5.00	
1942 (32,600)..657,796,000		.02	.02	.02	.03	.03	.10	.15	1.00	
1942, Proof										15.00
1942D..........206,698,000		.02	.02	.02	.03	.03	.10	.15	2.00	
1942S..........85,590,000		.02	.02	.02	.03	.10	1.00	2.00	8.00	

Variety 2 – Zinc-Coated Steel (1943)

	Mintage	F-12	VF-20	EF-40	MS-60	MS-63	MS-65
1943 684,628,670		$.05	$.10	$.15	$.30	$.70	$2.00
1943D 217,660,000		.05	.10	.15	.35	1.25	3.00
1943S 191,550,000		.06	.12	.20	.60	1.50	5.00

Variety 1 (Bronze) Resumed (1944–1958)

	Mintage	VF-20	EF-40	MS-63	MS-65
1944.......................... 1,435,400,000		$.02	$.03	$.15	$.50
1944D.......................... 430,578,000		.02	.03	.20	.50
1944D, D Over S........................ *		75.00	90.00	225.00	600.00
1944S.......................... 282,760,000		.02	.03	.15	1.50
1945.......................... 1,040,515,000		.02	.03	.20	.50
1945D.......................... 266,268,000		.02	.03	.15	.50
1945S.......................... 181,770,000		.02	.03	.10	2.00
1946.......................... 991,655,000		.02	.03	.10	.50
1946D.......................... 315,690,000		.02	.03	.15	1.00
1946S.......................... 198,100,000		.02	.03	.15	1.25
1947.......................... 190,555,000		.02	.03	.25	.50
1947D.......................... 194,750,000		.02	.02	.12	.50

* Included in number above.

1944-D, D Over S

1955, Doubled-Die Error

	Mintage	VF-20	EF-40	MS-63	MS-65
1947S 99,000,000		$.02	$.03	$.15	$1.50
1948 317,570,000		.02	.02	.15	.50
1948D 172,637,500		.02	.02	.12	.60
1948S 81,735,000		.02	.03	.20	1.50
1949 217,775,000		.02	.02	.30	.75
1949D 153,132,500		.02	.02	.20	.75

Chart continued on next page.

	Mintage	VF-20	EF-40	MS-63	MS-65	PF-65
1949S	64,290,000	$.03	$.05	$.50	$2.00	
1950 ....(51,386)	272,635,000	.02	.02	.25	.50	$30.00
1950D	334,950,000	.02	.02	.10	.50	
1950S	118,505,000	.02	.03	.25	.80	
1951 ....(57,500)	284,576,000	.02	.02	.25	.80	35.00
1951D	625,355,000	.02	.02	.10	.50	
1951S	136,010,000	.02	.03	.30	.60	
1952 ....(81,980)	186,775,000	.02	.02	.15	.60	25.00
1952D	746,130,000	.02	.02	.15	.60	
1952S	137,800,004	.02	.03	.50	1.50	
1953 ....(128,800)	256,755,000	.02	.03	.10	.50	25.00
1953D	700,515,000	.02	.02	.10	.50	
1953S	181,835,000	.02	.03	.12	.50	
1954 ....(233,300)	6,940,050	.03	.05	.10	.50	11.00
1954D	251,552,500	.02	.02	.05	.30	
1954S	96,190,000	.02	.03	.05	.30	
1955, Doubled-Die Obv	*	475.00	650.00	(a)1,000.00	1,100.00	
1955 ....(378,200)	330,958,200	.02	.02	.06	.30	10.00
1955D	563,257,500	.02	.02	.05	.25	
1955S	44,610,000	.10	.15	.15	.50	
1956 ....(669,384)	420,745,000	.02	.02	.05	.25	1.75
1956D	1,098,201,100	.02	.02	.05	.30	
1957 ....(1,247,952)	282,540,000	.02	.02	.05	.30	1.75
1957D	1,051,342,000	.02	.02	.03	.30	
1958 ....(875,652)	252,525,000	.02	.02	.03	.30	2.00
1958D	800,953,300	.02	.02	.03	.30	

* Included in regular mintage. **a.** Value for MS-60 Uncirculated is $800.00.

LINCOLN, MEMORIAL REVERSE (1959 TO DATE)

Small Date   Large Date

	Mintage	MS-63	MS-65	PF-65
1959	(1,149,291) 609,715,000	$.01	$.10	$1.00
1959D	1,279,760,000	.01	.10	
1960, Large Date	(1,691,602) 586,405,000	.01	.10	.50
1960, Small Date	(1,691,602) ....*	1.00	2.50	9.00
1960D, Large Date	1,580,884,000	.01	.10	
1960D, Small Date	*	.02	.10	
1961	(3,028,244) 753,345,000	.01	.10	.50
1961D	1,753,266,700	.01	.10	
1962	(3,218,019) 606,045,000	.01	.10	.50
1962D	1,793,148,140	.01	.10	
1963	(3,075,645) 754,110,000	.01	.10	.50
1963D	1,774,020,400	.01	.10	
1964	(3,950,762) .. 2,648,575,000	.01	.10	.50
1964D	3,799,071,500	.01	.10	
1965	1,497,224,900	.02	.12	
1966	2,188,147,783	.04	.12	
1967	3,048,667,100	.03	.12	
1968	1,707,880,970	.02	.12	
1968D	2,886,269,600	.01	.10	
1968S	(3,041,506) 258,270,001	.02	.10	.50
1969	1,136,910,000	.05	.20	
1969D	4,002,832,200	.03	.10	
1969S	(2,934,631) 544,375,000	.03	.10	.50
1969S, Doubled-Die Obverse	*	—	—	

* Included in number above.

SMALL CENTS

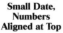

Small Date,
Numbers
Aligned at Top

Large Date,
Low 7 in Date

Enlarged Detail of 1972
Doubled-Die Error

1969-S, Doubled-
Die Error

	Mintage	MS-63	MS-65	PF-65
1970	1,898,315,000	$.05	$.10	
1970D	2,891,438,900	.02	.10	
1970S, Small Date (High 7) ....(2,632,810)	690,560,004	13.00	22.00	$25.00
1970S, Large Date (Low 7)	*	.03	.10	.25
1971	1,919,490,000	.05	.20	
1971D	2,911,045,600	.03	.20	
1971S	(3,220,733) 525,133,459	.03	.20	.25
1972, Doubled-Die Obverse	**	175.00	250.00	
1972	2,933,255,000	.01	.05	
1972D	2,665,071,400	.02	.10	
1972S	(3,260,996) 376,939,108	.02	.10	.25
1973	3,728,245,000	.01	.10	
1973D	3,549,576,588	.01	.10	
1973S	(2,760,339) 317,177,295	.02	.10	.25
1974	4,232,140,523	.01	.10	
1974D	4,235,098,000	.01	.10	
1974S	(2,612,568) 409,426,660	.03	.10	.25
1975	5,451,476,142	.01	.10	
1975D	4,505,275,300	.01	.10	
1975S	(2,845,450)			1.50
1976	4,674,292,426	.01	.10	
1976D	4,221,592,455	.02	.10	
1976S	(4,149,730)			1.25
1977	4,469,930,000	.01	.10	
1977D	4,194,062,300	.01	.10	
1977S	(3,251,152)			1.00
1978	5,558,605,000	.01	.10	
1978D	4,280,233,400	.01	.10	
1978S	(3,127,781)			1.00
1979	6,018,515,000	.01	.10	
1979D	4,139,357,254	.01	.10	
1979S, Filled S				1.50
1979S, Clear S				1.75
1980	7,414,705,000	.01	.10	
1980D	5,140,098,660	.01	.10	
1980S	(3,554,806)			1.00
1981	7,491,750,000	.01	.10	
1981D	5,373,235,677	.01	.10	
1981S, Filled S	(4,063,083)			1.50
1981S, Clear S	*			1.75
1982, Large Date	10,712,525,000	.01	.10	
1982, Small Date	*	.02	.12	
1982D, Large Date	6,012,979,368	.01	.10	
1982S	(3,857,479)			.80

* Included in number above.   ** Included in number below.

Large Date

Small Date

1995, Doubled Die showing strong doubling on word "LIBERTY".

Copper-Plated Zinc (1982 to Date)

	Mintage	MS-63	MS-65	PF-65		Mintage	MS-63	MS-65	PF-65
1982, Large Date	........*	$.01	$.05		1994D	7,131,765,000	$.01	$.05	
1982, Small Date	........*	.01	.05		1994S	.......(3,269,923)			$2.00
1982D, Large Date	......*	.05	.50		1995	6,411,440,000	.01	.05	
1982D, Small Date	......*	.01	.05		1995, DblDie Obv	....		10.00	
1983	7,752,355,000	.01	.05		1995D	7,128,560,000	.01	.05	
1983D	6,467,199,428	.01	.05		1995S	.......(2,797,481)			2.00
1983S	.......(3,279,126)	.01	.05	$1.10	1996	6,612,465,000	.01	.05	
1984	8,151,079,000	.01	.05		1996D	6,510,795,000	.01	.05	
1984, Doubled Ear	....	50.00	100.00		1996S	.......(2,525,265)			1.25
1984D	5,569,238,906	.01	.05		1997	4,622,800,000	.01	.05	
1984S	.......(3,065,110)			1.10	1997D	4,576,555,000	.01	.05	
1985	5,648,489,887	.01	.05		1997S	.......(2,796,678)			2.00
1985D	5,287,339,926	.01	.05		1998	5,032,155,000	.01	.05	
1985S	3,362,821			1.25	1998, Wide AM **(a)**	....		6.00	
1986	4,491,395,493	.01	.05		1998D	5,225,353,500	.01	.05	
1986D	4,442,866,698	.01	.05		1998S	.......(2,086,507)			2.00
1986S	.......(3,010,497)			2.00	1999	5,237,600,000	.01	.05	
1987	4,682,466,931	.01	.05		1999, Wide AM **(a)**	....		—	
1987D	4,879,389,514	.01	.05		1999D	6,360,065,000	.01	.05	
1987S	.......(4,227,728)			1.10	1999S	.......(2,543,401)			1.00
1988	6,092,810,000	.01	.05		1999S, Close AM	....			—
1988D	5,253,740,443	.01	.05		2000	5,503,200,000	.01	.05	
1988S	.......(3,262,948)			3.25	2000, Wide AM **(a)**	....	2.00	2.50	
1989	7,261,535,000	.01	.05		2000D	8,774,220,000	.01	.05	
1989D	5,345,467,111	.01	.05		2000S	.......(3,082,483)			1.00
1989S	.......(3,220,194)			3.00	2001	4,959,600,000	.01	.05	
1990	6,851,765,000	.01	.05		2001D	5,374,990,000	.01	.05	
1990D	4,922,894,533	.01	.05		2001S	.......(2,294,043)			1.00
1990S	.......(3,299,559)			2.00	2002	3,260,800,000	.01	.05	
1990, Pf, No S	....			—	2002D	4,028,055,000	.01	.05	
1991	5,165,940,000	.01	.05		2002S	.......(2,277,720)			1.00
1991D	4,158,446,076	.01	.05		2003	3,330,000,000	.01	.05	
1991S	.......(2,867,787)			10.00	2003D	3,548,000,000	.01	.05	
1992	4,648,905,000	.01	.05		2003S	....			1.00
1992D	4,448,673,300	.01	.05		2004	3,379,600,000	.01	.05	
1992D, Close AM **(a)**	......	—	—		2004D	3,456,400,000	.01	.05	
1992S	.......(4,176,560)			1.10	2004S	....			1.00
1993	5,684,705,000	.01	.05		2005	....	.01	.05	
1993D	6,426,650,571	.01	.05		2005D	....	.01	.05	
1993S	.......(3,394,792)			2.00	2005S	....			1.00
1994	6,500,850,000	.01	.05						

* Included in previous page's mintages. **a.** Varieties were made using Proof dies that have a wide space between AM in AMERICA. The letters nearly touch on other Uncirculated cents.

TWO-CENT PIECES (1864–1873)

The Act of April 22, 1864, which changed the weight and composition of the cent, included a provision for the bronze two-cent piece. The weight was specified as 96 grains, the alloy being the same as for the cent. There are two varieties for the first year of issue, 1864: the Small Motto and the Large Motto. The differences are illustrated in the closeups below.

1864, Small Motto

1864, Large Motto

On the obverse the D in GOD is narrow on the Large Motto variety. The stem to the leaf shows plainly on the Small Motto variety.

G-4 GOOD—At least part of IN GOD visible.
VG-8 VERY GOOD—WE weakly visible
F-12 FINE—Complete motto visible. The word WE weak.
EF-40 EXTREMELY FINE—The word WE bold.
AU-50 ABOUT UNCIRCULATED—Traces of wear visible on leaf tips, arrow points, and the word WE.
MS-60 UNCIRCULATED—No trace of wear. Light blemishes.
MS-63 UNCIRCULATED—Some distracting contact marks or blemishes in prime focal areas. Some impairment of luster possible.
PF-63 CHOICE PROOF—Reflective surfaces with only a few blemishes in secondary focal places. No major flaws.

Brilliant red choice Uncirculated and Proof coins are worth more than prices shown. Cleaned or discolored pieces are worth less.

	Mintage	G-4	VG-8	F-12	VF-20	EF-40	AU-50	MS-60	MS-63	PF-63
1864, Small Motto	19,847,500	$55.	$70.	$90.	$175.	$280.	$350.	$435.	$560.	$9,000.
1864, Large										
Motto . . . . .*(100+)*.	*	7.	8.	10.	15.	22.	30.	55.	90.	275.
1865 . . . .*(500+)*. .	13,640,000	7.	8.	10.	15.	22.	30.	55.	90.	275.
1866 . . . .*(725+)*. . .	3,177,000	7.	8.	10.	15.	22.	30.	55.	90.	275.
1867 . . . .*(625+)*. . .	2,938,750	7.	8.	10.	15.	22.	30.	60.	100.	275.
1868 . . . .*(600+)*. . .	2,803,750	7.	8.	10.	15.	25.	35.	65.	110.	275.
1869 . . . .*(600+)*. . .	1,546,500	8.	9.	12.	17.	32.	60.	120.	140.	325.
1870 . . . .*(1,000+)*	861,250	10.	12.	18.	25.	60.	80.	150.	220.	375.
1871 . . . .*(960+)*	721,250	12.	14.	20.	30.	65.	90.	165.	225.	400.
1872 . . . .*(950+)*	65,000	120.	160.	180.	230.	350.	400.	500.	650.	550.
1873 . . . .*(1,000+)*.										1,000.

* Included in number above.

SILVER THREE-CENT PIECES (TRIMES) (1851–1873)

This smallest of United States silver coins was authorized by Congress March 3, 1851. The first three-cent silver pieces had no lines bordering the six-pointed star. From 1854 through 1858 there were three lines, while issues of the last 15 years show only two lines. Issues from 1854 through 1873 have an olive sprig over the III and a bundle of three arrows beneath.

G-4 GOOD—Star worn smooth. Legend and date readable.
VG-8 VERY GOOD—Outline of shield defined. Legend and date clear.
F-12 FINE—Only star points worn smooth.
VF-20 VERY FINE—Only partial wear on star ridges.
EF-40 EXTREMELY FINE—Ridges on star points visible.
AU-50 ABOUT UNCIRCULATED—Trace of wear visible at each star point. Center of shield possibly weak.
MS-60 UNCIRCULATED—No trace of wear. Light blemishes.
MS-63 CHOICE UNCIRCULATED—Some distracting contact marks or blemishes in prime focal areas. Some impairment of luster possible.
PF-63 CHOICE PROOF—Reflective surfaces with only a few blemishes in secondary focal places. No major flaws.

  Mintmark location. ←

No Outline Around Star

Well-struck specimens command higher prices.

	Mintage	G-4	VG-8	F-12	VF-20	EF-40	AU-50	MS-60	MS-63	PF-63
1851	5,447,400	$12.	$15.	$17.	$23.	$33.	$70.	$85.	$130.	—
1851O	720,000	15.	18.	21.	40.	75.	100.	175.	225.	
1852	18,663,500	12.	15.	17.	23.	33.	70.	85.	135.	—
1853	11,400,000	12.	15.	17.	23.	33.	70.	85.	135.	

Three Outlines to Star, Large Date

	Mintage	G-4	VG-8	F-12	VF-20	EF-40	AU-50	MS-60	MS-63	PF-63
1854	671,000	$13.	$16.	$18.	$25.	$55.	$115.	$175.	$325.	$6,000.
1855	139,000	15.	25.	30.	50.	95.	135.	135.	300.	2,100.
1856	1,458,000	12.	15.	18.	25.	50.	100.	160.	340.	1,700.
1857	1,042,000	12.	15.	18.	25.	50.	100.	160.	340.	1,500.
1858 *(300+)*	1,603,700	12.	15.	18.	25.	50.	100.	160.	340.	1,100.

Two Outlines to Star, Small Date

1862, 2 Over 1

	Mintage	G-4	VG-8	F-12	VF-20	EF-40	AU-50	MS-60	MS-63	PF-63
1859	(800)...364,200	$12.	$15.	$17.	$22.	$40.	$75.	$90.	$175.	$300.
1860	(1,000)...286,000	12.	15.	17.	22.	40.	75.	90.	175.	300.
1861	(1,000)...497,000	12.	15.	17.	22.	40.	75.	90.	175.	300.
1862, 2 Over 1	*	13.	16.	19.	25.	45.	90.	120.	215.	
1862	(550)...343,550	12.	15.	17.	22.	40.	75.	90.	175.	270.
1863	(460)....21,000				150.	175.	275.	350.	500.	300.
1864	(470)....12,000				150.	175.	275.	350.	500.	300.

* Included in number below.

THREE-CENT PIECES

	Mintage	VF-20	EF-40	AU-50	MS-60	MS-63	PF-63
1865 . . . .(500). . . . 8,000		$175.	$200.	$300.	$375.	$525.	$315.
1866 . . . .(725). . . 22,000		150.	175.	275.	350.	500.	315.
1867 . . . .(625). . . . 4,000		175.	200.	300.	375.	525.	315.
1868 . . . .(600). . . . 3,500		175.	200.	300.	375.	600.	315.
1869 . . . .(600). . . . 4,500		175.	200.	300.	375.	500.	315.
1870 . . . .(1,000). . . . 3,000		175.	200.	300.	375.	500.	325.
1871 . . . .(960). . . . 3,400		175.	200.	300.	375.	500.	325.
1872 . . . .(950). . . . 1,000		200.	225.	300.	375.	600.	350.
1873, Proof only (600)							550.

NICKEL THREE-CENT PIECES (1865–1889)

The three-cent pieces struck in nickel composition were designed to replace the silver three-cent coins. Composition is 75% copper and 25% nickel. All were coined at Philadelphia and have plain edges.

G-4 GOOD—Date and legends complete though worn. III smooth.
VG-8 VERY GOOD—III half worn. Rims complete.
VF-20 VERY FINE—Three-quarters of hair details visible.
EF-40 EXTREMELY FINE—Slight, even wear.
AU-50 ABOUT UNCIRCULATED—Slight wear on hair curls, above forehead, and on wreath and numeral III.
MS-60 UNCIRCULATED—No trace of wear. Light blemishes.
MS-63 CHOICE UNCIRCULATED—Some distracting contact marks or blemishes in prime focal areas. Some impairment of luster possible.
PF-63 CHOICE PROOF—Reflective surfaces with only a few blemishes in secondary focal places. No major flaws.

Brilliant choice Uncirculated and Proof coins are worth more than prices shown. Spotted, cleaned, or discolored pieces are worth less.

	Mintage	G-4	VG-8	F-12	VF-20	EF-40	AU-50	MS-60	MS-63	PF-63
1865. . . . . . . (500+)	11,382,000	$6.	$8.	$9.	$10.	$12.	$25.	$50.	$90.	$650.
1866. . . . . . . (725+)	4,801,000	6.	8.	9.	10.	12.	25.	50.	90.	160.
1867. . . . . . . (625+)	3,915,000	6.	8.	9.	10.	12.	25.	50.	90.	160.
1868. . . . . . . (600+)	3,252,000	6.	8.	9.	10.	12.	25.	50.	90.	160.
1869. . . . . . . (600+)	1,604,000	6.	8.	9.	10.	12.	25.	50.	90.	160.
1870. . . . . . (1,000+)	1,335,000	6.	8.	9.	10.	12.	25.	50.	90.	160.
1871. . . . . . . (960+)	604,000	6.	8.	9.	10.	12.	25.	50.	100.	160.
1872. . . . . . . (950+)	862,000	6.	8.	9.	10.	12.	25.	50.	100.	160.
1873 . . . . . (1,100+)	390,000	6.	8.	9.	10.	12.	25.	50.	90.	160.
1874. . . . . . . (700+)	790,000	7.	9.	10.	12.	15.	27.	60.	110.	160.
1875 . . . . (700+)	228,000	8.	10.	11.	13.	18.	32.	90.	110.	160.
1876 . . . . . (1,150+)	162,000	8.	10.	11.	14.	20.	35.	110.	125.	175.
1877, Pf only (510+)					550.	600.				900.
1878, Pf only (2,350)					325.	375.				475.
1879 . . . . . . (3,200). . . . 38,000		30.	35.	40.	50.	60.	70.	140.	200.	200.
1880 . . . . . . (3,955). . . . 21,000		45.	55.	65.	75.	85.	100.	160.	200.	200.
1881 . . . . . . (3,575)	1,077,000	6.	8.	9.	10.	12.	25.	50.	90.	160.
1882 . . . . . . (3,100). . . . 22,200		30.	40.	45.	50.	60.	80.	150.	200.	200.
1883 . . . . . . (6,609). 4,000		75.	85.	100.	125.	150.	175.	225.	375.	225.
1884 . . . . . . (3,942). 1,700		150.	175.	200.	250.	275.	300.	450.	550.	300.
1885 . . . . . . (3,790). 1,000		175.	200.	250.	300.	325.	350.	480.	600.	300.
1886, Pf only (4,290)					175.	200.				250.
1887, All kinds . . . . . (2,960). 5,001		120.	140.	150.	180.	200.	225.	250.	275.	250.
1887, 7/6 . . . . . . *					175.	200.				300.
1888 . . . . . . (4,582). . . . 36,501		20.	23.	27.	35.	45.	60.	140.	175.	185.
1889 . . . . . . (3,436). . . . 18,125		35.	50.	60.	75.	85.	100.	150.	200.	185.

* Included in number above.

SHIELD (1866–1883)

The Shield type nickel was made possible by the Act of May 16, 1866. Its weight was set at 77-16/100 grains with the same composition as the nickel three-cent piece.

G-4 GOOD—All letters in motto readable.
VG-8 VERY GOOD—Motto clear and stands out. Rims slightly worn but even. Part of shield lines visible.
F-12 FINE—Half of each olive leaf worn smooth.
EF-40 EXTREMELY FINE—Slight wear to leaf tips and cross over shield.
AU-50 ABOUT UNCIRCULATED—Traces of light wear on only the high design points. Half of mint luster present.
MS-60 UNCIRCULATED—No trace of wear. Light blemishes.
MS-63 CHOICE UNCIRCULATED—Some distracting blemishes in prime focal areas. Impaired luster possible.
PF-63 CHOICE PROOF—Reflective surfaces. Only a few blemishes in secondary focal areas. No major flaws.

Brilliant choice Uncirculated and Proof coins are worth more than prices shown. Spotted, cleaned, or discolored pieces are worth less.

	Mintage	G-4	VG-8	F-12	EF-40	AU-50	MS-60	MS-63	PF-63
1866, Rays . . . . . . *(200+)*. . . . 14,742,500		$10.	$15.	$18.	$80.	$100.	$125.	$180.	$1,250.
1867, Rays . . . . *(25+)*. . . . 2,019,000		12.	16.	20.	90.	125.	225.	275.	12,000.
1867, No Rays . . . *(600+)*. . . 28,890,500		9.	10.	11.	20.	25.	70.	120.	200.

Without Rays (1867–1883)   **Typical Example of 1883, 3 Over 2**
Other varieties exist.

	Mintage	G-4	VG-8	F-12	EF-40	AU-50	MS-60	MS-63	PF-63
1868 . . . . *(600+)*. . . 28,817,000		$9.	$10.	$11.	$20.	$25.	$70.	$120.	$200.
1869 . . . . *(600+)*. . . 16,395,000		9.	10.	11.	20.	25.	70.	120.	200.
1870 . . . . *(1,000+)*. . . . 4,806,000		9.	10.	11.	20.	25.	70.	120.	200.
1871 . . . . *(960+)*. 561,000		22.	28.	40.	85.	110.	150.	175.	225.
1872 . . . . *(950+)*. . . . 6,036,000		9.	10.	11.	22.	27.	75.	120.	200.
1873, Close 3 *(1,100+)* 436,050		9.	10.	11.	27.	35.	80.	120.	200.
1873, Open 3 4,113,950		9.	10.	11.	20.	25.	70.	120.	
1874 . . . . *(700+)*. . . . 3,538,000		10.	11.	12.	24.	30.	70.	120.	200.
1875 . . . . *(700+)*. . . . 2,097,000		10.	12.	18.	40.	50.	100.	120.	200.
1876 . . . . *(1,150+)*. . . 2,530,000		12.	14.	20.	30.	40.	80.	120.	200.
1877, Pf only . . . *(510+)*.				400.	850.				1,200.
1878, Pf only . . *(2,350)*.				275.	450.				500.
1879 . . . . *(3,200)* 25,900		175.	225.	275.	325.	350.	400.	450.	400.
1880 . . . . *(3,955)* 16,000		180.	235.	270.	350.	375.	450.	500.	450.
1881 . . . . *(3,575)* 68,800		125.	150.	175.	250.	175.	350.	400.	350.
1882 . . . . *(3,100)*. . . 11,472,900		8.	9.	10.	19.	25.	65.	175.	175.
1883 . . . . *(5,419)*. . . . 1,451,500		8.	9.	10.	19.	25.	65.	175.	175.
1883, 3 Over 2 . . . . *		60.	70.	150.	200.	325.	450.		

* Included in number above.

LIBERTY HEAD (1883–1912)

In 1883 the design was changed to the familiar "Liberty head." This type first appeared without the word CENTS on the coin, merely a large letter V. These "CENTS-less" coins were goldplated by fraudsters and passed as $5 pieces. Later in that year the word CENTS was added.

NICKEL FIVE-CENT PIECES

G-4 GOOD—No details in head. LIBERTY obliterated.
VG-8 VERY GOOD—Some letters in LIBERTY legible.
F-12 FINE—All letters in LIBERTY legible.
VF-20 VERY FINE—LIBERTY bold, including letter L.
EF-40 EXTREMELY FINE—LIBERTY sharp. Corn grains at bottom of wreath visible on reverse.
AU-50 ABOUT UNCIRCULATED—Traces of light wear on only high points of design. Half of mint luster present.
MS-60 UNCIRCULATED—No trace of wear. Contact marks possible. Surface may be spotted, or luster faded.
MS-63 CHOICE UNCIRCULATED—No trace of wear. Light blemishes.
PF-63 CHOICE PROOF—Reflective surfaces. Only a few blemishes in secondary focal areas. No major flaws.

Variety 1, Without CENTS (1883 Only)

Brilliant choice Uncirculated and Proof coins are worth more than prices shown; spotted or cleaned coins, less.

	Mintage	G-4	VG-8	F-12	VF-20	EF-40	AU-50	MS-60	MS-63	PF-63
1883, Without CENTS ....(5,219)...	5,474,300	$2.25	$2.50	$3.00	$3.50	$4.50	$5.	$16.	$22.	$165.

Variety 2, With CENTS (1883–1913)

↑ Mintmark Location

	Mintage	G-4	VG-8	F-12	VF-20	EF-40	AU-50	MS-60	MS-63	PF-63
1883, w/CENTS (6,783)	16,026,200	$4.00	$5.00	$7.	$15.	$35.	$45.	$75.	$90.	$140.
1884 ....(3,942)	11,270,000	6.00	10.00	12.	20.	35.	45.	400.	120.	150.
1885 ....(3,790)	1,472,700	230.00	275.00	325.	450.	550.	625.	825.	1,000.	700.
1886 ....(4,290)	3,326,000	90.00	125.00	200.	250.	300.	350.	400.	500.	400.
1887 ....(2,960)	15,260,692	4.00	7.00	11.	20.	40.	45.	75.	125.	150.
1888 ....(4,582)	10,167,901	9.00	12.00	18.	40.	45.	50.	125.	175.	150.
1889 ....(3,336)	15,878,025	2.50	4.00	8.	12.	25.	30.	75.	125.	140.
1890 ....(2,740)	16,256,532	2.50	4.00	8.	12.	25.	30.	75.	125.	140.
1891 ....(2,350)	16,832,000	2.50	4.00	8.	12.	25.	30.	75.	125.	140.
1892 ....(2,745)	11,696,897	2.50	4.00	8.	12.	25.	30.	75.	125.	140.
1893 ....(2,195)	13,368,000	2.50	4.00	8.	12.	30.	35.	80.	135.	140.
1894 ....(2,632)	5,410,500	4.00	7.00	30.	60.	100.	150.	175.	185.	150.
1895 ....(2,062)	9,977,822	1.50	2.50	7.	10.	25.	30.	75.	130.	140.
1896 ....(1,862)	8,841,058	2.00	5.00	9.	12.	22.	25.	75.	140.	140.
1897 ....(1,938)	20,426,797	2.00	5.00	9.	12.	22.	24.	50.	125.	140.
1898 ....(1,795)	12,530,292	2.00	5.00	9.	12.	22.	22.	50.	125.	140.
1899 ....(2,031)	26,027,000	.75	1.00	3.	6.	14.	22.	50.	110.	140.
1900 ....(2,262)	27,253,733	.75	1.00	3.	6.	14.	20.	40.	100.	125.
1901 ....(1,985)	26,478,228	.75	1.00	3.	6.	14.	20.	40.	90.	125.
1902 ....(2,018)	31,487,561	.75	1.00	3.	6.	14.	20.	40.	90.	125.
1903 ....(1,790)	28,004,935	.60	.75	2.	4.	11.	20.	40.	90.	125.
1904 ....(1,817)	21,403,167	.60	.75	2.	4.	11.	20.	40.	90.	125.
1905 ....(2,152)	29,825,124	.60	.75	2.	4.	11.	20.	40.	90.	125.
1906 ....(1,725)	38,612,000	.60	.75	2.	4.	11.	20.	40.	90.	125.
1907 ....(1,475)	39,213,325	.60	.75	2.	4.	11.	20.	40.	90.	125.
1908 ....(1,620)	22,684,557	.60	.75	2.	4.	11.	20.	40.	90.	125.
1909 ....(4,763)	11,585,763	.60	.75	2.	4.	11.	20.	40.	90.	125.
1910 ....(2,405)	30,166,948	.60	.75	2.	4.	11.	20.	40.	90.	125.
1911 ....(1,733)	39,557,639	.60	.75	2.	4.	11.	20.	40.	90.	125.
1912 ....(2,145)	26,234,569	.60	.75	2.	4.	11.	20.	40.	90.	125.
1912D................	8,474,000	.75	.85	4.	10.	35.	85.	125.	150.	
1912S................	238,000	60.00	75.00	100.	175.	350.	500.	575.	700.	
1913 Liberty Head *(5 known)*......								2,000,000.		

INDIAN HEAD or BUFFALO (1913–1938)

The Buffalo nickel was designed by James E. Fraser, whose initial F is below the date. He modeled the bison after Black Diamond in the New York Central Park Zoo.

G-4 GOOD—Legends and date readable. Buffalo's horn worn off.
VG-8 VERY GOOD—Some of horn visible.
F-12 FINE—Part of horn visible. Obverse rim intact.
VF-20 VERY FINE—Most of horn visible. Indian's cheekbone worn.
EF-40 EXTREMELY FINE—Nearly full horn. Slight wear on Indian's hair ribbon.
AU-50 ABOUT UNCIRCULATED—Traces of light wear on high points of design. Half of mint luster present.
MS-60 UNCIRCULATED—No trace of wear. May have several blemishes.
MS-63 CHOICE UNCIRCULATED—No trace of wear. Light blemishes.
MATTE PF-63 CHOICE PROOF—Crisp surfaces. Only a few blemishes in secondary focal areas. No major flaws.

Variety 1 – FIVE CENTS on Raised Ground (1913)

Brilliant choice Uncirculated coins are worth more than prices shown. Spotted, cleaned, weakly struck, or discolored pieces are worth less.

	Mintage	G-4	VG-8	F-12	VF-20	EF-40	AU-50	MS-60	MS-63	MATTE PF-63
1913, Var. 1 . .(1,520)	30,992,000	$3.50	$4.	$5.	$6.	$10.	$11.	$18.	$25.	$625.
1913D, Variety 1	5,337,000	6.00	7.	8.	11.	15.	20.	32.	40.	
1913S, Variety 1	2,105,000	14.00	20.	22.	26.	37.	45.	65.	80.	

Variety 2 – FIVE CENTS in Recess (1913–1938)

Mintmark Below FIVE CENTS   **1916, Doubled-Die Obverse**   **1918-D, 8 Over 7**

	Mintage	G-4	VG-8	F-12	VF-20	EF-40	AU-50	MS-60	MS-63	MATTE PF-63
1913, Var. 2 . . . .(1,514)	29,857,186	$4.00	$5.00	$6.00	$7.00	$10.	$14.	$20.	$30.	$550.
1913D, Var. 2	4,156,000	40.00	50.00	60.00	80.00	100.	115.	125.	150.	
1913S, Var. 2	1,209,000	100.00	125.00	150.00	200.00	275.	300.	375.	475.	
1914 . .(1,275)	20,664,463	8.00	9.00	10.00	12.00	15.	20.	33.	40.	550.
1914D	3,912,000	30.00	40.00	50.00	75.00	110.	150.	200.	300.	
1914S	3,470,000	11.00	13.00	16.00	29.00	45.	75.	90.	230.	
1915 . .(1,050)	20,986,220	2.00	2.25	3.00	4.00	10.	25.	40.	45.	600.
1915D	7,569,000	7.00	9.00	15.00	30.00	60.	80.	125.	165.	
1915S	1,505,000	13.00	20.00	30.00	60.00	120.	175.	250.	400.	
1916 . . . .(600)	63,497,466	1.50	1.75	2.00	2.50	4.	9.	25.	30.	850.
1916, DblDie Obv . . . .*	1,000.00	1,800.00	3,500.00	5,500.00	8,000.	13,000.	32,000.	65,000.		
1916D	13,333,000	5.00	8.00	9.00	20.00	40.	50.	80.	125.	
1916S	11,860,000	3.00	4.00	7.00	20.00	40.	55.	90.	150.	
1917	51,424,019	1.50	2.00	2.50	3.00	6.	15.	25.	55.	
1917D	9,910,000	6.00	9.00	13.00	40.00	70.	100.	160.	350.	
1917S	4,193,000	8.00	12.00	18.00	40.00	75.	125.	200.	550.	
1918	32,086,314	1.25	1.50	2.00	5.00	15.	20.	50.	125.	

* Included in number above.

NICKEL FIVE-CENT PIECES

	Mintage	G-4	VG-8	F-12	VF-20	EF-40	AU-50	MS-60	MS-63
1918D, 8 Over 7 ....*	$450.00	$550.00	$1,000.00	$2,000.00	$4,000.	$4,700.	$14,000.	$30,000.
1918D 8,362,000	6.00	10.00	15.00	65.00	120.	160.	225.	500.
1918S 4,882,000	4.00	10.00	14.00	40.00	85.	125.	200.	1,400.
1919 60,868,000	.45	.50	.75	1.75	6.	13.	30.	50.
1919D (a) 8,006,000	4.00	8.00	18.00	55.00	120.	145.	300.	700.
1919S (a) 7,521,000	3.00	7.00	12.00	55.00	120.	145.	300.	850.
1920 63,093,000	.40	.50	1.00	2.00	5.	12.	30.	65.
1920D (a) 9,418,000	2.50	4.50	10.00	60.00	140.	150.	275.	750.
1920S 968,900	1.25	2.25	8.00	45.00	100.	125.	220.	700.
1921 10,663,000	.75	1.00	1.50	8.00	22.	30.	65.	130.
1921S 1,557,000	25.00	40.00	70.00	275.00	425.	450.	800.	1,100.
1923 35,715,000	.40	.50	.75	3.00	6.	15.	30.	75.
1923S (a) 6,142,000	2.00	2.50	4.00	75.00	150.	175.	225.	500.
1924 21,620,000	.35	.50	.60	3.00	8.	20.	37.	70.
1924D 5,258,000	2.00	3.00	8.00	35.00	100.	125.	180.	425.
1924S 1,437,000	7.00	16.00	35.00	225.00	700.	750.	1,100.	2,000.

* Included in number below. **a.** Uncirculated pieces with full, sharp details are worth considerably more.

1937-D, "3-Legged" Variety

1938-D, D Over S

Brilliant choice Uncirculated coins are worth more than prices shown. Spotted, cleaned, weakly struck, or discolored pieces are worth less.

	Mintage	G-4	VG-8	F-12	VF-20	EF-40	AU-50	MS-60	MS-63	PF-63
1925 35,565,100	$.50	$.75	$1.00	$3.00	$8.00	$15.00	$25.	$45.	
1925D 4,450,000	2.75	6.00	15.00	45.00	85.00	110.00	225.	300.	
1925S 6,256,000	1.50	5.00	8.00	45.00	85.00	110.00	225.	1,000.	
1926 44,693,000	.30	.40	.50	2.00	4.00	10.00	20.	30.	
1926D 5,638,000	1.75	4.00	8.00	40.00	80.00	120.00	150.	225.	
1926S 970,000	8.00	14.00	25.00	230.00	450.00	1,200.00	1,800.	3,000.	
1927 37,981,000	.30	.40	.50	1.00	5.00	9.00	22.	35.	
1927D 5,730,000	.75	1.75	2.00	11.00	30.00	45.00	80.	150.	
1927S 3,430,000	.50	.80	1.50	14.00	35.00	70.00	225.	950.	
1928 23,411,000	.35	.40	.50	1.00	4.00	9.00	20.	29.	
1928D 6,436,000	.40	.75	1.50	5.00	18.00	22.00	25.	45.	
1928S 6,936,000	.50	.60	1.00	4.00	12.00	48.00	100.	270.	
1929 36,446,000	.30	.35	.50	1.00	3.00	8.00	15.	30.	
1929D 8,370,000	.40	.50	.75	2.50	13.00	16.00	30.	60.	
1929S 7,754,000	.35	.50	.65	.80	4.50	10.00	23.	40.	
1930 22,849,000	.35	.40	.60	.75	3.00	8.00	15.	30.	
1930S 5,435,000	.35	.40	.60	.75	5.00	12.00	22.	55.	
1931S 1,200,000	5.00	6.00	7.50	8.50	12.00	20.00	26.	40.	
1934 20,213,003	.30	.40	.50	.65	2.00	8.00	15.	25.	
1934D 7,480,000	.30	.40	.50	1.00	6.00	18.00	27.	50.	
1935 58,264,000	.30	.40	.50	.65	1.00	3.00	9.	20.	
1935D 12,092,000	.30	.40	.50	.65	2.50	15.00	18.	30.	
1935S 10,300,000	.30	.40	.50	.65	1.50	6.00	14.	35.	
1936 (4,420)...118,997,000	.30	.40	.50	.65	1.00	3.00	9.	22.	$600.
1936D 24,814,000	.40	.50	.65	1.25	4.00	10.00	14.	17.	
1936S 14,930,000	.30	.40	.50	.65	1.00	3.50	10.	15.	
1937 (5,769)....79,480,000	.30	.40	.50	.65	1.00	2.50	12.	15.	500.
1937D 17,826,000	.30	.40	.50	.65	1.00	3.00	10.	15.	
1937D, 3-Legged...........*	130.00	250.00	300.00	350.00	400.00	500.00	850.	2,250.	
1937S 5,635,000	.30	.40	.50	.65	1.00	3.00	10.	19.	
1938D 7,020,000	.30	.40	.50	.65	1.00	3.00	10.	14.	
1938D, D Over S ....*			3.00	3.50	6.00	10.00	20.	30.	

* Included in number above.

JEFFERSON (1938 TO DATE)

This nickel was designed by Felix Schlag. He won an award of $1,000 in a competition with some 390 artists. It established the definite public approval of portrait and pictorial rather than symbolic devices on our coinage. On October 8, 1942, the wartime five-cent piece composed of copper (56%), silver (35%), and manganese (9%) was introduced to eliminate nickel, a critical war material. A larger mintmark was placed above the dome. Letter P (Philadelphia) was used for the first time, indicating the change of alloy. The designer's initials FS were added below the bust starting in 1966. The mintmark position was moved to the obverse starting in 1968.

VG-8 VERY GOOD—Second porch pillar from right nearly gone, other three still visible but weak.
F-12 FINE—Jefferson's cheekbone worn flat. Hair lines and eyebrow faint. Second pillar weak, especially at bottom.
VF-20 VERY FINE—Second pillar plain and complete on both sides.
EF-40 EXTREMELY FINE—Cheekbone, hair lines, eyebrow slightly worn but well defined. Base of triangle above pillars visible but weak.
MS-63 SELECT UNCIRCULATED—No trace of wear. Slight blemishes.
MS-65 CHOICE UNCIRCULATED—No trace of wear. Barely noticeable blemishes.
PF 65 GEM PROOF—Brilliant surfaces. No noticeable blemishes or flaws. May have a few barely noticeable marks or hairlines.

Mintmark Located at Right of Building   **Wartime Silver**   **Mintmark, Starting 1968**

Uncirculated pieces with fully struck steps are valued higher.

	Mintage	VG-8	F-12	VF-20	EF-40	MS-63	MS-65	PF-65
1938 . . . . (19,365)	19,496,000	$.07	$.10	$.20	$.25	$1.00	$5.00	$45.00
1938D	5,376,000	.25	.35	.50	.75	1.50	7.00	
1938S	4,105,000	.40	.60	.85	1.50	2.00	8.00	
1939 . . . . (12,535)	120,615,000	.08	.10	.12	.25	1.00	2.00	45.00
1939D	3,514,000	1.20	1.60	2.25	3.50	30.00	45.00	
1939S	6,630,000	.25	.30	.35	1.25	12.00	20.00	
1940 . . . . (14,158)	176,485,000			.05	.10	1.00	2.00	40.00
1940D	43,540,000			.05	.10	1.25	3.50	
1940S	39,690,000			.05	.10	1.25	3.50	
1941 . . . . (18,720)	203,265,000			.05	.10	.50	2.00	40.00
1941D	53,432,000			.05	.10	1.25	3.00	
1941S	43,445,000			.05	.10	1.50	3.50	
1942 . . . . (29,600)	49,789,000			.05	.10	1.25	3.00	40.00
1942D	13,938,000	.10	.15	.25	.50	11.00	22.00	

Wartime Silver Alloy (1942–1945)

	Mintage	VG-8	F-12	VF-20	EF-40	MS-63	MS-65	PF-65
1942P . . . . (27,600)	57,873,000	$.20	$.20	$.25	$0.35	$4.00	$8.00	$70.00
1942S	32,900,000	.20	.20	.25	0.35	4.00	9.00	
1943P, 3 Over 2	*		15.00	20.00	30.00	130.00	320.00	
1943P	271,165,000	.20	.20	.25	0.35	3.00	6.00	
1943D	15,294,000	.20	.30	.35	0.50	5.00	7.00	
1943S	104,060,000	.20	.20	.25	0.35	3.00	6.00	
1944P	119,150,000	.20	.30	.25	0.35	5.00	8.00	
1944D	32,309,000	.20	.20	.25	0.35	5.00	8.00	
1944S	21,640,000	.20	.20	.25	0.35	4.00	9.00	
1945P	119,408,100	.20	.20	.25	0.35	3.00	8.00	
1945D	37,158,000	.20	.20	.25	0.35	3.00	7.00	
1945S	58,939,000	.20	.20	.25	0.35	3.00	7.00	

* Included in number below.

Prewar Composition, Mintmark Style Resumed (1946–1967)

	Mintage	VF-20	EF-40	MS-63	MS-65	PF-65
1946	161,116,000	$.05	$.05	$.25	$2.00	
1946D	45,292,200	.05	.05	.25	2.00	
1946S	13,560,000	.05	.06	.15	1.50	
1947	95,000,000	.05	.05	.25	2.00	
1947D	37,822,000	.05	.05	.25	2.00	
1947S	24,720,000	.05	.06	.20	1.75	
1948	89,348,000	.05	.05	.20	1.75	
1948D	44,734,000	.05	.06	.25	2.00	
1948S	11,300,000	.05	.06	.20	1.75	
1949	60,652,000	.05	.05	.50	2.50	
1949D	36,498,000	.05	.05	.25	2.00	
1949D, D Over S	*	18.00	30.00	120.00	150.00	
1949S	9,716,000	.05	.10	.35	1.75	
1950	(51,386)..9,796,000	.05	.10	.50	2.50	$24.00
1950D	2,630,030	2.00	2.25	3.00	4.00	
1951	(57,500)..28,552,000	.05	.05	.50	2.50	20.00
1951D	20,460,000	.05	.05	.75	3.00	
1951S	7,776,000	.05	.10	.50	2.50	
1952	(81,980)..63,988,000	.05	.05	.20	1.75	11.00
1952D	30,638,000	.05	.05	2.00	3.00	
1952S	20,572,000	.05	.05	.50	1.00	
1953	(128,800)..46,644,000	.05	.05	.10	.25	16.00
1953D	59,878,600	.05	.05	.10	.25	
1953S	19,210,900	.05	.05	.20	.25	
1954	(233,300)..47,684,050	.05	.05	.15	.25	8.00
1954D	117,183,060	.05	.05	.15	.25	
1954S	29,384,000	.05	.05	.25	.25	
1954S, S Over D	*	2.50	5.00	20.00	35.00	
1955	(378,200)...7,888,000	.06	.08	.40	.50	6.00

* Included in number above.

1943, 3 Over 2	1954-S, S Over D	1955-D, D Over S (a)

	Mintage	VF-20	EF-40	MS-63	MS-65	PF-65
1955D	74,464,100	$.05	$.05	$.10	$.40	
1955D, D Over S (a)	*	3.00	5.00	30.00	35.00	
1956	(669,384)....35,216,000		.05	.10	.50	$1.00
1956D	67,222,940		.05	.10	.50	
1957	(1,247,952)....38,408,000		.05	.10	.50	1.00
1957D	136,828,900		.05	.10	.50	
1958	(875,652)....17,088,000		.05	.10	.60	1.50
1958D	168,249,120		.05	.10	.50	
1959	(1,149,291)....27,248,000		.05	.10	.50	.75
1959D	160,738,240		.05	.10	.20	
1960	(1,691,602)....55,416,000		.05	.10	.20	.75
1960D	192,582,180		.05	.10	.20	
1961	(3,028,144)....73,640,100		.05	.10	.20	.75
1961D	229,342,760		.05	.10	.20	
1962	(3,218,019)....97,384,000		.05	.10	.20	.75
1962D	280,195,720		.05	.10	.25	
1963	(3,075,645)....175,776,000		.05	.10	.20	.75
1963D	276,829,460			.10	.20	
1964	(3,950,762)....1,024,672,000			.10	.20	.75
1964D	1,787,297,160			.10	.20	
1965	136,131,380			.10	.20	

* Included in number above. **(a)** Varieties exist. Value is for that illustrated.

Chart continues on next page.

1966 Through 2003

	Mintage	MS-63	MS-65	PF-65		Mintage	MS-63	MS-65	PF-65
1966	156,208,283	$.10	$.20		1971D	316,144,800	$.10	$.20	
1967	107,325,800	.10	.20		1971S	(3,220,733)			$1.00
1968D	91,227,880	.10	.20		1972	202,036,000	.10	.20	
1968S	(3,041,506)				1972D	351,694,600	.10	.20	
	100,396,004	.10	.20	$.75	1972S	(3,260,996)			1.00
1969D	202,807,500	.10	.20		1973	384,396,000	.10	.20	
1969S	(2,934,631)				1973D	261,405,000	.10	.20	
	120,165,000	.10	.20	.75	1973S	(2,760,339)			1.00
1970D	515,485,380	.10	.20		1974	601,752,000	.10	.20	
1970S	(2,632,810)				1974D	277,373,000	.10	.20	
	238,832,004	.10	.20	.75	1974S	(2,612,568)			.75
1971	106,884,000	.25	.35						

	Mintage	MS-65	PF-65		Mintage	MS-65	PF-65
1975	181,772,000	$.20		1989D	570,842,474	$.20	
1975D	401,875,300	.20		1989S	(3,220,194)		$1.50
1975S	(2,845,450)		$.75	1990P	661,636,000	.20	
1976	367,124,000	.20		1990D	663,938,503	.20	
1976D	563,964,147	.20		1990S	(3,299,559)		1.75
1976S	(4,149,730)		.75	1991P	614,104,000	.20	
1977	585,376,000	.20		1991D	436,496,678	.20	
1977D	297,313,422	.50		1991S	(2,867,787)		2.00
1977S	(3,251,152)		.75	1992P	399,552,000	1.00	
1978	391,308,000	.20		1992D	450,565,113	.20	
1978D	313,092,780	.20		1992S	(4,176,560)		1.50
1978S	(3,127,781)		.75	1993P	412,076,000	.20	
1979	463,188,000	.20		1993D	406,084,135	.20	
1979D	325,867,672	.20		1993S	(3,394,792)		1.50
1979S, Filled S	(3,677,175)		.75	1994P	722,160,000	.20	
1979S, Clear S	*		1.00	1994D	715,762,110	.20	
1980P	593,004,000	.20		1994S	(3,269,923)		1.50
1980D	502,323,448	.20		1995P	774,156,000	.40	
1980S	(3,554,806)		.75	1995D	888,112,000	.20	
1981P	657,504,000	.20		1995S	(2,797,481)		1.75
1981D	364,801,843	.20		1996P	829,332,000	.20	
1981S	(4,063,083)		.75	1996D	817,736,000	.20	
1982P	292,355,000	2.00		1996S	(2,525,265)		1.00
1982D	373,726,544	1.50		1997P	470,972,000	.20	
1982S	(3,857,479)		1.00	1997D	466,640,000	.20	
1983P	561,615,000	1.75		1997S	(2,796,678)		2.00
1983D	536,726,276	1.25		1998P	688,272,000	.20	
1983S	(3,279,126)		1.00	1998D	635,360,000	.20	
1984P	746,769,000	1.25		1998S	(2,086,507)		2.00
1984D	517,675,146	.20		1999P	1,212,000,000	.20	
1984S	(3,065,110)		1.50	1999D	1,066,720,000	.20	
1985P	647,114,962	.20		1999S	(2,543,401)		1.00
1985D	459,747,446	.20		2000P	846,240,000	.20	
1985S	(3,362,821)		1.25	2000D	1,509,520,000	.20	
1986P	536,883,483	.25		2000S	(3,082,483)		1.00
1986D	361,819,140	.60		2001P	675,704,000	.20	
1986S	(3,010,497)		2.00	2001D	627,680,000	.20	
1987P	371,499,481	.20		2001S	(2,294,043)		1.00
1987D	410,590,604	.20		2002P	539,280,000	.20	
1987S	(4,227,728)		1.00	2002D	691,200,000	.20	
1988P	771,360,000	.20		2002S	(2,277,720)		1.00
1988D	663,771,652	.20		2003P	441,840,000	.20	
1988S	(3,262,948)		2.00	2003D	383,040,000	.20	
1989P	898,812,000	.20		2003S			1.00

* Included in number above.

NICKEL FIVE-CENT PIECES

"Westward Journey" Nickels

The United States Mint began the Westward Journey Nickel Series™ in 2004. The coins in this special program commemorate the bicentennial of the Louisiana Purchase and the journey of Lewis and Clark to explore the vast area recently acquired by the American government.

The reverse design of the first nickel of 2004 is a depiction of the original Jefferson Peace Medal designed in 1801. Lewis and Clark gave these medals as tokens to Native Americans they met during their journey. The second nickel design of 2004 features the keelboat that transported Lewis and Clark. Those of 2005 feature a bison and a view of the Pacific Ocean, as well as a new likeness of President Thomas Jefferson on the obverse.

| 2004 Obverse | Peace Medal | Keelboat |
| 2005 Obverse | American Bison | Ocean In View |

	Mintage	MS-65	PF-65
2004P, Peace Medal	361,440,000	$.25	
2004D, Peace Medal	372,000,000	.25	
2004S, Peace Medal			$1.10
2004P, Keelboat	366,720,000	.25	
2004D, Keelboat	344,880,000	.25	
2004S, Keelboat			1.10
2005P, American Bison		.25	
2005D, American Bison		.25	
2005S, American Bison			1.10
2005P, Ocean In View		.25	
2005D, Ocean In View		.25	
2005S, Ocean In View			1.10

The half dime types present the same general characteristics as larger United States silver coins. Authorized by the Act of April 2, 1792, they were not coined until February, 1795, although dated 1794. At first the weight was 20.8 grains, and fineness .8924. By the Act of January 18, 1837, the weight was slightly reduced to 20-5/8 grains and the fineness changed to .900. Finally, the weight was reduced to 19.2 grains by the Act of February 21, 1853.

FLOWING HAIR (1794–1795)

AG-3 ABOUT GOOD—Details clear enough to identify.
G-4 GOOD—Eagle, wreath, bust outlined but lack details.
VG-8 VERY GOOD—Some details on face. All lettering legible.
F-12 FINE—Hair ends visible. Hair at top smooth.
VF-20 VERY FINE—Hair lines at top visible. Hair about ear defined.
EF-40 EXTREMELY FINE—Hair above forehead and at neck well defined but shows some wear.
AU-50 ABOUT UNCIRCULATED—Slight wear on high waves of hair, near ear and face, and on head and tips of eagle's wings.
MS-60 UNCIRCULATED—No trace of wear. Light blemishes.
MS-63 CHOICE UNCIRCULATED—Some distracting marks or blemishes in prime focal areas. Some impairment of luster possible.

Weakly-struck Uncirculated coins are worth less than values shown.

	Mintage	AG-3	G-4	VG-8	F-12	VF-20	EF-40	AU-50	MS-60	MS-63
1794	86,416	$250.	$475.	$600.	$900.	$1,400.	$2,500.	$4,250.	$7,100.	$9,250.
1795	*	175.	400.	500.	725.	1,000.	1,800.	3,000.	5,250.	7,500.

* Included in number above.

DRAPED BUST (1796–1797)

AG-3 ABOUT GOOD—Details clear enough to identify.
G-4 GOOD—Date, stars, LIBERTY readable. Bust of Liberty outlined, but no details.
VG-8 VERY GOOD—Some details visible.
F-12 FINE—Hair and drapery lines worn, but visible.
VF-20 VERY FINE—Only left side of drapery indistinct.
EF-40 EXTREMELY FINE—Details visible in all hair lines.
AU-50 ABOUT UNCIRCULATED—Slight wear on bust, shoulder, and hair; wear on eagle's head and top of wings.
MS-60 UNCIRCULATED—No trace of wear. Light blemishes.
MS-63 CHOICE UNCIRCULATED—Some distracting marks or blemishes in prime focal areas. Impaired luster possible.

Small Eagle Reverse (1796–1797)

	Mintage	AG-3	G-4	VG-8	F-12	VF-20	EF-40	AU-50	MS-60	MS-63
1796, 6 Over 5	10,230	$275.	$500.	$575.	$1,000.	$1,600.	$2,600.	$4,250.	$9,500.	$15,500.
1796	*	225.	475.	550.	900.	1,400.	2,100.	3,600.	5,000.	11,000.
1796, LIBERTY	*	225.	475.	550.	900.	1,400.	2,100.	3,600.	5,250.	13,000.
1797, 15 Stars	44,527	200.	450.	525.	800.	1,300.	2,100.	3,600.	5,000.	11,000.
1797, 16 Stars	*	200.	450.	525.	800.	1,300.	2,100.	3,600.	5,000.	11,000.
1797, 13 Stars	*	275.	500.	575.	1,000.	1,600.	3,250.	4,750.	11,000.	16,000.

* Included in number above.

Heraldic Eagle Reverse (1800–1805)

1800 LIBEKTY

	Mintage	AG-3	G-4	VG-8	F-12	VF-20	EF-40	AU-50	MS-60	MS-63
1800	24,000	$125.	$275.	$325.	$550.	$825.	$1,500.	$2,500.	$3,500.	$5,000.
1800, LIBEKTY	16,000	125.	275.	325.	550.	825.	1,500.	2,500.	3,500.	5,000.
1801	27,760	140.	300.	375.	650.	900.	1,600.	2,750.	5,000.	6,750.
1802	3,060	3,600.	9,000.	11,000.	18,000.	30,000.	45,000.	—	—	—
1803	37,850	160.	350.	425.	600.	900.	1,600.	2,500.	3,750.	5,500.
1805	15,600	175.	400.	450.	625.	950.	2,100.	4,500.	—	—

CAPPED BUST (1829–1837)

G-4 GOOD—Bust of Liberty outlined, no detail. Date and legend legible.
VG-8 VERY GOOD—Complete legend and date plain. At least three letters of LIBERTY on edge of cap show clearly.
F-12 FINE—All letters in LIBERTY visible.
VF-20 VERY FINE—Full rims. Ear and shoulder clasp show plainly.
EF-40 EXTREMELY FINE—Ear very distinct; eyebrow and hair well defined.
AU-50 ABOUT UNCIRCULATED—Traces of light wear on many of the high points. At least half of mint luster still present.
MS-60 UNCIRCULATED—No trace of wear. Light blemishes.
MS-63 CHOICE UNCIRCULATED—No trace of wear. Light blemishes. Attractive mint luster.

	Mintage	G-4	VG-8	F-12	VF-20	EF-40	AU-50	MS-60	MS-63
1829	1,230,000	$12.	$15.	$19.	$35.	$65.	$100.	$150.	$350.
1830	1,240,000	12.	15.	19.	35.	65.	100.	150.	350.
1831	1,242,700	12.	15.	19.	35.	65.	100.	150.	350.
1832	965,000	12.	15.	19.	35.	65.	100.	150.	350.
1833	1,370,000	12.	15.	19.	35.	65.	100.	150.	350.
1834	1,480,000	12.	15.	19.	35.	65.	100.	150.	350.
1835, All kinds	2,760,000	12.	15.	19.	35.	65.	100.	150.	350.
1836	1,900,000	12.	15.	19.	35.	65.	100.	150.	350.
1837, Small 5C	871,000	14.	18.	27.	55.	100.	175.	475.	950.
1837, Large 5C	*	12.	15.	19.	35.	65.	100.	150.	350.

* Included in number above.

LIBERTY SEATED (1837–1873)

G-4 GOOD—LIBERTY on shield smooth. Date and letters legible.
VG-8 VERY GOOD—At least three letters in LIBERTY visible.
F-12 FINE—Entire LIBERTY visible, weak spots.
VF-20 VERY FINE—Entire LIBERTY strong and even.
EF-40 EXTREMELY FINE—LIBERTY and scroll edges distinct.
AU-50 ABOUT UNCIRCULATED—Traces of light wear on many of the high points. At least half of mint luster still present.
MS-60 UNCIRCULATED—No trace of wear. Light blemishes.
MS-63 CHOICE UNCIRCULATED—No trace of wear. Light blemishes. Attractive mint luster.

Variety 1 – No Stars on Obverse (1837–1838)

See next page for chart.

	Mintage	G-4	VG-8	F-12	VF-20	EF-40	AU-50	MS-60	MS-63
1837	1,405,000	$12.	$19.	$26.	$55.	$100.	$160.	$325.	$425.
18380, No Stars	70,000	32.	50.	85.	175.	325.	475.	850.	3,250.

Variety 2 – Stars on Obverse (1838–1853)

From 1838 through 1859 the mintmark is located above bow on reverse. Large, medium, or small mintmark varieties occur for several dates.

	Mintage	G-4	VG-8	F-12	VF-20	EF-40	AU-50	MS-60	MS-63
1838	2,255,000	$5.	$6.	$9.	$12.	$27.	$60.	$160.	$175.
1839	1,034,039	5.	6.	9.	12.	27.	60.	160.	175.
1840	1,344,085	5.	6.	9.	12.	27.	60.	160.	175.
1841	1,150,000	5.	6.	9.	12.	27.	60.	100.	125.
18410	815,000	6.	8.	13.	20.	40.	110.	350.	600.
1842	815,000	5.	6.	9.	12.	27.	60.	90.	125.
18420	350,000	11.	14.	25.	70.	200.	300.	525.	850.
1843	1,165,000	5.	6.	9.	12.	27.	60.	90.	125.
1844	430,000	5.	6.	9.	12.	27.	60.	90.	125.
18440	220,000	27.	40.	65.	225.	475.	1,100.	2,200.	5,500.
1845	1,564,000	5.	6.	9.	12.	27.	60.	90.	125.
1846	27,000	100.	150.	275.	350.	950.	1,600.	3,200.	
1847	1,274,000	5.	6.	9.	12.	27.	65.	100.	200.
1848	668,000	5.	6.	9.	12.	27.	65.	100.	125.
18480	600,000	7.	9.	13.	23.	40.	100.	190.	250.
1849, 9 Over 6	*	8.	10.	15.	23.	40.	90.	200.	550.
1849, 9 Over 8	*	8.	11.	19.	25.	50.	110.	250.	700.
1849, Normal Date	1,309,000	5.	6.	9.	12.	27.	60.	90.	200.
18490	140,000	11.	17.	33.	90.	200.	400.	800.	1,800.
1850	955,000	5.	6.	9.	12.	27.	60.	90.	125.
18500	690,000	6.	8.	10.	20.	45.	125.	325.	650.
1851	781,000	5.	6.	9.	12.	27.	60.	90.	125.
18510	860,000	6.	8.	10.	17.	45.	100.	225.	350.
1852	1,000,500	5.	6.	9.	12.	27.	60.	90.	125.
18520	260,000	11.	16.	26.	50.	110.	200.	375.	750.
1853, No Arrows	135,000	12.	17.	26.	50.	100.	175.	300.	450.
18530, No Arrows	160,000	75.	125.	150.	250.	500.	1,000.	2,200.	5,000.

* Included in number below.

Variety 3 – Arrows at Date (1853–1855)

As on the dimes, quarters, and halves, arrows were placed at the sides of the date for a short period starting in 1853 to denote the reduction of weight.

	Mintage	G-4	VG-8	F-12	VF-20	EF-40	AU-50	MS-60	MS-63	PF-63
1853	13,210,020	$6.	$7.	$9.	$13.	$30.	$55.	$110.	$130.	
18530	2,200,000	7.	8.	11.	18.	30.	70.	125.	400.	
1854	5,740,000	6.	7.	9.	12.	25.	60.	110.	125.	$4,000.
18540	1,560,000	7.	8.	11.	18.	30.	70.	135.	350.	
1855	1,750,000	6.	7.	9.	13.	30.	55.	110.	130.	3,500.
18550	600,000	6.	9.	12.	24.	70.	100.	275.	450.	

Variety 2 Resumed (1856–1859: Weight Standard of 1853)

1858 Over Inverted Date

	Mintage	G-4	VG-8	F-12	VF-20	EF-40	AU-50	MS-60	MS-63	PF-63
1856 4,880,000		$6.	$7.	$9.	$12.	$25.	$50.	$80.	$120.	$2,000.
1856O 1,100,000		6.	7.	10.	20.	40.	100.	210.	450.	
1857 7,280,000		6.	7.	9.	12.	25.	50.	80.	120.	1,500.
1857O 1,380,000		6.	7.	10.	16.	30.	80.	175.	210.	
1858 3,500,000		6.	7.	9.	12.	25.	50.	80.	120.	750.
1858, Over Inverted Date . . .		15.	20.	30.	50.	95.	150.	275.	550.	
1858O 1,660,000		6.	7.	10.	18.	28.	60.	125.	180.	
1859 340,000		7.	8.	12.	20.	50.	90.	130.	150.	650.
1859O 560,000		7.	8.	12.	20.	50.	90.	150.	150.	

Variety 4 – Legend on Obverse (1860–1873)

	Mintage	G-4	VG-8	F-12	VF-20	EF-40	AU-50	MS-60	MS-63	PF-63
1860 . .(1,000) 799,000		$6.00	$7.	$9.	$11.	$18.	$30.	$70.	$100.	$320.
1860O 1,060,000		6.00	7.	9.	11.	18.	35.	100.	135.	
1861 . .(1,000) . . 3,360,000		6.00	7.	9.	11.	18.	30.	70.	100.	320.
1862 . . . .(550) . . . 1,492,000		8.00	10.	17.	20.	25.	40.	110.	125.	320.
1863 . . . .(460) 18,000		60.00	70.	95.	125.	200.	270.	300.	400.	350.
1863S 100,000		10.00	14.	17.	21.	60.	160.	350.	450.	
1864 . . . .(470) 48,000		110.00	170.	200.	275.	400.	500.	550.	600.	350.
1864S 90,000		18.00	20.	35.	50.	110.	180.	310.	700.	
1865 . . . .(500) 13,000		100.00	125.	180.	210.	275.	300.	400.	600.	350.
1865S 120,000		10.00	14.	17.	22.	60.	200.	450.	800.	
1866 . . . .(725) 10,000		100.00	115.	150.	200.	300.	320.	375.	600.	320.
1866S 120,000		10.00	14.	17.	22.	60.	180.	200.	400.	
1867 . . . .(625) 8,000		175.00	200.	250.	300.	350.	400.	450.	620.	350.
1867S 120,000		6.50	12.	17.	25.	60.	140.	210.	500.	
1868 . . . .(600) 88,600		20.00	25.	40.	70.	120.	200.	300.	400.	350.
1868S 280,000		6.00	8.	10.	12.	19.	40.	125.	250.	
1869 . . . .(600) 208,000		6.00	8.	10.	12.	19.	60.	120.	150.	320.
1869S 230,000		6.00	8.	10.	12.	19.	50.	150.	350.	
1870 . .(1,000) 535,000		6.00	8.	9.	10.	19.	30.	70.	120.	320.
1870S *(unique)*							—			
1871 . . . .(960) . . 1,873,000		6.00	8.	9.	10.	19.	30.	70.	120.	320.
1871S 161,000		7.00	10.	15.	25.	40.	70.	125.	200.	
1872 . . . .(950) . . 2,947,000		6.00	8.	9.	10.	19.	30.	70.	120.	320.
1872S, All kinds 837,000		6.00	8.	9.	10.	19.	30.	70.	120.	
1873 . . . .(600) . . 7,126,000		6.00	8.	9.	10.	19.	30.	70.	120.	320.
1873S 324,000		6.00	8.	9.	10.	19.	30.	70.	120.	

The designs of the dimes, first coined in 1796, followed closely those of the half dimes up through the Liberty Seated type. The dimes in each instance weigh twice as much as the half dimes.

DRAPED BUST (1796–1807)
Small Eagle Reverse (1796–1797)

AG-3 ABOUT GOOD—Details clear enough to identify.
G-4 GOOD—Date legible. Bust outlined, but no detail.
VG-8 VERY GOOD—All but deepest drapery folds worn smooth. Hair lines nearly gone and curls lacking in detail.
F-12 FINE—All drapery lines visible. Hair partly worn.
VF-20 VERY FINE—Only left side of drapery indistinct.
EF-40 EXTREMELY FINE—Hair well outlined with details visible.
AU-50 ABOUT UNCIRCULATED—Traces of light wear on many of the high points. At least half of mint luster still present.
MS-60 UNCIRCULATED—No trace of wear. Light blemishes.
MS-63 CHOICE UNCIRCULATED—Some distracting marks or blemishes in prime focal areas. Impaired luster possible.

1797, 16 Stars

1797, 13 Stars

	Mintage	AG-3	G-4	VG-8	F-12	VF-20	EF-40	AU-50	MS-60	MS-63
1796	22,135	$300.	$600.	$900.	$1,100.	$1,700.	$3,200.	$3,750.	$5,500.	$11,000.
1797, 16 Stars	25,261	325.	650.	950.	1,200.	1,800.	3,400.	4,250.	6,000.	12,000.
1797, 13 Stars	*	325.	650.	950.	1,200.	1,800.	3,400.	4,250.	6,000.	12,000.

* Included in number above.

Heraldic Eagle Reverse (1798–1807)

	Mintage	AG-3	G-4	VG-8	F-12	VF-20	EF-40	AU-50	MS-60	MS-63
1798, All kinds	27,550									
1798, 98/97, 16 Stars on Reverse		$125.	$250.	$350.	$450.	$650.	$1,200.	$2,000.	$3,000.	$5,000.
1798, 98/97, 13 Stars on Reverse		250.	800.	1,000.	1,500.	3,000.	4,000.	—	—	
1798		125.	225.	250.	425.	600.	1,100.	1,600.	2,500.	5,000.
1800	21,760	125.	225.	250.	425.	600.	1,100.	1,600.	2,700.	4,750.
1801	34,640	125.	250.	275.	500.	900.	1,800.	3,200.	5,000.	7,000.
1802	10,975	150.	325.	450.	650.	1,200.	2,500.	4,000.	9,000.	
1803	33,040	110.	225.	300.	400.	600.	1,500.	3,500.	5,000.	
1804	8,265	250.	500.	700.	1,200.	2,000.	5,000.	12,000.	17,000.	
1805	120,780	100.	200.	225.	350.	500.	900.	1,100.	2,800.	4,200.
1807	165,000	100.	200.	225.	350.	500.	900.	1,100.	2,500.	4,200.

CAPPED BUST (1809–1837)

G-4 GOOD—Date, letters, and stars discernible. Bust outlined, no details.
VG-8 VERY GOOD—Legends and date plain. Some letters in LIBERTY visible.
F-12 FINE—Clear LIBERTY. Ear and shoulder clasp visible. Part of rim visible on both sides.
VF-20 VERY FINE—LIBERTY distinct. Full rim. Ear and clasp plain and distinct.
EF-40 EXTREMELY FINE—LIBERTY sharp. Ear distinct. Hair above eye well defined.
AU-50 ABOUT UNCIRCULATED—Traces of light wear on only the high points of the design. Half of mint luster present.
MS-60 UNCIRCULATED—No trace of wear. Light blemishes.
MS-63 CHOICE UNCIRCULATED—Some distracting marks or blemishes in prime focal areas. Impaired luster possible.

Variety 1 – Wide Border (1809–1828)

	Mintage	G-4	VG-8	F-12	VF-20	EF-40	AU-50	MS-60	MS-63
1809	51,065	$55.	$85.	$150.	$250.	$500.	$800.	$1,900.	$2,750.
1811/9	65,180	40.	60.	125.	225.	500.	800.	1,700.	2,500.
1814	421,500	13.	15.	28.	70.	200.	275.	500.	1,100.
1820	942,587	12.	14.	25.	60.	200.	275.	500.	1,100.
1821	1,186,512	12.	14.	25.	60.	200.	275.	500.	1,100.
1822	100,000	175.	300.	425.	700.	1,400.	2,300.	5,000.	8,000.
1823, 3 Over 2, All kinds	440,000								
1823, 3 Over 2, Small E's	*	12.	14.	25.	60.	200.	275.	550.	1,100.
1823, 3 Over 2, Large E's	*	12.	14.	25.	60.	200.	275.	550.	1,100.

* Included in number above.

1823, 3 Over 2 **1824, 4 Over 2** **1828, Large Date** **1828, Small Date**

	Mintage	G-4	VG-8	F-12	VF-20	EF-40	AU-50	MS-60	MS-63
1824, 4 Over 2	510,000	$14.	$18.	$40.	$140.	$300.	$600.	$1,000.	$1,800.
1825	*	12.	14.	20.	50.	175.	275.	500.	1,100.
1827	1,215,000	12.	14.	20.	50.	175.	275.	500.	1,100.
1828, Large Date, Curl Base 2	125,000	16.	30.	50.	140.	300.	600.	1,000.	1,800.

* Included in number above.

Variety 2 – Modified Design (1828–1837)

1829, Small 10c 1829, Large 10c **1830, 30 Over 29**

	Mintage	G-4	VG-8	F-12	VF-20	EF-40	AU-50	MS-60	MS-63
1828, Small Date, Square Base 2	*	$13.	$17.	$30.	$65.	$200.	$325.	$625.	$1,100.
1829, Small 10c	770,000	12.	13.	15.	35.	120.	170.	400.	750.
1829, Medium 10c	*	12.	13.	15.	35.	120.	170.	350.	650.
1829, Large 10c	*	12.	15.	21.	50.	135.	200.	400.	675.
1830, 30 Over 29	510,000	17.	25.	45.	90.	250.	275.	500.	1,100.
1830, Large 10c	*	12.	13.	15.	35.	120.	170.	350.	675.
1830, Small 10c	*	12.	13.	15.	35.	120.	170.	350.	675.
1831	771,350	12.	13.	15.	35.	120.	170.	350.	675.
1832	522,500	12.	13.	15.	35.	120.	170.	350.	675.
1833	485,000	12.	13.	15.	35.	120.	170.	350.	675.
1834	635,000	12.	13.	15.	35.	120.	170.	350.	675.
1835	1,410,000	12.	13.	15.	35.	120.	170.	350.	675.
1836	1,190,000	12.	13.	15.	35.	120.	170.	350.	675.
1837	359,500	12.	13.	15.	35.	120.	170.	350.	675.

* Included in number above.

LIBERTY SEATED (1837–1891)
Variety 1 – No Stars on Obverse (1837–1838)

G-4 GOOD—LIBERTY on shield smooth. Date and letters legible.
F-12 FINE—LIBERTY visible, weak spots.
VF-20 VERY FINE—LIBERTY strong and even.
EF-40 EXTREMELY FINE—LIBERTY and scroll edges distinct.
AU-50 ABOUT UNCIRCULATED—Wear on Liberty's shoulder and hair high points; slight wear on eagle's breast, tail, and wing tips.
MS-60 UNCIRCULATED—No trace of wear. Light blemishes.
MS-63 CHOICE UNCIRCULATED—Some distracting contact marks or blemishes in prime focal areas. Impaired luster possible.

**No Drapery From Elbow
No Stars on Obverse**

*Mintmarks on Liberty Seated
dimes on reverse, within or below the wreath.
Size of mintmark varies on many dates.*

	Mintage	G-4	F-12	VF-20	EF-40	AU-50	MS-60	MS-63
1837	682,500	$13.	$32.	$110.	$220.	$325.	$600.	$800.
1838O	406,034	16.	50.	150.	285.	500.	1,200.	2,500.

Variety 2 – Stars on Obverse (1838–1853)

**No Drapery From Elbow, Tilted Shield
(1838–1840)**

1838, Small Stars   **1838, Large Stars**

**Drapery From Elbow, Upright Shield
(1840–1891)**

Obverse   **Reverse**

	Mintage	G-4	F-12	VF-20	EF-40	AU-50	MS-60	MS-63
1838, Small Stars	1,992,500	$8.	$18.	$35.	$70.	$175.	$400.	$600.
1838, Large Stars	*	6.	10.	13.	40.	100.	150.	350.
1838, Partial Drapery	*	8.	18.	35.	75.	210.	425.	1,000.
1839	1,053,115	6.	10.	13.	40.	100.	150.	350.
1839O	1,323,000	7.	12.	15.	45.	120.	175.	500.
1840	981,500	6.	10.	13.	40.	100.	150.	350.
1840O	1,175,000	7.	12.	18.	50.	120.	475.	900.
1840	377,500	12.	30.	55.	125.	170.	425.	2,000.
1841	1,622,500	6.	9.	12.	20.	50.	135.	250.
1841O	2,007,500	7.	12.	15.	28.	90.	425.	900.
1842	1,887,500	6.	9.	12.	20.	50.	135.	250.
1842O	2,020,000	8.	12.	15.	75.	475.	1,300.	2,600.
1843	1,370,000	6.	9.	12.	20.	50.	135.	250.
1843O	150,000	13.	45.	100.	250.	425.	1,000.	
1844	72,500	100.	225.	325.	550.	750.	1,100.	3,100.
1845	1,755,000	6.	9.	12.	20.	50.	135.	275.
1845O	230,000	8.	20.	80.	175.	400.	1,000.	
1846	31,300	30.	70.	150.	400.	900.	1,900.	4,000.
1847	245,000	7.	15.	27.	55.	120.	400.	1,000.
1848	451,500	6.	10.	15.	35.	60.	210.	400.
1849	839,000	6.	9.	12.	20.	50.	150.	425.
1849O	300,000	7.	15.	50.	110.	300.	1,000.	2,000.

* Included in number above.

	Mintage	G-4	F-12	VF-20	EF-40	AU-50	MS-60	MS-63
1850	1,931,500	$6.	$9.	$12.	$20.	$50.	$125.	$300.
1850O	510,000	7.	12.	33.	65.	150.	425.	900.
1851	1,026,500	6.	9.	12.	20.	50.	160.	325.
1851O	400,000	8.	16.	35.	100.	175.	1,000.	1,400.
1852	1,535,500	6.	9.	12.	20.	50.	150.	300.
1852O	430,000	8.	18.	45.	100.	175.	900.	1,300.
1853, No Arrows	95,000	20.	40.	75.	135.	175.	350.	400.

Variety 3 – Arrows at Date (1853–1855)

Arrows at Date (1853–1855)   **Small Date, Arrows Removed (1856–1860)**

	Mintage	G-4	F-12	VF-20	EF-40	AU-50	MS-60	MS-63	PF-63
1853, With Arrows	12,078,010	$6.	$7.	$10.	$21.	$50.	$150.	$300.	
1853O	1,100,000	6.	7.	15.	40.	100.	325.	1,100.	
1854	4,470,000	6.	7.	10.	21.	50.	150.	300.	$5,250.
1854O	1,770,000	6.	7.	12.	35.	60.	285.	500.	
1855	2,075,000	6.	7.	10.	21.	50.	175.	400.	5,250.

Variety 2 Resumed (1856–1860)

	Mintage	G-4	F-12	VF-20	EF-40	AU-50	MS-60	MS-63	PF-63
1856, Large Date	5,780,000	$6.	$7.	$10.	$17.	$40.	$140.	$250.	
1856, Small Date	*	6.	7.	10.	17.	40.	140.	250.	$1,800.
1856O	1,180,000	6.	7.	10.	22.	90.	300.	600.	
1856S	70,000	30.	120.	200.	375.	600.	1,000.	—	
1857	5,580,000	6.	7.	9.	17.	40.	135.	250.	1,800.
1857O	1,540,000	6.	7.	10.	17.	70.	190.	250.	
1858 . . . . *(300+)* . . .	1,540,000	6.	7.	9.	17.	40.	135.	250.	900.
1858O	290,000	7.	15.	35.	75.	125.	300.	450.	
1858S	60,000	35.	90.	150.	325.	525.	1,100.		
1859 . . . . *(800+)*	429,200	6.	7.	10.	25.	50.	135.	250.	700.
1859O	480,000	6.	8.	17.	37.	100.	180.	325.	
1859S	60,000	35.	110.	175.	450.	850.	2,000.		
1860S	140,000	10.	20.	50.	125.	350.	900.	1,750.	

* Included in number above.

Variety 4 – Legend on Obverse (1860–1873)

	Mintage	G-4	F-12	VF-20	EF-40	AU-50	MS-60	MS-63	PF-63
1860 . . . .(1,000)	606,000	$6.00	$7.	$9.	$17.	$40.	$135.	$250.	$400.
1860O	40,000	150.00	350.	600.	1,200.	2,000.	5,000.	—	
1861 . . . .(1,000) . .	1,883,000	6.00	7.	9.	17.	40.	100.	180.	400.
1861S	172,500	12.00	40.	75.	125.	200.	550.	1,750.	
1862 . . . .(550) . . .	847,000	5.00	6.	8.	13.	25.	100.	120.	350.
1862S	180,750	9.00	21.	50.	100.	125.	600.	1,000.	
1863 . . . .(460)	14,000	100.00	200.	300.	350.	400.	550.	600.	400.
1863S	157,500	8.50	20.	40.	70.	125.	450.	1,200.	

Chart continues on next page.   **83**

	Mintage	G-4	F-12	VF-20	EF-40	AU-50	MS-60	MS-63	PF-63
1864 . . . .(470)	11,000	$70.00	$150.00	$200.	$350.	$425.	$550.	$600.	$400.
1864S	230,000	7.00	16.00	32.	60.	110.	500.	550.	
1865 . . . .(500)	10,000	75.00	200.00	250.	310.	375.	525.	600.	400.
1865S	175,000	7.00	16.00	32.	100.	250.	800.	1,900.	
1866 . . . .(725)	8,000	120.00	235.00	375.	400.	600.	700.	800.	400.
1866S	135,000	10.00	20.00	40.	100.	135.	550.	1,100.	
1867 . . . .(625)	6,000	175.00	275.00	400.	475.	550.	675.	800.	450.
1867S	140,000	8.00	20.00	40.	100.	220.	600.	900.	
1868 . . . .(600)	464,000	5.50	6.50	15.	31.	60.	175.	375.	300.
1868S	260,000	6.00	12.00	30.	50.	75.	185.	450.	
1869 . . . .(600)	256,000	6.00	12.00	25.	40.	70.	185.	400.	300.
1869S	450,000	6.00	10.00	15.	35.	65.	185.	375.	
1870 . . . .(1,000)	470,500	5.00	7.00	9.	18.	40.	110.	200.	300.
1870S	50,000	100.00	150.00	200.	180.	350.	750.	1,000.	
1871 . . . .(960)	906,750	5.00	7.00	9.	15.	65.	140.	180.	300.
1871CC	20,100	350.00	1,000.00	1,500.	3,000.	4,250.	—	—	
1871S	320,000	6.00	20.00	28.	65.	120.	275.	650.	
1872 . . . .(950) . . .	2,395,500	5.00	6.00	9.	13.	30.	75.	110.	300.
1872CC	35,480	170.00	375.00	900.	2,100.	4,500.	—	—	
1872S	190,000	7.50	30.00	45.	95.	175.	500.	1,000.	
1873, Close 3 (1,100) . . .	1,506,900	5.00	6.00	9.	13.	30.	100.	125.	300.
1873, Open 3	60,000	8.00	20.00	30.	60.	90.	195.	550.	
1873CC *(unique)*	12,400								

Variety 5 – Arrows at Date (1873–1874)

In 1873, the dime was increased in weight to 2.50 grams. Arrows at the date in 1873 and 1874 indicate this change.

	Mintage	G-4	F-12	VF-20	EF-40	AU-50	MS-60	MS-63	PF-63
1873 . . . .(800) . . .	2,377,700	$6.	$9.	$20.	$50.	$100.	$275.	$425.	$700.
1873CC	18,791	400.	1,200.	2,750.	4,000.	7,500.	—		
1873S	455,000	7.	15.	28.	65.	150.	450.	900.	
1874 . . . .(700) . . .	2,939,300	6.	9.	20.	50.	125.	285.	425.	700.
1874CC	10,817	1,000.	2,250.	4,000.	7,500.	11,000.	—		
1874S	240,000	9.	25.	45.	90.	200.	400.	900.	

Variety 4 Resumed (1875–1891)

	Mintage	G-4	F-12	VF-20	EF-40	AU-50	MS-60	MS-63	PF-63
1875 . . . .(700) . . .	10,350,000	$5.	$6.	$8.	$12.	$30.	$75.	$110.	$250.
1875CC	4,645,000	5.	6.	8.	15.	32.	125.	170.	
1875S	9,070,000	5.	6.	8.	12.	30.	75.	110.	
1876 . . . .(1,150) . . .	11,145,000	5.	6.	8.	12.	30.	75.	110.	250.
1876CC	8,270,000	5.	6.	8.	15.	32.	100.	150.	
1876S	10,420,000	5.	6.	8.	12.	30.	75.	110.	
1877 . . . .(510) . . .	7,310,000	5.	6.	8.	12.	30.	75.	110.	275.
1877CC	7,700,000	5.	6.	8.	12.	30.	100.	150.	
1877S	2,340,000	5.	6.	8.	12.	30.	75.	110.	
1878 . . . .(800) . . .	1,677,200	5.	6.	8.	12.	30.	80.	110.	250.
1878CC	200,000	19.	45.	70.	135.	200.	400.	650.	
1879 . . . .(1,100)	14,000	70.	120.	180.	210.	275.	325.	350.	250.
1880 . . . .(1,355)	36,000	50.	100.	125.	175.	225.	275.	350.	250.
1881 . . . .(975)	24,000	50.	100.	125.	175.	225.	300.	350.	250.
1882 . . . .(1,100) . . .	3,910,000	5.	6.	8.	12.	30.	75.	110.	250.

	Mintage	G-4	F-12	VF-20	EF-40	AU-50	MS-60	MS-63	PF-63
1883 . . . . (1,039). . . .	7,674,673	$5.	$6.	$8.	$12.	$30.	$75.	$110.	$250.
1884 . . . . (875). . . .	3,365,505	5.	6.	8.	12.	30.	75.	110.	250.
1884S	564,969	8.	12.	20.	35.	100.	325.	575.	
1885 . . . . (930). . . .	2,532,497	5.	6.	8.	12.	30.	75.	110.	250.
1885S	43,690	150.	325.	600.	950.	1,600.	2,500.	3,000.	
1886 . . . . (886). . . .	6,376,684	5.	6.	8.	12.	30.	75.	110.	250.
1886S	206,524	9.	20.	30.	50.	90.	275.	500.	
1887 . . . . (710). . .	11,283,229	5.	6.	8.	12.	30.	75.	110.	250.
1887S	4,454,450	5.	6.	8.	12.	30.	75.	110.	
1888 . . . . (832). . . .	5,495,655	5.	6.	8.	12.	30.	75.	110.	250.
1888S	1,720,000	5.	6.	8.	13.	40.	120.	300.	
1889 . . . . (711). . . .	7,380,000	5.	6.	8.	12.	30.	75.	110.	250.
1889S	972,678	6.	10.	20.	35.	60.	200.	400.	
1890 . . . . (590). . . .	9,910,951	5.	6.	8.	12.	30.	75.	110.	250.
1890S	1,423,076	6.	8.	17.	30.	60.	135.	275.	
1891 . . . . (600). . .	15,310,000	5.	6.	8.	12.	30.	75.	110.	250.
1891O	4,540,000	5.	6.	8.	15.	40.	100.	150.	
1891S	3,196,116	5.	6.	8.	13.	35.	100.	125.	

BARBER OR LIBERTY HEAD (1892–1916)

This type was designed by Charles E. Barber, chief engraver of the Mint. His initial B is at the truncation of the neck. He also designed the quarters and half dollars of the same period.

G-4 GOOD—Date and letters plain. LIBERTY obliterated.
VG-8 VERY GOOD—Some letters visible in LIBERTY.
F-12 FINE—Letters in LIBERTY visible, though some weak.
VF-20 VERY FINE—Letters of LIBERTY evenly plain.
EF-40 EXTREMELY FINE—All letters in LIBERTY sharp, distinct. Headband edges distinct.
AU-50 ABOUT UNCIRCULATED—Slight traces of wear on hair cheekbone and on leaf tips in wreath.
MS-60 UNCIRCULATED—No trace of wear. Light blemishes.
MS-63 CHOICE UNCIRCULATED—Some distracting blemishes in prime focal areas. Impaired luster possible.

Mintmark location is on reverse, below wreath.

	Mintage	G-4	VG-8	F-12	VF-20	EF-40	AU-50	MS-60	MS-63	PF-63
1892 . . (1,245). . .	12,120,000	$1.50	$2.00	$6.00	$10.00	$12.	$25.	$70.	$90.	$225.
1892O	3,841,700	2.50	5.00	10.00	15.00	25.	32.	90.	150.	
1892S	990,710	18.00	30.00	65.00	75.00	100.	120.	200.	275.	
1893, 3 Over 2	*					90.	110.	275.	800.	475.
1893 . . . (792). . . .	3,340,792	3.00	4.00	7.00	10.00	15.	25.	90.	120.	250.
1893O	1,760,000	9.00	12.00	40.00	50.00	60.	75.	150.	300.	
1893S	2,491,401	4.00	8.00	10.00	18.00	25.	40.	135.	325.	
1894 . . . (972). . . .	1,330,000	5.00	10.00	35.00	50.00	60.	75.	150.	300.	250.
1894O	720,000	22.00	40.00	85.00	125.00	175.	300.	600.	950.	
1894S	24							400,000.		
1895 . . . (880)	690,000	35.00	40.00	50.00	200.00	250.	300.	350.	500.	275.
1895O	440,000	135.00	170.00	325.00	600.00	900.	1,000.	2,200.	2,700.	
1895S	1,120,000	12.00	17.00	50.00	75.00	85.	100.	225.	450.	
1896 . . . (762). . . .	2,000,000	3.00	7.00	15.00	20.00	30.	40.	90.	200.	250.
1896O	610,000	27.00	45.00	100.00	125.00	185.	220.	475.	1,000.	
1896S	575,056	25.00	40.00	90.00	125.00	175.	200.	400.	650.	
1897 . . . (731). .	10,868,533	.85	1.00	2.00	3.50	10.	18.	65.	75.	250.
1897O	666,000	24.00	35.00	100.00	140.00	175.	200.	400.	600.	
1897S	1,342,844	4.00	8.00	30.00	35.00	50.	75.	180.	350.	

* Included in number below.

Chart continues on next page.

	Mintage	G-4	VG-8	F-12	VF-20	EF-40	AU-50	MS-60	MS-63	PF-63
1898 ....(735)...	16,320,000	$.85	$1.00	$2.00	$4.00	$11.	$15.	$50.	$75.	$250.
1898O	2,130,000	2.00	5.00	25.00	40.00	60.	75.	210.	450.	
1898S	1,702,507	1.50	4.00	10.00	15.00	25.	50.	130.	450.	
1899 ....(846)...	19,580,000	.85	1.00	2.00	4.00	11.	15.	50.	75.	250.
1899O	2,650,000	1.00	4.00	22.00	36.00	50.	75.	175.	325.	
1899S	1,867,493	1.00	3.00	6.00	12.00	16.	35.	120.	300.	
1900 ....(912)...	17,600,000	.85	1.00	2.00	4.00	11.	15.	50.	75.	250.
1900O	2,010,000	3.00	14.00	30.00	36.00	80.	115.	260.	325.	
1900S	5,168,270	1.50	1.75	3.00	4.50	12.	25.	90.	150.	
1901 ....(813)...	18,859,665	.85	1.00	2.00	4.00	11.	22.	60.	75.	250.
1901O	5,620,000	1.00	1.50	3.00	7.00	22.	35.	180.	300.	
1901S...........	593,022	25.00	40.00	150.00	200.00	250.	275.	500.	600.	
1902 ....(777)...	21,380,000	.75	.85	1.50	3.50	11.	20.	60.	75.	250.
1902O	4,500,000	1.00	1.50	4.00	10.00	20.	40.	160.	375.	
1902S	2,070,000	2.50	4.00	16.00	25.00	40.	65.	160.	375.	
1903 ....(755)...	19,500,000	.75	.85	1.50	3.50	11.	20.	60.	75.	250.
1903O	8,180,000	1.00	1.50	4.00	6.00	15.	32.	135.	250.	
1903S...........	613,300	25.00	40.00	150.00	225.00	375.	450.	650.	800.	
1904 ....(670)...	14,600,357	.75	.85	1.50	3.50	11.	20.	60.	75.	250.
1904S...........	800,000	15.00	25.00	60.00	75.00	125.	200.	375.	700.	
1905 ....(727)...	14,551,623	.75	.85	1.50	3.50	11.	20.	60.	75.	250.
1905O	3,400,000	.80	1.50	12.00	18.00	25.	40.	125.	200.	
1905S	6,855,199	.80	1.50	3.00	5.00	15.	25.	120.	175.	
1906 ....(675)...	19,957,731	.75	.85	1.50	3.50	11.	20.	60.	75.	250.
1906D	4,060,000	.80	1.50	3.00	6.00	12.	25.	80.	140.	
1906O	2,610,000	1.00	3.00	18.00	25.00	32.	50.	115.	150.	
1906S	3,136,640	1.00	1.50	4.00	8.00	15.	35.	110.	130.	
1907 ....(575)...	22,220,000	.75	.85	1.50	3.50	11.	20.	60.	75.	250.
1907D	4,080,000	.80	2.00	3.00	6.00	15.	40.	130.	425.	
1907O	5,058,000	.80	3.00	9.00	12.00	20.	30.	100.	165.	
1907S	3,178,470	1.00	2.00	5.00	9.00	16.	35.	175.	300.	
1908 ....(545)...	10,600,000	.75	.85	1.50	3.50	11.	20.	60.	75.	250.
1908D	7,490,000	.80	1.20	3.00	4.00	12.	25.	65.	140.	
1908O	1,789,000	1.00	4.00	18.00	25.00	35.	60.	140.	250.	
1908S	3,220,000	.80	2.00	4.00	6.00	14.	60.	140.	260.	
1909 ....(650)...	10,240,000	.75	.85	1.50	3.00	11.	20.	60.	75.	250.
1909D	954,000	2.00	7.00	25.00	35.00	50.	80.	200.	425.	
1909O	2,287,000	1.00	2.00	4.00	8.00	16.	40.	95.	240.	
1909S	1,000,000	2.00	6.00	30.00	40.00	70.	130.	220.	500.	
1910 ....(551)...	11,520,000	.75	.85	1.50	3.00	11.	20.	60.	75.	250.
1910D	3,490,000	.80	2.00	3.00	5.00	15.	35.	110.	200.	
1910S	1,240,000	.80	3.00	20.00	32.00	45.	65.	175.	350.	
1911 ....(543)...	18,870,000	.75	.85	1.50	3.00	11.	20.	60.	75.	250.
1911D	11,209,000	.80	.85	1.50	3.00	11.	20.	60.	75.	
1911S	3,520,000	.80	2.00	4.00	6.00	13.	35.	90.	170.	
1912 ....(700)...	19,349,300	.75	.85	1.50	3.00	11.	20.	60.	75.	250.
1912D	11,760,000	.80	.85	1.50	3.00	11.	20.	60.	75.	
1912S	3,420,000	.80	2.00	3.00	6.00	13.	40.	85.	150.	
1913 ....(622)...	19,760,000	.75	.85	1.50	3.00	11.	20.	60.	75.	250.
1913S...........	510,000	5.00	10.00	32.00	45.00	75.	140.	225.	325.	
1914 ....(425)...	17,360,230	.75	.85	1.50	3.00	11.	20.	60.	75.	250.
1914D	11,908,000	.80	.85	1.50	3.00	11.	20.	60.	75.	
1914S	2,100,000	.80	2.00	4.00	6.00	11.	20.	75.	160.	
1915 ....(450)...	5,620,000	.75	.85	1.50	3.00	11.	20.	60.	75.	250.
1915S............	960,000	.80	2.00	15.00	18.00	25.	60.	120.	240.	
1916	18,490,000	.75	.85	1.50	3.00	11.	20.	60.	75.	
1916S	5,820,000	.80	.90	1.50	3.00	11.	20.	60.	75.	

DIMES

WINGED LIBERTY HEAD or MERCURY (1916–1945)

Although this coin is commonly called the Mercury dime, the main device is in fact a representation of Liberty. The wings crowning her cap are intended to symbolize liberty of thought. The designer's monogram AW is at the right of the neck.

G-4 GOOD—Letters and date clear. Lines and bands in fasces obliterated.
VG-8 VERY GOOD—Half of sticks discernible in fasces.
F-12 FINE—All sticks in fasces defined. Diagonal bands worn nearly flat.
VF-20 VERY FINE—Diagonal bands definitely visible.
EF-40 EXTREMELY FINE—Only slight wear on diagonal bands. Braids and hair before ear clearly visible.
AU-50 ABOUT UNCIRCULATED—Slight trace of wear. Most mint luster present.
MS-63 CHOICE UNCIRCULATED—No trace of wear. Light blemishes. Attractive mint luster.
MS-65 GEM UNCIRCULATED—Only light, scattered marks that are not distracting. Strong luster, good eye appeal.

Mintmark location is on reverse, left of fasces.

Uncirculated values shown are for average pieces with minimum blemishes; those with sharp strikes and split bands on reverse are worth much more.

	Mintage	G-4	VG-8	F-12	VF-20	EF-40	MS-60	MS-63	MS-65
1916	22,180,080	$1.00	$2.00	$3.00	$4.00	$5.00	$16.	$22.	$45.
1916D	264,000	400.00	550.00	900.00	1,400.00	2,000.00	3,000.	4,000.	10,000.
1916S	10,450,000	2.00	3.00	4.00	5.00	8.00	16.	32.	90.
1917	55,230,000	.50	.75	1.00	1.50	3.00	12.	24.	70.
1917D	9,402,000	2.00	3.00	4.00	6.00	18.00	60.	175.	550.
1917S	27,330,000	.50	.85	1.00	2.50	5.00	28.	80.	225.
1918	26,680,000	.50	.75	1.10	5.00	12.00	35.	80.	200.
1918D	22,674,800	.50	.75	1.00	5.00	11.00	50.	135.	325.
1918S	19,300,000	.50	.75	1.00	4.00	7.00	40.	135.	325.
1919	35,740,000	.50	.75	1.00	2.50	4.00	25.	65.	160.
1919D	9,939,000	.50	.85	2.00	9.00	18.00	80.	250.	700.
1919S	8,850,000	.50	.75	1.50	6.50	16.00	100.	300.	550.
1920	59,030,000	.50	.75	1.00	3.00	3.50	22.	38.	135.
1920D	19,171,000	.50	.75	1.00	4.50	10.00	75.	200.	400.
1920S	13,820,000	.50	.75	1.00	4.25	9.00	50.	150.	600.
1921	1,230,000	25.00	35.00	65.00	150.00	275.00	600.	900.	1,700.
1921D	1,080,000	32.00	55.00	80.00	175.00	320.00	625.	1,000.	1,700.
1923	50,130,000	.50	.75	1.00	2.50	3.00	12.	22.	60.
1923S	6,440,000	.50	.75	2.00	3.50	25.00	70.	185.	475.
1924	24,010,000	.50	.75	1.00	2.50	4.00	18.	40.	100.
1924D	6,810,000	.50	.75	2.00	3.50	10.00	85.	200.	500.
1924S	7,120,000	.50	.75	2.00	3.25	10.00	80.	275.	525.
1925	25,610,000	.50	.75	1.00	2.50	5.00	22.	35.	80.
1925D	5,117,000	2.00	3.00	5.00	18.00	45.00	140.	325.	800.
1925S	5,850,000	.50	.75	2.00	3.50	15.00	80.	210.	700.
1926	32,160,000	.50	.75	1.00	2.50	6.00	20.	25.	100.
1926D	6,828,000	.50	.75	1.00	4.00	16.00	45.	80.	210.
1926S	1,520,000	2.50	3.50	8.00	20.00	135.00	375.	800.	1,700.
1927	28,080,000	.50	.75	1.00	2.50	5.00	8.	20.	65.
1927D	4,812,000	.50	.75	2.00	8.00	27.00	90.	200.	675.
1927S	4,770,000	.50	.75	1.00	2.50	16.00	100.	250.	700.
1928	19,480,000	.50	.75	1.00	2.50	5.00	20.	40.	65.
1928D	4,161,000	.50	.75	3.00	8.00	18.00	75.	160.	420.
1928S	7,400,000	.50	.75	1.00	1.50	7.00	28.	110.	180.
1929	25,970,000	.50	.75	1.00	1.50	2.50	8.	15.	28.
1929D	5,034,000	.50	.75	1.00	2.00	4.00	12.	18.	30.
1929S	4,730,000	.50	.75	1.00	1.50	3.00	14.	20.	45.
1930	6,770,000	.50	.75	1.00	1.50	3.00	10.	20.	45.
1930S	1,843,000	.60	1.25	1.50	1.75	3.75	25.	50.	85.
1931	3,150,000	.50	.75	1.00	1.50	4.50	14.	32.	65.
1931D	1,260,000	3.00	3.50	4.50	8.00	15.00	42.	55.	100.
1931S	1,800,000	1.00	1.50	2.00	3.00	6.00	30.	42.	90.

1942, 2 Over 1

1942-D, 2 Over 1

	Mintage	VG-8	F-12	VF-20	EF-40	MS-60	MS-63	MS-65	PF-63
1934	24,080,000	$.30	$.40	$.50	$.60	$7.	$10.	$20.	
1934D	6,772,000	.30	.40	.50	.60	16.	20.	30.	
1935	58,830,000	.30	.40	.50	.60	6.	8.	13.	
1935D	10,477,000	.30	.40	.50	.60	17.	20.	35.	
1935S	15,840,000	.30	.40	.50	.60	10.	14.	20.	
1936 ...... (4,130)	87,500,000	.30	.40	.50	.60	7.	10.	12.	$800.
1936D	16,132,000	.30	.40	.50	.60	12.	14.	20.	
1936S	9,210,000	.30	.40	.50	.60	9.	12.	15.	
1937 ...... (5,756)	56,860,000	.30	.40	.50	.60	5.	8.	10.	275.
1937D	14,146,000	.30	.40	.50	.60	12.	14.	20.	
1937S	9,740,000	.30	.40	.50	.60	9.	12.	16.	
1938 ...... (8,728)	22,190,000	.30	.40	.50	.60	5.	8.	10.	175.
1938D	5,537,000	.30	.40	.50	.60	8.	9.	12.	
1938S	8,090,000	.30	.40	.50	.60	7.	8.	10.	
1939 ...... (9,321)	67,740,000	.30	.40	.50	.60	4.	6.	8.	175.
1939D	24,394,000	.30	.40	.50	.60	4.	6.	9.	
1939S	10,540,000	.30	.40	.50	.60	10.	14.	22.	
1940 ..... (11,827)	65,350,000	.30	.40	.50	.60	4.	5.	10.	150.
1940D	21,198,000	.30	.40	.50	.60	4.	7.	12.	
1940S	21,560,000	.30	.40	.50	.60	4.	6.	11.	
1941 ..... (16,557)	175,090,000	.30	.40	.50	.60	4.	5.	10.	120.
1941D	45,634,000	.30	.40	.50	.60	4.	7.	12.	
1941S	43,090,000	.30	.40	.50	.60	4.	6.	11.	
1942, 2 Over 1	*	175.00	225.00	275.00	350.00	950.	1,800.	5,000.	
1942 ..... (22,329)	205,410,000	.30	.40	.50	.60	4.	5.	10.	120.
1942D, 2 Over 1	*	175.00	225.00	275.00	350.00	850.	1,600.	4,000.	
1942D	60,740,000	.30	.40	.50	.60	5.	7.	11.	
1942S	4,930,000	.30	.40	.50	.60	6.	8.	12.	
1943	191,710,000	.30	.40	.50	.60	4.	5.	10.	
1943D	71,949,000	.30	.40	.50	.60	5.	6.	11.	
1943S	60,400,000	.30	.40	.50	.60	5.	6.	11.	
1944	231,410,000	.30	.40	.50	.60	4.	5.	10.	
1944D	62,224,000	.30	.40	.50	.60	4.	5.	10.	
1944S	49,490,000	.30	.40	.50	.60	4.	5.	10.	
1945	159,130,000	.30	.40	.50	.60	4.	5.	10.	
1945D	40,245,000	.30	.40	.50	.60	4.	5.	12.	
1945S	41,920,000	.30	.40	.50	.60	4.	6.	12.	
1945S, Micro S	*	.30	.40	.50	.60	8.	14.	40.	

* Included in regular mintage.

ROOSEVELT (1946 TO DATE)

John R. Sinnock (whose initials JS are at the truncation of the neck) designed this dime showing a portrait of Franklin D. Roosevelt. The design has heavier lettering and a more modernistic character than preceding types.

VF-20 EXTREMELY FINE—Moderate wear on high points of design. All major details are clear.

EF-40 EXTREMELY FINE—All lines of torch, flame, and hair very plain.

MS-63 CHOICE UNCIRCULATED—Some distracting contact marks or blemishes in prime focal areas. Impaired luster possible.

MS-65 GEM UNCIRCULATED—Only light, non-distracting scattered marks. Strong luster, good eye appeal.

PF-65 GEM PROOF—Nearly perfect.

Mintmark on reverse (1946–1964).

Silver Coinage (1946–1964)

	Mintage	VF-20	EF-40	MS-63	MS-65	PF-65
1946	255,250,000	$.30	$.40	$.90	$1.50	
1946D	61,043,500	.30	.40	.65	1.40	
1946S	27,900,000	.30	.40	2.00	3.00	
1947	121,520,000	.30	.40	1.50	2.50	
1947D	46,835,000	.30	.40	2.50	3.50	
1947S	34,840,000	.30	.40	2.00	4.00	
1948	74,950,000	.30	.40	1.50	4.00	
1948D	52,841,000	.30	.40	1.50	4.00	
1948S	35,520,000	.30	.40	2.00	5.00	
1949	30,940,000	.30	.40	10.00	15.00	
1949D	26,034,000	.30	.40	4.25	7.00	
1949S	13,510,000	.30	.40	16.00	23.00	
1950 (51,386)	50,130,114	.30	.40	2.50	3.50	$16.
1950D	46,803,000	.30	.40	2.00	3.00	
1950S	20,440,000	.30	.40	12.00	17.00	
1951 (57,500)	103,880,102	.30	.40	.60	1.50	20.
1951D	56,529,000	.30	.40	.60	1.50	
1951S	31,630,000	.30	.40	4.00	9.50	
1952 (81,980)	99,040,093	.30	.40	.60	1.50	13.
1952D	122,100,000	.30	.40	.60	1.50	
1952S	44,419,500	.30	.40	2.00	7.00	
1953 (128,800)	53,490,120	.30	.40	.85	2.00	13.
1953D	136,433,000	.30	.40	.85	2.00	
1953S	39,180,000	.30	.40	1.00	1.50	
1954 (233,300)	114,010,203	.30	.40	.75	1.35	9.
1954D	106,397,000	.30	.40	.75	1.35	
1954S	22,860,000	.30	.40	.75	1.35	
1955 (378,200)	12,450,181	.30	.40	1.00	2.00	9.
1955D	13,959,000	.30	.40	.75	1.35	
1955S	18,510,000	.30	.40	.75	1.35	
1956 (669,384)	108,640,000	.30	.40	.75	1.35	1.
1956D	108,015,100	.30	.40	.75	1.35	
1957 (1,247,952)	160,160,000	.30	.40	.75	1.35	1.
1957D	113,354,330	.30	.40	.75	1.35	
1958 (875,652)	31,910,000	.30	.40	.60	1.25	1.
1958D	136,564,600	.30	.40	.60	1.25	
1959 (1,149,291)	85,780,000	.30	.40	.60	1.25	1.
1959D	164,919,790	.30	.40	.60	1.25	
1960 (1,691,602)	70,390,000	.30	.40	.60	1.25	1.
1960D	200,160,400	.30	.40	.60	1.25	
1961 (3,028,244)	93,730,000	.30	.40	.60	1.25	1.
1961D	209,146,550	.30	.40	.60	1.25	
1962 (3,218,019)	72,450,000	.30	.40	.60	1.25	1.
1962D	334,948,380	.30	.40	.60	1.25	
1963 (3,075,645)	123,650,000	.30	.40	.60	1.25	1.
1963D	421,476,530	.30	.40	.60	1.25	
1964 (3,950,762)	929,360,000	.30	.40	.60	1.25	1.
1964D	1,357,517,180	.30	.40	.60	1.25	

Clad Coinage and Silver Proofs (1965 to Date)

Mintmark on obverse starting 1968.

	Mintage	MS-63	MS-65	PF-65		Mintage	MS-63	MS-65	PF-65
1965	1,652,140,570	$.15	$.25		1969	145,790,000	$.25	$.50	
1966	1,382,734,540	.15	.25		1969D	563,323,870	.15	.20	
1967	2,244,007,320	.15	.25		1969S	(2,394,631)			$.50
1968	424,470,400	.15	.20		1970	345,570,000	.15	.25	
1968D	480,748,280	.15	.20		1970D	754,942,100	.15	.25	
1968S	(3,041,506)			$.50	1970S	(2,632,810)			.50

Chart continues on next page.

Mintage	MS-63	MS-65	PF-65	Mintage	MS-63	MS-65	PF-65
1971 162,690,000	$.18	$.30		1990S . . . . . .(3,299,559)			$1.00
1971D 377,914,240	.16	.20		1991P 927,220,000	$.10	$.20	
1971S . . . . . .(3,220,733)			$.50	1991D 601,241,114	.12	.20	
1972 431,540,000	.15	.25		1991S . . . . . .(2,867,787)			1.20
1972D 330,290,000	.15	.25		1992P 593,500,000	.10	.15	
1972S . . . . . .(3,260,996)			.50	1992D 616,273,932	.10	.15	
1973 315,670,000	.15	.25		1992S . . . . . .(2,858,981)			2.00
1973D 455,032,426	.15	.25		1992S, Silver . .(1,317,579)			3.00
1973S . . . . . .(2,760,339)			.50	1993P 766,180,000	.10	.15	
1974 470,248,000	.15	.25		1993D 750,110,166	.10	.15	
1974D 571,083,000	.15	.25		1993S . . . . . .(2,633,439)			2.00
1974S . . . . . .(2,612,568)			.50	1993S, Silver . . .(761,353)			2.50
1975 585,673,900	.15	.25		1994P 1,189,000,000	.10	.15	
1975D 313,705,300	.15	.25		1994D 1,303,268,110	.10	.15	
1975S . . . . . .(2,845,450)			.60	1994S . . . . . .(2,484,594)			2.00
1976 568,760,000	1.50	.25		1994S, Silver . . .(785,329)			2.50
1976D 695,222,774		.15		1995P 1,125,500,000	.10	.20	
1976S . . . . . .(4,149,730)			.50	1995D 1,274,890,000	.15	.25	
1977 796,930,000	.15	.25		1995S, Proof . .(2,117,496)			3.00
1977D 376,607,228	.15	.25		1995S, Silver . . .(679,985)			4.00
1977S . . . . . .(3,251,152)			.50	1996P 1,421,163,000	.10	.20	
1978 663,980,000		.15		1996D 1,400,300,000	.10	.20	
1978D 282,847,540		.15		1996W 1,457,000	5.00	9.00	
1978S . . . . . .(3,127,781)			.40	1996S . . . . . .(1,750,244)			2.00
1979 315,440,000	.15	.25		1996S, Silver . . .(775,021)			3.00
1979D 390,921,184	.15	.25		1997P 991,640,000	.10	.15	
1979S, Filled S (3,677,175)			.50	1997D 979,810,000	.10	.15	
1979S, Clear S . . . .*			.75	1997S . . . . . .(2,055,000)			3.00
1980P 735,170,000	.15	.25		1997S, Silver . . .(741,678)			8.50
1980D 719,354,321	.15	.25		1998P 1,163,000,000	.10	.15	
1980S . . . . . .(3,554,806)			.40	1998D 1,172,250,000	.10	.15	
1981P 676,650,000	.15	.25		1998S . . . . . .(2,086,507)			2.00
1981D 712,284,143	.15	.25		1998S, Silver . . .(878,792)			3.00
1981S . . . . . .(4,063,083)			.40	1999P 2,164,000,000	.10	.15	
1982, No Mintmark	75.00	100.00		1999D 1,397,750,000	.10	.15	
1982P 519,475,000	1.50	2.00		1999S . . . . . .(2,543,401)			1.00
1982D 542,713,584	.60	1.10		1999S, Silver . . .(800,000)			3.00
1982S . . . . . .(3,857,479)			.60	2000P 1,842,500,000	.10	.15	
1983P 647,025,000	1.25	1.50		2000D 1,818,700,000	.10	.15	
1983D 730,129,224	.35	.60		2000S . . . . . .(3,082,483)			1.00
1983S . . . . . .(3,279,126)			.50	2000S, Silver . . .(856,400)			2.00
1984P 856,669,000	.15	.25		2001P 1,369,590,000	.10	.15	
1984D 704,803,976	.20	.35		2001D 1,412,800,000	.10	.15	
1984S . . . . . .(3,065,110)			.75	2001S . . . . . .(2,294,043)			.50
1985P 705,200,962	.15	.25		2001S, Silver . . .(889,697)			2.00
1985D 587,979,970	.15	.25		2002P 1,187,500,000	.10	.15	
1985S . . . . . .(3,362,821)			.50	2002D 1,379,500,000	.10	.15	
1986P 682,649,693	.25	.35		2002S . . . . . .(2,277,720)			.75
1986D 473,326,970	.25	.35		2002S, Silver . . .(888,826)			1.50
1986S . . . . . .(3,010,497)			1.00	2003P 1,085,500,000	.10	.15	
1987P 762,709,481	.15	.35		2003D 986,500,000	.10	.15	
1987D 653,203,402	.15	.35		2003S			.50
1987S . . . . . .(4,227,728)			.60	2003S, Silver			1.50
1988P 1,030,550,000	.12	.20		2004P 1,328,000,000	.10	.15	
1988D 962,385,489	.12	.20		2004D 1,159,500,000	.10	.15	
1988S . . . . . .(3,262,948)			1.00	2004S			.50
1989P 1,298,400,000	.10	.20		2004S, Silver			.50
1989D 896,535,597	.10	.20		2005P	.10	.15	
1989S . . . . . .(3,220,194)			1.00	2005D	.10	.15	
1990P 1,034,340,000	.10	.20		2005S			.50
1990D 839,995,824	.10	.20		2005S, Silver			1.50

* Included in number above.

LIBERTY SEATED (1875–1878)

The twenty-cent piece was a short-lived coin authorized by the Act of March 3, 1875. The edge of the coin is plain. Most of the 1876-CC coins were melted at the Mint and never released. The mintmark is on the reverse below the eagle.

G-4 GOOD—LIBERTY on shield obliterated. Letters and date legible.
VG-8 VERY GOOD—One or two letters in LIBERTY barely visible. Other details bold.
F-12 FINE—Some letters of LIBERTY possibly visible.
VF-20 VERY FINE—LIBERTY readable, but partly weak.
EF-40 EXTREMELY FINE—LIBERTY mostly sharp. Only slight wear on high points of coin.
AU-50 ABOUT UNCIRCULATED—Slight trace of wear on breast, head, and knees.
MS-60 UNCIRCULATED—No trace of wear. Light blemishes.
MS-63 CHOICE UNCIRCULATED—Some distracting blemishes in prime focal areas. Some impairment of luster possible.
PF-63 CHOICE PROOF—Reflective surfaces with only a few blemishes in secondary focal places. No major flaws.

	Mintage	G-4	VG-8	F-12	VF-20	EF-40	AU-50	MS-60	MS-63	PF-63
1875 . . . . .(2,790). . . 36,910		$45.	$50.	$60.	$90.	$150.	$200.	$325.	$475.	$1,100.
1875CC 133,290		50.	60.	100.	150.	200.	250.	425.	825.	
1875S 1,155,000		45.	50.	60.	90.	125.	175.	300.	450.	
1876 . . . . .(1,260). . . 14,640		50.	60.	100.	150.	200.	250.	450.	550.	1,200.
1876CC 10,000								60,000.		
1877 . . . .(350)					750.	850.				1,600.
1878 . . . .(600)					650.	800.				1,500.

QUARTER DOLLARS

Authorized in 1792, this denomination was not issued until four years later. The first type weighed 104 grains which remained standard until modified to 103-1/8 grains by the Act of January 18, 1837. As with the dime and half dime, the weight was reduced and arrows placed at the date in 1853. Rays were placed in the field of the reverse during that year only.

DRAPED BUST (1796–1807)

AG-3 ABOUT GOOD—Details clear enough to identify.
G-4 GOOD—Date readable. Bust outlined, but no detail.
VG-8 VERY GOOD—All but deepest drapery folds worn smooth. Hairlines nearly gone and curls lacking in detail.
F-12 FINE—All drapery lines visible. Hair partly worn.
VF-20 VERY FINE—Only left side of drapery indistinct.
EF-40 EXTREMELY FINE—Hair well outlined and detailed.
AU-50 ABOUT UNCIRCULATED—Slight trace of wear on shoulder and highest waves of hair.
MS-60 UNCIRCULATED—No trace of wear. Light blemishes.
MS-63 CHOICE UNCIRCULATED—Some distracting contact marks or blemishes in prime focal areas. Impaired luster possible.

Small Eagle Reverse (1796)

	Mintage	AG-3	G-4	VG-8	F-12	VF-20	EF-40	AU-50	MS-60	MS-63
1796	6,146	$1,800.	$3,250.	$4,000.	$6,000.	$9,000.	$11,000.	$15,000.	$23,000.	$30,000.

Heraldic Eagle Reverse (1804–1807)

	Mintage	AG-3	G-4	VG-8	F-12	VF-20	EF-40	AU-50	MS-60	MS-63
1804	6,738	$350.	$800.	$1,000.	$1,650.	$2,400.	$4,750.	$9,000.	—	
1805	121,394	50.	100.	135.	210.	425.	850.	1,400.	$2,600.	$3,500.
1806, 6 Over 5	*	50.	100.	135.	210.	425.	950.	1,500.	2,850.	6,500.
1806	206,124	50.	100.	135.	210.	425.	850.	1,400.	2,600.	3,500.
1807	220,643	50.	100.	135.	210.	425.	850.	1,400.	2,600.	3,500.

* Included in number below.

CAPPED BUST (1815–1838)
Variety 1 – Large Diameter (1815–1828)

AG-3 ABOUT GOOD—Details clear enough to identify.
G-4 GOOD—Date, letters, stars legible. Hair under Liberty's headband smooth. Cap lines worn smooth.
VG-8 VERY GOOD—Rim well defined. Main details visible. Full LIBERTY on cap. Hair above eye nearly smooth.
F-12 FINE—All hair lines visible, but only partial detail visible in drapery. Shoulder clasp distinct.
VF-20 VERY FINE—All details visible, but some wear evident. Clasp and ear sharp.
EF-40 EXTREMELY FINE—All details distinct. Hair well outlined.
AU-50 ABOUT UNCIRCULATED—Slight trace of wear on tips of curls and above the eye, and on the wing and claw tips.
MS-60 UNCIRCULATED—No trace of wear. Light blemishes.
MS-63 CHOICE UNCIRCULATED—Some distracting contact marks or blemishes in prime focal areas. Impaired luster possible.

	Mintage	AG-3	G-4	VG-8	F-12	VF-20	EF-40	AU-50	MS-60	MS-63
1815	89,235	$14.	$30.	$40.	$60.	$175.	$475.	$575.	$1,200.	$2,200.
1818, 8 Over 5	*	14.	30.	40.	60.	175.	450.	575.	1,400.	2,400.
1818, Normal Date	361,174	14.	30.	35.	55.	150.	400.	525.	1,100.	2,200.
1819	144,000	14.	30.	35.	55.	150.	400.	525.	1,100.	2,200.
1820	127,444	14.	30.	35.	55.	150.	400.	525.	1,100.	2,200.
1821	216,851	14.	30.	35.	55.	150.	400.	525.	1,100.	2,200.
1822, All kinds.	604,080	14.	30.	40.	70.	175.	425.	575.	1,300.	2,400.
1822, 25 Over 50c		275.	650.	1,300.	2,000.	2,650.	4,500.	7,000.	10,000.	
1823, 3 Over 2.	17,800	2,500.	4,000.	7,000.	10,000.	16,000.	22,000.			
1824, 4 Over 2	*	25.	40.	60.	100.	300.	700.	1,400.	3,000.	
1825, All kinds.	168,000	14.	30.	33.	50.	150.	400.	525.	1,200.	2,250.
1827, Original (Curl Base 2 in 25c)	4,000									60,000.
1827, Restrike (Square Base 2 in 25c).										25,000.
1828, All kinds.	102,000	14.	30.	33.	50.	150.	300.	700.	1,300.	2,500.
1828, 25 Over 50c		30.	60.	100.	200.	400.	800.	1,400.	3,000.	

* Included in number below.

Variety 2 – Reduced Diameter (1831–1838)

G-4 GOOD—Bust of Liberty well defined. Hair under headband smooth. Date, letters, stars legible. Scant rims.
VG-8 VERY GOOD—Details apparent but worn on high spots. Rims strong. Full LIBERTY.
F-12 FINE—All hair lines visible. Drapery partly worn. Shoulder clasp distinct.
VF-20 VERY FINE—Only top spots worn. Clasp sharp. Ear distinct.
EF-40 EXTREMELY FINE—Hair details and clasp bold and clear.
AU-50 ABOUT UNCIRCULATED—Slight trace of wear on hair around forehead, on cheek, and at top and bottom tips of eagle's wings and left claw.
MS-60 UNCIRCULATED—No trace of wear. Light blemishes.
MS-63 CHOICE UNCIRCULATED—Some distracting contact marks or blemishes in prime focal areas. Impaired luster possible.

	Mintage	G-4	VG-8	F-12	VF-20	EF-40	AU-50	MS-60	MS-63
1831.	398,000	$25.	$30.	$35.	$60.	$140.	$250.	$450.	$1,000.
1832.	320,000	25.	30.	35.	60.	140.	250.	450.	1,000.
1833.	156,000	25.	32.	40.	65.	175.	285.	600.	1,250.
1834.	286,000	25.	30.	35.	60.	140.	250.	450.	1,000.
1835.	1,952,000	25.	30.	35.	60.	140.	250.	450.	1,000.
1836.	472,000	25.	30.	35.	60.	140.	250.	450.	1,000.
1837.	252,400	25.	30.	35.	60.	140.	250.	450.	1,000.
1838.	366,000	25.	30.	35.	60.	140.	250.	450.	1,000.

LIBERTY SEATED (1838–1891)

G-4 GOOD—Scant rim. LIBERTY on shield worn off. Date and letters legible.
VG-8 VERY GOOD—Rim fairly defined, at least three letters in LIBERTY evident.
F-12 FINE—LIBERTY complete, but partly weak.
VF-20 VERY FINE—LIBERTY strong.
EF-40 EXTREMELY FINE—Complete LIBERTY and edges of scroll. Clasp clear.
AU-50 ABOUT UNCIRCULATED—Slight wear on Liberty's knees and breast and on eagle's neck, wing tips, and claws.
MS-60 UNCIRCULATED—No trace of wear. Light blemishes.
MS-63 CHOICE UNCIRCULATED—Some distracting contact marks or blemishes in prime focal areas. Impaired luster possible.

Variety 1 – No Motto Above Eagle (1838–1853)

Mintmark location is on reverse, below eagle.

	Small Date					Large Date		
	Mintage	G-4	VG-8	F-12	VF-20	EF-40	AU-50	MS-60	MS-63
1838	466,000	$8.	$10.	$16.	$30.	$100.	$200.	$600.	$1,500.
1839	491,146	8.	10.	16.	30.	100.	200.	550.	1,500.
1840	188,127	9.	12.	21.	35.	70.	110.	550.	1,000.
1840O	425,200	9.	12.	21.	35.	70.	110.	550.	1,000.
1841	120,000	16.	25.	42.	60.	110.	125.	425.	600.
1841O	452,000	8.	10.	16.	30.	90.	120.	425.	600.
1842, Small Date (Proof Only)	.....								13,000.
1842, Large Date	88,000	30.	40.	75.	130.	175.	225.	800.	12,500.
1842O, Small Date	769,000	135.	250.	425.	700.	1,350.	2,600.	—	
1842O, Large Date	*	9.	10.	16.	30.	70.	125.	650.	1,800.
1843	645,600	8.	9.	15.	20.	40.	60.	275.	600.
1843O	968,000	9.	13.	20.	40.	100.	275.	700.	1,300.
1844	421,200	8.	9.	15.	20.	40.	60.	225.	600.
1844O	740,000	8.	9.	17.	30.	80.	110.	550.	1,000.
1845	922,000	8.	9.	15.	20.	40.	60.	225.	600.
1846	510,000	8.	9.	15.	20.	40.	60.	225.	600.
1847	734,000	8.	9.	15.	20.	40.	60.	225.	600.
1847O	368,000	10.	15.	27.	50.	100.	275.	800.	2,000.
1848	146,000	12.	16.	28.	50.	80.	100.	450.	1,000.
1849	340,000	9.	10.	18.	26.	70.	90.	400.	600.
1849O	(a)	140.	230.	410.	800.	1,400.	1,900.	—	
1850	190,800	13.	16.	25.	35.	65.	100.	400.	700.
1850O	412,000	13.	16.	25.	35.	65.	180.	550.	1,000.
1851	160,000	14.	18.	28.	50.	80.	100.	400.	700.
1851O	88,000	65.	100.	200.	300.	650.	1,100.	2,000.	
1852	177,060	15.	20.	30.	55.	90.	110.	375.	650.
1852O	96,000	80.	120.	175.	300.	550.	1,400.	3,000.	5,500.
1853, Recut Date, No Arrows or Rays	44,200	100.	120.	150.	250.	400.	700.	1,300.	1,800.

** Included in number above. **a.** Mintage for 1849-O included with 1850-O.*

Variety 2 – Arrows at Date, Rays Around Eagle (1853)

1853, 3 Over 4

QUARTER DOLLARS

	Mintage	G-4	VG-8	F-12	VF-20	EF-40	AU-50	MS-60	MS-63
1853	15,210,020	$8.	$10.	$13.	$20.	$60.	$125.	$500.	$800.
1853, 3 Over 4	*	20.	35.	75.	125.	150.	200.	900.	1,850.
1853O	1,332,000	7.	11.	16.	30.	90.	400.	1,100.	3,000.
* Included in number above									

Variety 3 – Arrows at Date, No Rays (1854–1855)

	Mintage	G-4	VG-8	F-12	VF-20	EF-40	AU-50	MS-60	MS-63
1854	12,380,000	$7.	$8.	$10.	$17.	$35.	$90.	$250.	$550.
1854O	1,484,000	7.	8.	10.	17.	35.	90.	300.	800.
1855	2,857,000	7.	8.	10.	17.	35.	90.	275.	550.
1855O	176,000	16.	25.	45.	100.	150.	340.	1,000.	3,000.
1855S	396,400	16.	25.	32.	60.	125.	300.	850.	2,000.

Variety 1 Resumed (1856–1865; Weight Standard of 1853)

	Mintage	G-4	VG-8	F-12	VF-20	EF-40	AU-50	MS-60	MS-63	PF-63
1856	7,264,000	$8.	$9.	$11.	$17.	$23.	$60.	$170.	$300.	$1,850.
1856O	968,000	7.	9.	13.	18.	40.	90.	500.	675.	
1856S	286,000	14.	20.	30.	80.	160.	275.	1,000.	3,750.	
1857	9,644,000	7.	8.	10.	17.	23.	60.	150.	275.	1,200.
1857O	1,180,000	7.	8.	10.	17.	27.	100.	400.	850.	
1857S	82,000	20.	35.	55.	150.	250.	400.	1,200.	2,500.	
1858 . . . . (300+) . . .	7,368,000	7.	8.	10.	17.	23.	60.	150.	275.	900.
1858O	520,000	7.	8.	10.	20.	45.	150.	550.	1,000.	
1858S	121,000	18.	30.	45.	100.	200.	400.	2,000.		
1859 . . . . . (800) . .	1,343,200	7.	8.	10.	17.	23.	60.	150.	425.	625.
1859O	260,000	8.	13.	18.	26.	45.	150.	475.	1,000.	
1859S	80,000	30.	50.	90.	150.	400.	2,700.	—		
1860 . . . (1,000) . .	804,400	7.	8.	10.	17.	23.	60.	175.	300.	525.
1860O	388,000	7.	9.	12.	18.	32.	150.	450.	800.	
1860S	56,000	60.	100.	150.	325.	1,000.	1,800.			
1861 . . . (1,000) . .	4,853,600	7.	8.	10.	17.	23.	60.	175.	300.	525.
1861S	96,000	18.	35.	75.	125.	300.	800.			
1862 . . . . . (550) . .	932,000	7.	8.	10.	17.	23.	60.	175.	325.	525.
1862S	67,000	15.	22.	50.	90.	200.	400.	1,000.	2,500.	
1863 . . . . . (460) . .	191,600	9.	13.	20.	30.	50.	120.	350.	425.	525.
1864 . . . . . (470) . .	93,600	15.	25.	35.	55.	100.	175.	400.	550.	525.
1864S	20,000	100.	120.	250.	350.	850.	1,100.			
1865 . . . . . (500) . .	58,800	16.	25.	40.	55.	110.	150.	350.	550.	525.
1865S	41,000	20.	35.	55.	120.	190.	400.	1,200.	1,500.	

Variety 4 – Motto Above Eagle (1866–1873)

	Mintage	G-4	VG-8	F-12	VF-20	EF-40	AU-50	MS-60	MS-63	PF-63
1866 . . . . . . (725) . . .	16,800	$90.	$175.	$200.	$300.	$400.	$500.	$750.	$1,000.	$425.
1866S	28,000	70.	100.	200.	350.	450.	600.	1,400.	2,000.	
1867 . . . . . . (625) . . .	20,000	70.	100.	150.	200.	250.	350.	475.	1,500.	425.
1867S	48,000	70.	100.	130.	175.	300.	400.	1,750.		
1868 . . . . . . (600) . . .	29,400	35.	50.	75.	100.	125.	200.	400.	600.	425.
1868S	96,000	30.	40.	50.	90.	200.	350.	1,100.	1,500.	
1869 . . . . . . (600) . . .	16,000	90.	110.	170.	200.	275.	400.	600.	1,000.	425.
1869S	76,000	21.	35.	70.	110.	180.	450.	1,000.	1,750.	
1870 . . . . . . (1,000) . . .	86,400	18.	21.	35.	60.	90.	175.	400.	500.	425.

Chart continues on next page.

	Mintage	G-4	VG-8	F-12	VF-20	EF-40	AU-50	MS-60	MS-63	PF-63
1870CC	8,340	$900.	$1,400.	$2,600.	$4,750.	$8,000.	$10,000.			
1871 . . . (960) . . .	118,200	10.	14.	20.	40.	60.	125.	$225.	$400.	$400.
1871CC	10,890	600.	1,000.	1,600.	4,000.	8,000.	—	—		
1871S	30,900	90.	125.	175.	250.	400.	600.	1,300.	1,800.	
1872 . . . (950) . . .	182,000	10.	13.	20.	30.	50.	90.	300.	700.	400.
1872CC	22,850	150.	250.	500.	950.	1,700.	2,500.	5,500.		
1872S	83,000	210.	325.	475.	650.	950.	1,300.	2,750.		
1873 . . . (600) . . .	212,600	10.	13.	22.	35.	50.	90.	200.	400.	400.
1873CC	4,000				—					

Variety 5 – Arrows at Date (1873–1874)

	Mintage	G-4	VG-8	F-12	VF-20	EF-40	AU-50	MS-60	MS-63	PF-63
1873 . . . (540) . . .	1,271,160	$9.	$10.	$15.	$35.	$90.	$175.	$425.	$600.	$800.
1873CC	12,462	550.	1,000.	1,800.	3,250.	5,500.	9,000.	16,000.	27,000.	
1873S	156,000	10.	13.	22.	45.	110.	200.	600.	1,000.	
1874 . . . (700) . . .	471,200	9.	10.	15.	35.	90.	175.	450.	600.	800.
1874S	392,000	10.	12.	20.	45.	110.	175.	450.	600.	

Variety 4 Resumed (1875–1891)

1877-S, S Over Horizontal S

	Mintage	G-4	VG-8	F-12	VF-20	EF-40	AU-50	MS-60	MS-63	PF-63
1875 . . . . (700)	4,292,800	$7.	$8.	$10.	$15.	$20.	$60.	$125.	$200.	$350.
1875CC	140,000	20.	30.	60.	125.	200.	300.	700.	1,000.	
1875S	680,000	9.	14.	22.	35.	70.	125.	275.	500.	
1876 . . . (1,150) . . .	17,816,000	7.	8.	10.	15.	20.	60.	175.	200.	350.
1876CC	4,944,000	8.	13.	16.	20.	35.	75.	200.	400.	
1876S	8,596,000	7.	8.	10.	15.	20.	60.	125.	200.	
1877 . . . (510) . . .	10,911,200	7.	8.	10.	15.	20.	60.	125.	200.	350.
1877CC	4,192,000	8.	13.	16.	20.	35.	75.	200.	350.	
1877S	8,996,000	7.	8.	10.	15.	20.	60.	125.	200.	
1877S, S Over										
Horizontal S	*	10.	15.	40.	50.	90.	125.	300.	500.	
1878 . . . . (800)	2,260,000	7.	8.	10.	15.	20.	60.	125.	200.	350.
1878CC	996,000	8.	13.	17.	25.	50.	90.	225.	400.	
1878S	140,000	27.	50.	75.	100.	175.	250.	600.	900.	
1879 . . . (1,100)	13,600	40.	45.	75.	80.	100.	135.	200.	350.	350.
1880 . . . (1,355)	13,600	40.	45.	75.	80.	100.	135.	200.	350.	350.
1881 . . . . (975)	12,000	50.	65.	85.	100.	120.	190.	225.	375.	400.
1882 . . . (1,100)	15,200	45.	50.	80.	100.	110.	150.	275.	375.	350.
1883 . . . (1,039)	14,400	45.	50.	80.	100.	110.	150.	275.	375.	350.
1884 . . . . (875)	8,000	90.	100.	120.	125.	150.	200.	350.	400.	350.

* Included in number above

QUARTER DOLLARS

	Mintage	G-4	VG-8	F-12	VF-20	EF-40	AU-50	MS-60	MS-63	PF-63
1885 .....(930).....13,600		$40.	$50.	$75.	$100.	$110.	$200.	$300.	$400.	$350.
1886 .....(886)......5,000		90.	110.	150.	175.	275.	375.	475.	500.	400.
1887 .....(710).....10,000		80.	90.	100.	125.	175.	200.	300.	400.	350.
1888 .....(832).....10,001		70.	80.	90.	135.	200.	225.	300.	375.	350.
1888S...........1,216,000		7.	8.	10.	15.	22.	65.	150.	250.	
1889 .....(711).....12,000		50.	60.	90.	110.	120.	200.	325.	425.	450.
1890 .....(590).....80,000		20.	25.	35.	50.	80.	125.	275.	375.	375.
1891 .....(600)...3,920,000		7.	8.	10.	15.	22.	65.	150.	250.	375.
18910.............68,000		50.	65.	110.	325.	475.	525.	1,600.	2,200.	
1891S...........2,216,000		7.	8.	10.	15.	23.	65.	150.	250.	

BARBER or LIBERTY HEAD (1892–1916)

Like other silver coins of this type, the quarter dollars minted from 1892 to 1916 were designed by Charles E. Barber. His initial B is found at the truncation of the neck of Liberty.

G-4 GOOD—Date and legends legible. LIBERTY worn off headband.
VG-8 VERY GOOD—Some letters in LIBERTY legible.
F-12 FINE—LIBERTY completely legible but not sharp.
VF-20 VERY FINE—All letters in LIBERTY evenly plain.
EF-40 EXTREMELY FINE—LIBERTY bold, and its ribbon distinct.
AU-50 ABOUT UNCIRCULATED—Slight trace of wear above forehead, on cheek, and on eagle's head, wings, and tail.
MS-60 UNCIRCULATED—No trace of wear. Light blemishes.
MS-63 CHOICE UNCIRCULATED—Some distracting contact marks or blemishes in prime focal areas. Impaired luster possible.
PF-63 CHOICE PROOF—Reflective surfaces with only a few blemishes in secondary focal places. No major flaws.

	Mintage	G-4	VG-8	F-12	VF-20	EF-40	AU-50	MS-60	MS-63	PF-63
1892 ...(1,245)...8,236,000		$2.00	$3.00	$8.	$12.	$27.	$50.	$115.	$125.	$300.
1892O 2,460,000		3.00	5.00	10.	18.	35.	60.	150.	200.	
1892S 964,079		8.00	15.00	20.	30.	60.	125.	200.	425.	
1893 ....(792)...5,444,023		2.00	3.00	8.	13.	30.	50.	115.	165.	300.
1893O 3,396,000		3.00	4.00	9.	14.	35.	60.	160.	220.	
1893S 1,454,535		3.00	8.00	15.	30.	60.	125.	200.	500.	
1894 ....(972)...3,432,000		2.00	2.50	9.	15.	30.	60.	110.	200.	300.
1894O 2,852,000		2.50	3.00	10.	20.	35.	90.	160.	300.	
1894S 2,648,821		3.00	3.50	10.	20.	35.	90.	160.	300.	
1895 ....(880)...4,440,000		2.00	2.50	9.	14.	30.	60.	110.	200.	300.
1895O 2,816,000		2.50	3.50	12.	25.	38.	90.	185.	400.	
1895S 1,764,681		3.00	6.00	15.	30.	40.	110.	225.	450.	
1896 ....(762)...3,874,000		2.50	3.00	8.	13.	32.	60.	125.	200.	300.
1896O 1,484,000		3.00	10.00	30.	100.	150.	275.	450.	750.	
1896S 1,888,039		225.00	350.00	475.	900.	1,200.	1,800.	2,400.	3,600.	
1897 ....(731)...8,140,000		2.00	3.00	8.	12.	28.	50.	90.	125.	300.
1897O 1,414,800		3.00	10.00	30.	90.	120.	275.	425.	750.	
1897S 542,229		8.00	18.00	60.	100.	125.	275.	425.	750.	
1898 ....(735)...11,100,000		2.00	2.50	8.	13.	30.	50.	90.	125.	300.
1898O 1,868,000		3.00	6.00	18.	50.	100.	150.	300.	650.	
1898S 1,020,592		3.00	5.00	12.	16.	30.	90.	200.	600.	
1899 ....(846)...12,624,000		2.00	2.50	8.	12.	26.	50.	90.	125.	300.
1899O 2,644,000		3.00	5.00	9.	16.	32.	100.	200.	400.	
1899S 708,000		4.00	8.00	16.	30.	40.	125.	225.	550.	
1900 ....(912)...10,016,000		2.00	2.50	7.	12.	25.	60.	90.	125.	300.
1900O 3,416,000		3.00	7.00	15.	25.	45.	150.	250.	400.	
1900S 1,858,585		2.50	4.00	10.	16.	30.	50.	175.	450.	

Chart continues on next page.

	Mintage	G-4	VG-8	F-12	VF-20	EF-40	AU-50	MS-60	MS-63	PF-63
1901 ...(813)...	8,892,000	$2.00	$3.00	$7.00	$12.	$30.	$60.	$100.	$120.	$300.
1901O.........	1,612,000	12.00	21.00	50.00	100.	175.	250.	400.	900.	
1901S	72,664	1,800.00	3,000.00	3,500.00	5,750.	8,500.	10,000.	12,000.	17,500.	
1902 ...(777)..	12,196,967	2.00	2.50	7.00	12.	30.	50.	90.	125.	300.
1902O.........	4,748,000	2.50	3.00	12.00	25.	50.	90.	200.	600.	
1902S.........	1,524,612	4.00	6.00	12.00	25.	50.	100.	220.	475.	
1903 ...(755)...	9,759,309	2.00	2.50	7.00	12.	30.	50.	90.	175.	300.
1903O.........	3,500,000	3.00	4.00	11.00	20.	32.	100.	150.	600.	
1903S.........	1,036,000	4.00	6.00	14.00	25.	45.	100.	210.	400.	
1904 ...(670)...	9,588,143	2.00	2.50	7.00	12.	25.	50.	90.	125.	300.
1904O.........	2,456,000	3.00	4.00	16.00	30.	90.	175.	350.	600.	
1905 ...(727)...	4,967,523	2.50	3.50	8.50	12.	30.	50.	90.	150.	300.
1905O.........	1,230,000	3.00	9.00	30.00	50.	90.	150.	200.	550.	
1905S.........	1,884,000	2.50	3.00	12.00	18.	40.	90.	175.	500.	
1906 ...(675)...	3,655,760	2.50	3.00	7.00	12.	25.	50.	90.	125.	300.
1906D.........	3,280,000	2.50	3.00	9.00	15.	26.	60.	110.	200.	
1906O.........	2,056,000	2.50	3.00	12.00	15.	30.	90.	135.	250.	
1907 ...(575)...	7,132,000	2.50	3.00	7.00	12.	25.	50.	90.	125.	300.
1907D.........	2,484,000	2.50	3.00	9.00	15.	26.	60.	125.	350.	
1907O.........	4,560,000	2.50	3.00	8.00	12.	25.	55.	100.	250.	
1907S.........	1,360,000	2.50	3.00	15.00	19.	45.	90.	200.	400.	
1908 ...(545)...	4,232,000	2.50	3.00	7.00	12.	25.	50.	90.	125.	300.
1908D.........	5,788,000	2.50	3.00	7.00	12.	25.	50.	110.	200.	
1908O.........	6,244,000	2.00	2.50	7.00	12.	25.	50.	100.	125.	
1908S.........	784,000	4.00	12.00	30.00	40.	100.	200.	350.	550.	
1909 ...(650)...	9,268,000	2.00	2.50	7.00	12.	25.	50.	90.	125.	300.
1909D.........	5,114,000	2.00	2.50	7.00	12.	25.	60.	110.	160.	
1909O	712,000	4.00	12.00	30.00	70.	125.	225.	400.	850.	
1909S.........	1,348,000	2.00	2.50	10.00	16.	30.	90.	150.	350.	
1910 ...(551)...	2,244,000	2.00	2.50	7.00	12.	25.	60.	90.	150.	300.
1910D.........	1,500,000	2.00	2.50	15.00	18.	35.	110.	175.	400.	
1911 ...(543)...	3,720,000	2.00	2.50	7.00	12.	25.	50.	90.	125.	300.
1911D.........	933,600	2.00	2.50	30.00	90.	130.	225.	325.	600.	
1911S	988,000	2.00	2.50	18.00	20.	50.	120.	175.	350.	
1912 ...(700)...	4,400,000	2.00	2.50	7.00	12.	25.	50.	90.	125.	300.
1912S.........	708,000	2.00	2.50	15.00	18.	35.	100.	175.	400.	
1913 ...(613)...	484,000	5.00	8.00	23.00	65.	185.	210.	550.	600.	375.
1913D.........	1,450,800	2.00	2.50	10.00	15.	32.	70.	140.	175.	
1913S	40,000	425.00	625.00	1,000.00	1,900.	2,500.	3,000.	3,500.	4,000.	
1914 ...(380)...	6,244,230	2.00	2.50	7.00	12.	25.	50.	90.	125.	375.
1914D.........	3,046,000	2.00	2.50	7.00	12.	25.	50.	90.	125.	
1914S	264,000	22.00	35.00	60.00	100.	185.	275.	450.	600.	
1915 ...(450)...	3,480,000	2.00	2.50	7.00	12.	25.	50.	90.	125.	375.
1915D.........	3,694,000	2.00	2.50	7.00	12.	25.	50.	90.	125.	
1915S	704,000	2.00	2.50	8.00	15.	32.	90.	125.	200.	
1916	1,788,000	2.00	2.50	7.00	12.	25.	50.	90.	125.	
1916D.........	6,540,800	2.00	2.50	7.00	12.	25.	50.	90.	125.	

STANDING LIBERTY (1916–1930)

This design is by Hermon A. MacNeil, whose initial M is above and to the right of the date. Liberty bears a shield of protection in her left arm, while the right hand holds the olive branch of peace. There was a modification in 1917. The reverse had a new arrangement of stars and the eagle was higher. After 1924 the date was "recessed," thereby giving it greater protection from the effects of circulation.

G-4 GOOD—Date and lettering legible. Top of date worn. Liberty's right leg and toes worn off. Much wear evident on left leg and drapery lines.
VG-8 VERY GOOD—Distinct date. Toes faintly visible. Drapery lines visible above Liberty's left leg.
F-12 FINE—High curve of right leg flat from thigh to ankle. Only slight wear evident on left leg. Drapery lines over right thigh seen only at sides of leg.
VF-20 VERY FINE—Garment line across right leg worn, but visible at sides.
EF-40 EXTREMELY FINE—Flattened only at high spots. Liberty's toes are sharp. Drapery lines across right leg evident.
AU-50 ABOUT UNCIRCULATED—Slight trace of wear on head, kneecap, shield's center, and highest point on eagle's body.
MS-60 UNCIRCULATED—No trace of wear, but contact marks, surface spots, or faded luster possible.
MS-63 CHOICE UNCIRCULATED—No trace of wear. Light blemishes. Attractive mint luster.

Variety 1 – No Stars Below Eagle (1916–1917)

Mintmark location is on obverse, to left of date.

	Mintage	G-4	VG-8	F-12	VF-20	EF-40	AU-50	MS-60	MS-63
1916	52,000	$2,000.	$3,200.	$3,750.	$5,000.	$6,500.	$8,000.	$10,000.	$12,000.
1917, Variety	18,740,000	13.	18.	26.	32.	50.	100.	140.	180.
1917D, Variety	11,509,200	13.	18.	26.	32.	55.	110.	150.	200.
1917S, Variety	11,952,000	16.	21.	28.	40.	75.	125.	170.	250.

Variety 2 – Stars Below Eagle (1917–1930)
Pedestal Date (1917–1924)

1918-S, 8 Over 7

	Mintage	G-4	VG-8	F-12	VF-20	EF-40	AU-50	MS-60	MS-63
1917, Variety 2	13,880,000	$11.	$13.	$16.	$18.	$27.	$55.	$100.	$140.
1917D, Variety 2	6,224,400	15.	21.	30.	35.	50.	75.	125.	175.
1917S, Variety 2	5,552,000	15.	21.	30.	35.	50.	75.	125.	175.
1918	14,240,000	8.	9.	15.	17.	25.	50.	100.	145.
1918D	7,380,000	13.	15.	25.	30.	40.	75.	125.	200.
1918S, Normal Date	11,072,000	9.	11.	17.	20.	30.	50.	120.	175.
1918S, 8 Over 7	*	950.	1,000.	1,300.	2,000.	3,000.	5,500.	9,500.	17,500.
1919	11,324,000	18.	22.	27.	35.	40.	60.	100.	125.
1919D	1,944,000	50.	70.	100.	150.	225.	300.	375.	800.
1919S	1,836,000	50.	70.	100.	150.	300.	350.	500.	900.
1920	27,860,000	8.	10.	15.	20.	25.	40.	100.	125.
1920D	3,586,400	25.	30.	40.	45.	65.	100.	125.	450.
1920S	6,380,000	9.	12.	16.	20.	30.	50.	110.	400.
1921	1,916,000	80.	110.	160.	200.	275.	400.	500.	700.
1923	9,716,000	8.	10.	15.	17.	20.	35.	100.	150.
1923S	1,360,000	150.	200.	225.	350.	450.	500.	550.	650.
1924	10,920,000	8.	10.	12.	15.	20.	45.	100.	150.
1924D	3,112,000	20.	30.	40.	60.	100.	125.	150.	175.
1924S	2,860,000	12.	15.	20.	22.	100.	125.	150.	500.

* Included in number above

Recessed Date (1925–1930)

	Mintage	G-4	VG-8	F-12	VF-20	EF-40	AU-50	MS-60	MS-63
1925	12,280,000	$1.50	$2.50	$3.50	$7.	$16.	$35.	$75.	$150.
1926	11,316,000	1.50	2.50	3.50	7.	16.	35.	75.	150.
1926D	1,716,000	1.50	2.50	8.00	15.	25.	50.	100.	170.
1926S	2,700,000	1.50	2.50	6.00	11.	50.	125.	200.	400.
1927	11,912,000	1.50	2.50	3.50	7.	16.	35.	75.	150.
1927D	976,000	3.00	5.00	10.00	20.	50.	80.	160.	200.
1927S	396,000	10.00	12.00	30.00	125.	600.	1,750.	2,000.	4,000.
1928	6,336,000	1.50	2.50	3.50	7.	16.	35.	75.	140.
1928D	1,627,600	1.50	2.50	3.00	7.	16.	35.	75.	140.
1928S	2,644,000	1.50	2.50	3.50	7.	16.	35.	75.	150.
1929	11,140,000	1.50	2.50	3.50	7.	16.	35.	75.	150.
1929D	1,358,000	1.50	2.50	3.50	7.	16.	35.	75.	150.
1929S	1,764,000	1.50	2.50	3.50	7.	16.	35.	85.	150.
1930	5,632,000	1.50	2.50	3.50	7.	16.	35.	70.	140.
1930S	1,556,000	1.50	2.50	3.50	7.	16.	35.	70.	140.

WASHINGTON (1932 TO DATE)

This type was intended to be a commemorative issue marking the 200th anniversary of Washington's birth. John Flanagan, a New York sculptor, was the designer. The initials JF are found at the base of the neck. The mintmark is on the reverse below the wreath for coins from 1932 to 1964. Starting in 1968, the mintmark was moved to the obverse at the right of the ribbon.

F-12 FINE—Hair lines about Washington's ear visible. Tiny feathers on eagle's breast faintly visible.
VF-20 VERY FINE—Most hair details visible. Wing feathers clear.
EF-40 EXTREMELY FINE—Hair lines sharp. Wear spots confined to top of eagle's legs and center of breast.
MS-60 UNCIRCULATED—No trace of wear, but many contact marks, surface spotting, or faded luster possible.
MS-63 CHOICE UNCIRCULATED—No trace of wear. Light blemishes. Attractive mint luster.
MS-64 UNCIRCULATED—A few scattered contact marks. Good eye appeal and attractive luster.
MS-65 GEM UNCIRCULATED—Only light, scattered contact marks that are not distracting. Strong luster, good eye appeal.
PF-65 GEM PROOF—Hardly any blemishes, and no flaws.

Since 1968, the mintmark has been on obverse at the right of the ribbon.

Silver Coinage (1932–1964)

	Mintage	VG-8	F-12	VF-20	EF-40	MS-60	MS-63	MS-65	PF-65
1932	5,404,000	$2.00	$2.50	$3.00	$4.00	$12.	$23.	$175.	
1932D	436,800	45.00	60.00	75.00	150.00	475.	1,650.	12,000.	
1932S	408,000	45.00	60.00	65.00	75.00	225.	600.	3,300.	
1934	31,912,052	.75	1.25	1.40	3.00	9.	17.	45.	
1934D	3,527,200	1.00	1.25	1.40	5.00	80.	175.	400.	
1935	32,484,000	.75	1.00	1.25	2.00	9.	15.	45.	
1935D	5,780,000	1.00	1.25	2.00	5.00	85.	140.	350.	
1935S	5,660,000	1.00	1.25	1.40	4.00	40.	60.	140.	
1936 (3,837)	41,300,000		.75	.75	1.00	8.	16.	40.	$850.
1936D	5,374,000		1.00	5.00	18.00	170.	300.	650.	
1936S	3,828,000		.75	1.50	4.00	40.	75.	200.	
1937 (5,542)	19,696,000		.75	.75	.85	8.	15.	48.	325.
1937D	7,189,600		.75	1.50	3.00	25.	45.	70.	
1937S	1,652,000		.75	2.00	6.00	65.	100.	140.	
1938 (8,045)	9,472,000		.75	2.00	5.00	35.	60.	120.	200.
1938S	2,832,000		.75	1.50	4.00	35.	60.	120.	
1939 (8,795)	33,540,000		.75	.75	.85	5.	12.	25.	175.
1939D	7,092,000		.75	1.00	2.00	12.	20.	50.	
1939S	2,628,000		.75	1.00	4.00	45.	65.	150.	

	Mintage	F-12	VF-20	EF-40	MS-60	MS-63	MS-65	PF-65
1940 ....(11,246)...	35,704,000	$.75	$.75	$.85	$5.00	$12.	$30.	$100.
1940D	2,797,600	.75	1.00	5.00	50.00	100.	150.	
1940S	8,244,000	.75	.75	1.00	7.00	13.	25.	
1941 ....(15,287)...	79,032,000	.75	.75	.85	2.00	6.	20.	100.
1941D	16,714,800	.75	.75	.85	12.00	22.	25.	
1941S	16,080,000	.75	.75	.85	7.50	18.	35.	
1942 ....(21,123)...	102,096,000	.75	.75	.85	2.00	4.	10.	100.
1942D	17,487,200	.75	.75	1.00	6.00	12.	20.	
1942S	19,384,000	.75	.75	1.00	27.00	45.	95.	
1943	99,700,000	.75	.75	.85	2.00	4.	20.	
1943D	16,095,600	.75	.75	.85	8.00	16.	20.	
1943S	21,700,000	.75	.75	1.00	10.00	19.	25.	
1944	104,956,000	.75	.75	.85	2.00	4.	18.	
1944D	14,600,800	.75	.75	.85	4.00	10.	20.	
1944S	12,560,000	.75	.75	.85	5.00	12.	20.	
1945	74,372,000	.75	.75	.85	2.00	3.	20.	
1945D	12,341,600	.75	.75	.85	4.00	12.	20.	
1945S	17,004,001	.75	.75	.85	3.00	5.	15.	
1946	535,436,000	.75	.75	.85	2.00	3.	15.	
1946D	9,072,800	.75	.75	.85	2.00	3.	15.	
1946S	4,204,000	.75	.75	.85	2.00	3.	15.	
1947	22,556,000	.75	.75	.85	3.00	5.	15.	
1947D	15,338,400	.75	.75	.85	2.00	4.	15.	
1947S	5,532,000	.75	.75	.85	2.00	4.	15.	
1948	35,196,000	.75	.75	.85	2.00	3.	15.	
1948D	16,766,800	.75	.75	.85	2.00	4.	30.	
1948S	15,960,000	.75	.75	.85	2.00	3.	18.	
1949	9,312,000	.75	.75	.85	10.00	20.	30.	
1949D	10,068,400	.75	.75	.85	5.00	11.	22.	
1950 ....(51,386)...	24,920,126	.75	.75	.85	2.00	4.	13.	30.
1950D	21,075,600	.75	.75	.85	2.00	4.	13.	
1950D, D Over S	*		25.00	75.00	125.00	200.	700.	
1950S	10,284,004	.75	.75	.85	4.00	7.	30.	
1950S, S Over D	*		25.00	80.00	140.00	200.	400.	
1951 ....(57,500)...	43,448,102	.75	.75	.85	1.25	3.	14.	30.
1951D	35,354,800	.75	.75	.85	1.25	3.	14.	
1951S	9,048,000	.75	.75	.85	4.00	12.	18.	
1952 ....(81,980)...	3,780,093	.75	.75	.85	1.25	3.	18.	25.
1952D	49,795,200	.75	.75	.85	1.25	3.	16.	
1952S	13,707,800	.75	.75	.85	4.00	10.	16.	
1953 ....(128,800)...	18,536,120	.75	.75	.85	1.25	3.	16.	25.
1953D	56,112,400	.75	.75	.85	1.25	3.	14.	
1953S	14,016,000	.75	.75	.85	1.25	2.	12.	
1954 ....(233,300)...	54,412,203	.75	.75	.85	1.25	4.	13.	12.
1954D	42,305,500	.75	.75	.85	1.25	3.	16.	
1954S	11,834,722	.75	.75	.85	1.25	2.	15.	
1955 ....(378,200)...	18,180,181	.75	.75	.85	1.25	2.	10.	12.
1955D	3,182,400	.75	.75	.85	1.25	2.	20.	
1956 ....(669,384)...	44,144,000	.75	.75	.75	1.00	3.	8.	4.
1956D	32,334,500	.75	.75	.75	1.00	2.	10.	
1957 ....(1,247,952)...	3,532,000	.75	.75	.75	1.00	2.	10.	3.
1957D	77,924,160	.75	.75	.75	1.00	2.	10.	
1958 ....(875,652)...	6,360,000	.75	.75	.75	1.00	2.	9.	4.
1958D	78,124,900	.75	.75	.75	1.00	2.	9.	
1959 ....(1,149,291)...	24,384,000	.75	.75	.75	1.00	2.	9.	3.
1959D	62,054,232	.75	.75	.75	1.00	2.	9.	
1960 ....(1,691,602)...	29,164,000	.75	.75	.75	1.00	2.	6.	2.
1960D	63,000,324	.75	.75	.75	1.00	2.	6.	
1961 ....(3,028,244)...	37,036,000	.75	.75	.75	1.00	2.	6.	2.
1961D	83,656,928	.75	.75	.75	1.00	2.	6.	
1962 ....(3,218,019)...	36,156,000	.75	.75	.75	1.00	2.	6.	2.
1962D	127,554,756	.75	.75	.75	1.00	2.	6.	
1963 ....(3,075,645)...	74,316,000	.75	.75	.75	1.00	2.	6.	2.
1963D	135,288,184	.75	.75	.75	1.00	2.	6.	
1964 ....(3,950,762)...	560,390,585	.75	.75	.75	1.00	2.	6.	2.
1964D	704,135,528	.75	.75	.75	1.00	2.	6.	

* Included in number above

Clad Coinage and Silver Proofs (1965 to Date)

	Mintage	MS-63	MS-65	PF-65		Mintage	MS-63	MS-65	PF-65
1965	1,819,717,540	$.30	$1.00		1971	109,284,000	$.30	$1.00	
1966	821,101,500	.30	1.00		1971D	258,634,428	.30	.50	
1967	1,524,031,848	.30	1.00		1971S	(3,220,733)			$.50
1968	220,731,500	.50	1.50		1972	215,048,000	.30	.75	
1968D	101,534,000	.30	1.00		1972D	311,067,732	.30	1.00	
1968S	(3,041,506)			$.50	1972S	(3,260,996)			.50
1969	176,212,000	.75	1.50		1973	346,924,000	.30	1.00	
1969D	114,372,000	.50	1.25		1973D	232,977,400	.30	1.00	
1969S	(2,934,631)			.50	1973S	(2,760,339)			.50
1970	136,420,000	.25	1.00		1974	801,456,000	.30	1.00	
1970D	417,341,364	.25	1.00		1974D	353,160,300	.30	2.00	
1970S	(2,632,810)			.50	1974S	(2,612,568)			.50

Bicentennial (1776–1976)

	Mintage	MS-63	MS-65	PF-65
1776–1976, Copper-Nickel Clad	809,784,016	$.30	$1.00	
1776–1976D, Copper-Nickel Clad	860,118,839	.30	1.00	
1776–1976S, Copper-Nickel Clad	(7,059,099)			$.50
1776–1976S, Silver Clad (a)	11,000,000	1.00	2.00	
1776–1976S, Silver Clad (a)	(4,000,000)			2.00

a. Mintage is approximate. Several million were melted in 1982.

Eagle Reverse Resumed (1977–1998)
(Dies Slightly Modified to Lower Relief)

	Mintage	MS-63	MS-65	PF-65		Mintage	MS-63	MS-65	PF-65
1977	468,556,000	$.27			1985P	775,818,962	$.50	$2.50	
1977D	256,524,978	.27	$1.00		1985D	519,962,888	.35	1.25	
1977S	(3,251,152)			$.50	1985S	(3,362,821)			$.75
1978	521,452,000	.27	1.50		1986P	551,199,333	1.00	1.25	
1978D	287,373,152	.27	1.50		1986D	504,298,660	1.50	4.00	
1978S	(3,127,781)			.50	1986S	(3,010,497)			1.00
1979	515,708,000	.28	1.50		1987P	582,499,481	.27	1.50	
1979D	489,789,780	.27	1.25		1987D	655,594,696	.27	1.00	
1979S, Proof	(3,677,175)				1987S	(4,227,728)			1.00
Filled S				.50	1988P	562,052,000	.50	1.75	
Clear S				1.00	1988D	596,810,688	.27	1.50	
1980P	635,832,000	.27	1.50		1988S	(3,262,948)			.75
1980D	518,327,487	.27	1.25		1989P	512,868,000	.27	1.75	
1980S	(3,554,806)			.50	1989D	896,535,597	.27	1.00	
1981P	601,716,000	.27	1.50		1989S	(3,220,194)			.75
1981D	575,722,833	.27	1.00		1990P	613,792,000	.27	1.50	
1981S	(4,063,083)			.75	1990D	927,638,181	.28	1.00	
1982P	500,931,000	2.00	5.00		1990S	(3,299,559)			1.75
1982D	480,042,788	.70	4.00		1991P	570,968,000	.30	1.75	
1982S	(3,857,479)			.75	1991D	630,966,693	.30	1.50	
1983P	673,535,000	4.00	18.00		1991S	(2,867,787)			1.25
1983D	617,806,446	2.00	9.00		1992P	384,764,000	.27	4.00	
1983S	(3,279,126)			1.00	1992D	389,777,107	.35	1.50	
1984P	676,545,000	.30	1.25		1992S	(2,858,981)			1.25
1984D	546,483,064	.50	1.25		1992S, Silver	(1,317,579)			1.50
1984S	(3,065,110)			1.00	1993P	639,276,000	.30	1.75	

	Mintage	MS-63	MS-65	PF-65		Mintage	MS-63	MS-65	PF-65
1993D	645,476,128	$.30	$1.75		1996D	906,868,000	$.25	$1.75	
1993S	(2,633,439)			$1.25	1996S	(1,750,244)			$1.50
1993S, Silver	(761,353)			3.00	1996S, Silver	(775,021)			4.00
1994P	825,600,000	.30	4.00		1997P	595,740,000	.25	1.25	
1994D	880,034,110	.30	1.50		1997D	599,680,000	.25	1.25	
1994S	(2,484,594)			1.75	1997S	(2,055,000)			3.00
1994S, Silver	(785,329)			5.00	1997S, Silver	(741,678)			8.00
1995P	1,004,336,000	.30	1.75		1998P	896,268,000	.25	1.00	
1995D	1,103,216,000	.30	1.75		1998D	821,000,000	.25	1.00	
1995S	(2,117,496)			6.00	1998S	(2,086,507)			4.00
1995S, Silver	(679,985)			6.00	1998S, Silver	(878,792)			4.00
1996P	925,040,000	.25	1.25						

State Quarters (1999–2008)

The United States Mint 50 State Quarters® Program, which began in 1999, will produce a series of 50 quarter dollar coins with special designs honoring each state. Five different designs will be issued each year during the period 1999 to 2008. States are being commemorated in the order of their entrance into statehood.

These are all legal tender coins of standard weight and composition. The obverse side depicting President George Washington has been modified slightly to include some of the wording previously used on the reverse. The modification was authorized by special legislation, and carried out by Mint Sculptor-Engraver William Cousins, whose initials have been added to the truncation of Washington's neck adjacent to those of the original designer, John Flanagan.

Each state theme is being proposed and approved by the governor of the state. Final designs will be created by Mint personnel.

Circulation coins are made at the Philadelphia and Denver mints. Proof coins are made in San Francisco. Both copper-nickel and silver Proof coins are made each year.

	Mintage	AU-50	MS-63	PF-65
1999P, Delaware	373,400,000	$.25	$.50	
1999D, Delaware	401,424,000	.25	.50	
1999S, Delaware	(3,713,359)			$1.50
1999S, Delaware, Silver	(800,000)			2.50
1999P, Pennsylvania	349,000,000	.25	.50	
1999D, Pennsylvania	358,332,000	.25	.50	
1999S Pennsylvania	(3,713,359)			1.50
1999S, Pennsylvania, Silver	(800,000)			2.50
1999P, New Jersey	363,200,000	.25	.30	
1999D, New Jersey	299,028,000	.25	.35	
1999S, New Jersey	(3,713,359)			1.50
1999S, New Jersey, Silver	(800,000)			2.50
1999P, Georgia	451,188,000	.25	.30	
1999D, Georgia	488,744,000	.25	.30	
1999S, Georgia	(3,713,359)			1.50
1999S Georgia, Silver	(800,000)			2.50
1999P, Connecticut	688,744,000	.25	.30	
1999D, Connecticut	657,880,000	.25	.30	
1999S, Connecticut	(3,713,359)			1.50
1999S, Connecticut, Silver	(800,000)			2.50

	Mintage	AU-50	MS-63	PF-65
2000P, Massachusetts	628,600,000	$.25	$.30	
2000D, Massachusetts	535,184,000	.25	.30	
2000S, Massachusetts	(4,020,083)			$1.50
2000S, Massachusetts, Silver	(856,400)			2.50
2000P, Maryland	678,200,000	.25	.30	
2000D, Maryland	556,532,000	.25	.30	
2000S, Maryland	(4,020,083)			1.50
2000S, Maryland, Silver	(856,400)			2.50
2000P, South Carolina	742,576,000	.25	.30	
2000D, South Carolina	566,208,000	.25	.30	
2000S, South Carolina	(4,020,083)			1.50
2000S, South Carolina, Silver	(856,400)			2.50
2000P, New Hampshire	673,040,000	.25	.30	
2000D, New Hampshire	495,976,000	.25	.30	
2000S, New Hampshire	(4,020,083)			1.50
2000S, New Hampshire, Silver	(856,400)			2.50
2000P, Virginia	943,000,000	.25	.30	
2000D, Virginia	651,616,000	.25	.30	
2000S, Virginia	(4,020,083)			1.50
2000S, Virginia, Silver	(856,400)			2.50

	Mintage	AU-50	MS-63	PF-65
2001P, New York	655,400,000	$.25	$.30	
2001D, New York	619,640,000	.25	.30	
2001S, New York	(3,093,274)			$1.50
2001S, New York, Silver	(889,697)			2.50
2001P, North Carolina	627,600,000	.25	.30	
2001D, North Carolina	427,876,000	.25	.30	
2001S, North Carolina	(3,093,274)			1.50
2001S, North Carolina, Silver	(889,697)			2.50
2001P, Rhode Island	423,000,000	.25	.30	
2001D, Rhode Island	447,100,000	.25	.30	
2001S, Rhode Island	(3,093,274)			1.50
2001S, Rhode Island, Silver	(889,697)			2.50
2001P, Vermont	423,400,000	.25	.30	
2001D, Vermont	459,404,000	.25	.30	
2001S, Vermont	(3,093,274)			1.50
2001S, Vermont, Silver	(889,697)			2.50
2001P, Kentucky	353,000,000	.25	.30	
2001D, Kentucky	370,564,000	.25	.30	
2001S, Kentucky	(3,093,274)			1.50
2001S, Kentucky, Silver	(889,697)			2.50

QUARTER DOLLARS

	Mintage	AU-50	MS-63	PF-65
2002P, Tennessee	361,600,000	$.25	$.30	
2002D, Tennessee	286,468,000	.25	.30	
2002S, Tennessee	(3,039,320)			$1.50
2002S, Tennessee, Silver	(888,826)			2.50
2002P, Ohio	217,200,000	.25	.30	
2002D, Ohio	414,832,000	.25	.30	
2002S, Ohio	(761,600) 3,039,320			1.50
2002S, Ohio, Silver	(888,826)			2.50
2002P, Louisiana	362,000,000	.25	.30	
2002D, Louisiana	402,204,000	.25	.30	
2002S, Louisiana	(3,039,320)			1.50
2002S, Louisiana, Silver	(888,826)			2.50
2002P, Indiana	362,600,000	.25	.30	
2002D, Indiana	327,200,000	.25	.30	
2002S, Indiana	(3,039,320)			1.50
2002S, Indiana, Silver	(888,826)			2.50
2002P, Mississippi	290,000,000	.25	.30	
2002D, Mississippi	289,600,000	.25	.30	
2002S, Mississippi	(3,039,320)			1.50
2002S, Mississippi, Silver	(888,826)			2.50

	Mintage	AU-50	MS-63	PF-65
2003P, Illinois	225,800,000	$.25	$.30	
2003D, Illinois	237,400,000	.25	.30	
2003S, Illinois				$1.50
2003S, Illinois, Silver				2.50
2003P, Alabama	225,000,000	.25	.30	
2003D, Alabama	232,400,000	.25	.30	
2003S, Alabama				1.50
2003S, Alabama, Silver				2.50
2003P, Maine	217,400,000	.25	.30	
2003D, Maine	231,400,000	.25	.30	
2003S, Maine				1.50
2003S, Maine, Silver				2.50
2003P, Missouri	225,000,000	.25	.30	
2003D, Missouri	228,200,000	.25	.30	
2003S, Missouri				1.50
2003S, Missouri, Silver				2.50
2003P, Arkansas	228,000,000	.25	.30	
2003D, Arkansas	229,800,000	.25	.30	
2003S, Arkansas				1.50
2003S, Arkansas, Silver				2.50

	Mintage	AU-50	MS-63	PF-65
2004P, Michigan	233,800,000	$.35	$.50	
2004D, Michigan	225,800,000	.35	.50	
2004S, Michigan				$5.
2004S, Michigan, Silver				8.
2004P, Florida	240,200,000	.35	.50	
2004D, Florida	241,600,000	.35	.50	
2004S, Florida				5.
2004S, Florida, Silver				8.
2004P, Texas	278,800,000	.35	.50	
2004D, Texas	263,000,000	.35	.50	
2004S, Texas				5.
2004S, Texas, Silver				8.
2004P, Iowa	213,800,000	.35	.50	
2004D, Iowa	251,800,000	.35	.50	
2004S, Iowa				5.
2004S, Iowa, Silver				8.
2004P, Wisconsin	226,400,000	.35	.50	
2004D, Wisconsin	226,800,000	.35	.50	
2004S, Wisconsin				5.
2004S, Wisconsin, Silver				8.

	Mintage	AU-50	MS-63	PF-65
2005P, California		$.35	$.50	
2005D, California		.35	.50	
2005S, California				$5.
2005S, California, Silver				8.
2005P, Minnesota		.35	.50	
2005D, Minnesota		.35	.50	
2005S, Minnesota				5.
2005S, Minnesota, Silver				8.
2005P, Oregon		.35	.50	
2005D, Oregon		.35	.50	
2005S, Oregon				5.
2005S, Oregon, Silver				8.
2005P, Kansas		.35	.50	
2005D, Kansas		.35	.50	
2005S, Kansas				5.
2005S, Kansas, Silver				8.
2005P, West Virginia		.35	.50	
2005D, West Virginia		.35	.50	
2005S, West Virginia				5.
2005S, West Virginia, Silver				8.

The half dollar, authorized by the Act of April 2, 1792, was not minted until December, 1794. The weight of the half dollar was 208 grains and its fineness .8924 when first issued. This standard was not changed until 1837 when the Law of January 18, 1837 specified 206-1/4 grains, .900 fine. This fineness continued in use until 1965.

Arrows at the date in 1853 indicate the reduction of weight to 192 grains. During that year only, rays were added to the field on the reverse side. Arrows remained in 1854 and 1855. In 1873 the weight was raised to 192.9 grains and arrows were again placed at the date.

FLOWING HAIR (1794–1795)

AG-3 ABOUT GOOD—Clear enough to identify.
G-4 GOOD—Date and letters sufficient to be legible. Main devices outlined, but lacking in detail.
VG-8 VERY GOOD—Major details discernible. Letters well formed but worn.
F-12 FINE—Hair ends distinguishable. Top hair lines visible, but otherwise worn smooth.
VF-20 VERY FINE—Some detail visible in hair in center; other details more bold.
EF-40 EXTREMELY FINE—Hair above head and down neck detailed, with slight wear.
AU-50 ABOUT UNCIRCULATED—All hair visible; slight wear on bust of Liberty and on top edges of eagle's wings, head, and breast.

2 Leaves Under Wings   **3 Leaves Under Wings**

	Mintage	AG-3	G-4	VG-8	F-12	VF-20	EF-40	AU-50
1794 23,464		$600.	$1,200.	$1,800.	$3,000.	$6,000.	$14,000.	$25,000.
1795, All kinds 299,680		150.	325.	400.	650.	1,200.	3,000.	5,000.
1795, Recut Date		150.	325.	400.	700.	1,400.	3,500.	5,250.
1795, 3 Leaves Under Each Wing		250.	550.	850.	1,750.	2,750.	6,000.	9,500.

DRAPED BUST (1796–1807)

AG-3 ABOUT GOOD—Clear enough to identify.
G-4 GOOD—Date and letters sufficiently clear to be legible. Main devices outlined, but lacking in detail.
VG-8 VERY GOOD—Major details discernible. Letters well formed but worn.
F-12 FINE—Hair ends distinguishable. Top hair lines visible, but otherwise worn smooth.
VF-20 VERY FINE—Right side of drapery slightly worn. Left side to curls smooth.
EF-40 EXTREMELY FINE—All lines in drapery on bust distinctly visible around to hair curls.
AU-50 ABOUT UNCIRCULATED—Slight trace of wear on cheek, hair, and shoulder.

Small Eagle Reverse (1796–1797)

1796, 15 Stars   **1796, 16 Stars**

See next page for chart.

HALF DOLLARS

	Mintage	AG-3	G-4	VG-8	F-12	VF-20	EF-40	AU-50
1796, 15 Stars	3,918	$5,000.	$9,000.	$11,000.	$18,000.	$23,000.	$33,000.	$48,000.
1796, 16 Stars	*	5,500.	10,000.	12,000.	20,000.	25,000.	35,000.	60,000.
1797, 15 Stars	*	5,000.	9,000.	11,000.	18,000.	23,000.	33,000.	48,000.

* Included in number above.

Heraldic Eagle Reverse (1801–1807)

	Mintage	G-4	VG-8	F-12	VF-20	EF-40	AU-50	MS-60
1801	30,289	$120.	$175.	$350.	$650.	$1,300.	$4,750.	$9,000.
1802	29,890	100.	150.	300.	600.	1,100.	4,500.	9,000.
1803		75.	90.	150.	250.	475.	1,200.	4,000.

1805, 5 Over 4   **1806, 6 Over 5**

	Mintage	G-4	VG-8	F-12	VF-20	EF-40	AU-50	MS-60
1805, 5 Over 4	211,722	$100.	$150.	$275.	$375.	$1,100.	$2,500.	$10,000.
1805, Normal Date	*	75.	100.	120.	225.	500.	1,200.	3,300.
1806, All kinds	839,576							
1806, Normal Date		75.	100.	120.	200.	425.	1,100.	2,700.
1806, 6 Over 5		75.	100.	120.	200.	425.	1,100.	2,700.
1806, 6 Over Inverted 6		80.	120.	200.	450.	900.	2,200.	4,750.
1807	301,076	75.	100.	120.	200.	425.	1,100.	2,700.

* Included in number above.

CAPPED BUST, LETTERED EDGE (1807–1836)

John Reich designed this capped head concept of Liberty. The head of Liberty facing left was used on all U.S. coin denominations for the next thirty years.

G-4 GOOD—Date and letters legible. Bust worn smooth with outline distinct.
VG-8 VERY GOOD—LIBERTY faint. Legends distinguishable. Clasp at shoulder visible; curl above it nearly smooth.
F-12 FINE—Clasp and adjacent curl clearly outlined with slight details.
VF-20 VERY FINE—Clasp at shoulder clear. Wear visible on highest point of curl. Hair over brow distinguishable.
EF-40 EXTREMELY FINE—Clasp and adjacent curl fairly sharp. Brow and hair above distinct. Curls well defined.
AU-50 ABOUT UNCIRCULATED—Trace of wear on hair over eye and over ear.
MS-60 UNCIRCULATED—No trace of wear. Light blemishes. Possible slide marks from storage handling.
MS-63 CHOICE UNCIRCULATED—Some distracting contact marks or blemishes in prime focal areas. Impaired luster possible.

First Style (1807–1808)

	Mintage	G-4	VG-8	F-12	VF-20	EF-40	AU-50	MS-60	MS-63
1807	750,500	$25.	$30.	$45.	$90.	$220.	$600.	$1,250.	$3,500.
1808, 8 Over 7	*	25.	30.	40.	75.	150.	400.	1,000.	2,500.
1808	1,368,600	22.	25.	35.	50.	115.	250.	800.	1,200.

* Included in number below.

Remodeled Portrait and Eagle (1809–1836)

	Mintage	G-4	VG-8	F-12	VF-20	EF-40	AU-50	MS-60	MS-63
1809, All kinds	1,405,810	$20.	$25.	$35.	$50.	$100.	$250.	$700.	$1,400.
1810	1,276,276	20.	25.	35.	45.	100.	225.	675.	1,300.
1811, All kinds	1,203,644	18.	25.	32.	40.	85.	175.	600.	1,000.

1812, 2 Over 1	**1813, 50 C. Over UNI**	**1814, 4 Over 3**

	Mintage	G-4	VG-8	F-12	VF-20	EF-40	AU-50	MS-60	MS-63
1812, All kinds	1,628,059								
1812, 2 Over 1		$20.	$27.	$38.	$65.	$150.	$250.	$1,000.	$2,100.
1812		18.	25.	35.	55.	100.	200.	500.	950.
1813	1,241,903	18.	25.	35.	55.	100.	180.	500.	950.
1813, 50 C. Over UNI	*	20.	26.	40.	70.	140.	240.	600.	2,000.
1814, All kinds	1,039,075								
1814, 4 Over 3		18.	25.	36.	60.	125.	180.	500.	600.
1814		18.	25.	35.	55.	100.	180.	500.	950.

* Included in number above.

1817, 7 Over 3 | **1817, 7 Over 4** | **1817, Punctuated Date**

	Mintage	G-4	VG-8	F-12	VF-20	EF-40	AU-50	MS-60	MS-63
1815, 5 Over 2	47,150	$400.	$600.	$700.	$1,000.	$2,000.	$2,250.	$4,500.	$11,000.
1817, All kinds	1,215,567								
1817, 7 Over 3		24.	40.	90.	200.	350.	600.	1,500.	3,750.
1817, 7 Over 4				35,000.	50,000.	80,000.			
1817, Dated 181.7		18.	25.	32.	42.	85.	150.	475.	900.
1817		18.	25.	30.	40.	60.	140.	450.	850.

1818, 2nd 8 Over 7 | **1819, 9 Over 8** | **1820, 20 Over 19**

	Mintage	G-4	VG-8	F-12	VF-20	EF-40	AU-50	MS-60	MS-63
1818, 8 Over 7	*	$18.	$25.	$30.	$35.	$60.	$150.	$500.	$900.
1818	1,960,322	18.	25.	30.	35.	60.	140.	450.	825.
1819, 9 Over 8	*	18.	25.	30.	35.	60.	140.	450.	825.
1819	2,208,000	18.	25.	30.	35.	60.	140.	450.	825.
1820, 20 Over 19	*	18.	28.	35.	50.	120.	300.	600.	900.
1820	751,122	17.	25.	30.	35.	55.	130.	475.	850.
1821	1,305,797	17.	25.	30.	35.	55.	130.	450.	850.
1822	1,559,573	17.	25.	30.	35.	55.	130.	475.	900.
1823	1,694,200	17.	25.	30.	35.	55.	130.	375.	800.

* Included in number below.

"Various Dates" *Probably 4 Over 2 Over 0.* | **1824, 4 Over 1** | **1828, Curl Base, Knob 2** | **1828, Square Base 2**

	Mintage	G-4	VG-8	F-12	VF-20	EF-40	AU-50	MS-60	MS-63
1824, All kinds	3,504,954								
1824, 4 Over Various Dates		$17.	$23.	$30.	$35.	$55.	$130.	$350.	$750.
1824, 4 Over 1		18.	25.	30.	35.	55.	130.	375.	750.
1824		12.	23.	30.	35.	55.	130.	400.	775.
1825	2,943,166	17.	23.	30.	35.	55.	130.	325.	725.
1826	4,004,180	17.	23.	30.	35.	55.	130.	325.	725.
1827, All kinds	5,493,400								
1827, 7 Over 6		20.	30.	35.	40.	75.	140.	425.	800.
1827		17.	23.	30.	35.	55.	130.	325.	725.
1828, All kinds	3,075,200								
1828, Curl Base No Knob 2		17.	23.	30.	35.	55.	130.	325.	725.
1828, Curl Base Knob 2		22.	32.	40.	50.	75.	150.	485.	750.
1828, Square Base 2		17.	23.	30.	35.	55.	130.	325.	725.

	Mintage	G-4	VG-8	F-12	VF-20	EF-40	AU-50	MS-60	MS-63
1829, 9 Over 7 .... *		$18.	$24.	$32.	$38.	$60.	$140.	$325.	$850.
1829 3,712,156		17.	22.	30.	35.	55.	130.	300.	725.
1830 4,764,800		17.	22.	30.	35.	55.	130.	300.	725.
1831 5,873,660		17.	22.	30.	35.	55.	130.	300.	700.
1832 4,797,000		17.	22.	30.	35.	55.	130.	300.	700.
1833 5,206,000		17.	22.	30.	35.	55.	130.	300.	700.
1834 6,412,004		17.	22.	30.	35.	55.	130.	300.	700.
1835 5,352,006		17.	22.	30.	35.	55.	130.	300.	700.
1836 6,545,000		17.	22.	30.	35.	55.	130.	300.	700.
1836, 50 Over 00 ....*		20.	30.	40.	60.	100.	225.	650.	1,600.

* Included in regular mintage.

CAPPED BUST, REEDED EDGE (1836–1839)

G-4 GOOD—LIBERTY barely discernible on headband.
VG-8 VERY GOOD—Some letters in LIBERTY clear.
F-12 FINE—LIBERTY complete but faint.
VF-20 VERY FINE—LIBERTY sharp. Shoulder clasp clear.
EF-40 EXTREMELY FINE—LIBERTY sharp and strong. Hair details visible.
AU-50 ABOUT UNCIRCULATED—Slight trace of wear on cap, cheek, and hair above forehead, and on eagle's claws, wing tops, and head.
MS-60 UNCIRCULATED—No trace of wear. Light blemishes.
MS-63 CHOICE UNCIRCULATED—Some distracting contact marks or blemishes in prime focal areas. Impaired luster possible.

Reverse 50 CENTS (1836–1837)

	Mintage	G-4	VG-8	F-12	VF-20	EF-40	AU-50	MS-60	MS-63
1836 ....*1,200*		$400.	$500.	$600.	$900.	$1,100.	$2,000.	$5,000.	$7,500.
1837 3,629,820		20.	22.	27.	50.	75.	150.	425.	850.

Reverse HALF DOL. (1838–1839)

On half dollars of 1838 and 1839, the mintmark appears on the obverse; on those thereafter, it is on the reverse below the eagle.

	Mintage	G-4	VG-8	F-12	VF-20	EF-40	AU-50	MS-60	MS-63
1838 3,546,000		$20.	$25.	$35.	$50.	$75.	$150.	$425.	$800.
1838O ....(20)...........							70,000.	90,000.	
1839 1,392,976		20.	25.	35.	50.	75.	150.	525.	825.
1839O 178,976		65.	90.	125.	175.	300.	550.	1,500.	2,500.

LIBERTY SEATED (1839–1891)

G-4 GOOD—Scant rim. LIBERTY on shield worn off. Date and letters legible.
VG-8 VERY GOOD—Rim fairly defined. Some letters in LIBERTY evident.
F-12 FINE—LIBERTY complete, but weak.
VF-20 VERY FINE—LIBERTY mostly sharp.
EF-40 EXTREMELY FINE—LIBERTY entirely sharp. Scroll edges and clasp distinct.
AU-50 ABOUT UNCIRCULATED—Slight wear on Liberty's breast and knees; eagle's head, claws, and wing tops.
MS-60 UNCIRCULATED—No trace of wear. Light blemishes.
MS-63 CHOICE UNCIRCULATED—Some distracting blemishes in prime focal areas. Impaired luster possible.
PF-63 CHOICE PROOF—Reflective surfaces with only a few blemishes in secondary focal places. No major flaws.

Variety 1 – No Motto Above Eagle (1839–1853)

No Drapery From Elbow

Drapery From Elbow (Starting 1839)   **1842, Small Date**

	Mintage	G-4	VG-8	F-12	VF-20	EF-40	AU-50	MS-60	MS-63
1839, No Drapery From Elbow		$18.	$28.	$50.	$140.	$325.	$450.	$2,600.	$8,500.
1839, Drapery	1,972,400	10.	12.	18.	30.	50.	60.	275.	650.
1840	1,435,008	9.	13.	20.	35.	60.	70.	275.	650.
18400	855,100	9.	12.	17.	30.	48.	58.	300.	600.
1841	310,000	12.	14.	20.	65.	110.	140.	500.	800.
18410	401,000	9.	12.	17.	30.	50.	65.	375.	500.
1842, Small Date	2,012,764	9.	12.	17.	35.	55.	70.	350.	875.
1842, Medium Date	*	9.	12.	17.	30.	50.	65.	300.	850.
18420, Small Date	754,000	200.	375.	600.	1,100.	1,900.	2,750.	4,750.	—
18420, Medium Date	*	9.	11.	16.	28.	45.	60.	300.	600.
1843	3,844,000	9.	11.	16.	28.	45.	60.	300.	400.
18430	2,268,000	9.	11.	16.	28.	45.	60.	300.	450.
1844	1,766,000	9.	11.	16.	28.	45.	60.	300.	400.
18440	2,005,000	9.	11.	16.	28.	45.	60.	300.	450.
1845	589,000	9.	11.	18.	30.	50.	65.	380.	600.
18450	2,094,000	9.	11.	16.	23.	45.	60.	360.	400.
1846, All kinds . .	2,210,000	9.	11.	16.	23.	45.	60.	300.	500.
1846, Over Horizontal 6	*	40.	75.	120.	175.	300.	500.	1,000.	2,850.
18470	2,584,000	9.	11.	16.	23.	45.	60.	300.	575.
1848	580,000	14.	18.	28.	40.	75.	180.	420.	575.
18480	3,180,000	9.	11.	16.	23.	45.	60.	360.	575.
1849	1,252,000	9.	11.	16.	23.	45.	60.	340.	500.
18490	2,310,000	9.	11.	16.	23.	45.	60.	300.	650.
1850	227,000	50.	75.	140.	175.	275.	300.	700.	1,200.
18500	2,456,000	9.	11.	16.	23.	45.	60.	300.	425.

* Included in number above.

	Mintage	G-4	VG-8	F-12	VF-20	EF-40	AU-50	MS-60	MS-63
1851	200,750	$60.	$100.	$175.	$250.	$260.	$275.	$700.	$1,000.
1851O	402,000	9.	11.	16.	23.	45.	60.	300.	400.
1852	77,130	125.	180.	280.	360.	400.	550.	800.	1,000.
1852O	144,000	20.	30.	45.	70.	180.	225.	900.	2,500.
1853O				60,000.	70,000.	95,000.			

Variety 2 – Arrows at Date, Rays Around Eagle (1853)

	Mintage	G-4	VG-8	F-12	VF-20	EF-40	AU-50	MS-60	MS-63
1853	3,532,708	$9.	$11.	$20.	$60.	$120.	$300.	$950.	$1,250.
1853O	1,328,000	9.	12.	22.	65.	130.	340.	1,400.	1,800.

Variety 3 – Arrows at Date, No Rays (1854–1855)

	Mintage	G-4	VG-8	F-12	VF-20	EF-40	AU-50	MS-60	MS-63
1854	2,982,000	$8.	$11.	$18.	$30.	$55.	$85.	$360.	$650.
1854O	5,240,000	8.	11.	18.	30.	55.	85.	360.	650.
1855, Over 1854	*	15.	35.	70.	120.	220.	275.	675.	1,300.
1855	759,500	8.	11.	18.	30.	55.	85.	360.	650.
1855O	3,688,000	8.	11.	18.	30.	55.	85.	360.	650.
1855S	129,950	150.	185.	300.	600.	1,400.	2,500.	5,500.	

* Included in number below.

Variety 1 Resumed (1856–1866; Weight Standard of 1853)

	Mintage	G-4	VG-8	F-12	VF-20	EF-40	AU-50	MS-60	MS-63
1856	938,000	$7.50	$11.	$18.	$22.	$40.	$80.	$220.	$400.
1856O	2,658,000	7.50	11.	20.	24.	40.	80.	220.	400.
1856S	211,000	15.00	20.	37.	90.	200.	425.	1,700.	
1857	1,988,000	7.50	11.	18.	22.	40.	80.	220.	400.
1857O	818,000	7.50	11.	20.	24.	40.	80.	240.	650.
1857S	158,000	18.00	30.	40.	80.	175.	400.	1,400.	

	Mintage	G-4	VG-8	F-12	VF-20	EF-40	AU-50	MS-60	MS-63	PF-63
1858 ...(300+)	4,225,700	$9.	$10.	$17.	$22.	$40.	$80.	$220.	$400.	$1,300.
1858O	7,294,000	9.	10.	17.	22.	40.	80.	220.	400.	
1858S	476,000	11.	13.	20.	30.	55.	120.	525.	1,500.	
1859 .....(800)	747,200	9.	10.	17.	22.	45.	85.	225.	450.	900.
1859O	2,834,000	9.	10.	17.	22.	45.	85.	225.	450.	
1859S	566,000	11.	13.	20.	30.	80.	85.	250.	1,000.	
1860 ...(1,000)	302,700	11.	13.	19.	28.	50.	85.	225.	450.	600.
1860O	1,290,000	9.	10.	17.	22.	45.	80.	225.	450.	
1860S	472,000	11.	13.	20.	25.	45.	80.	350.	1,000.	
1861 ...(1,000)	2,887,400	9.	10.	17.	22.	45.	80.	225.	400.	600.
1861O	2,532,633	9.	10.	17.	22.	45.	80.	225.	400.	
1861S	939,500	9.	10.	17.	22.	45.	80.	275.	800.	
1862 ...(550)	253,000	12.	18.	25.	50.	75.	100.	450.	650.	600.
1862S	1,352,000	9.	10.	17.	22.	45.	80.	275.	450.	
1863 ...(460)	503,200	11.	14.	20.	28.	55.	85.	300.	675.	600.
1863S	916,000	9.	10.	17.	22.	45.	85.	275.	450.	
1864 ...(470)	379,100	12.	16.	21.	32.	55.	90.	300.	450.	600.
1864S	658,000	9.	10.	17.	22.	45.	85.	275.	425.	
1865 .....(500)	511,400	11.	13.	20.	28.	50.	90.	300.	450.	600.
1865S	675,000	9.	10.	17.	22.	45.	85.	275.	400.	
1866S, No Motto	60,000	35.	45.	90.	150.	350.	625.	2,300.	3,000.	

Variety 4 – Motto Above Eagle (1866–1873, 1875–1891)

	Mintage	G-4	VG-8	F-12	VF-20	EF-40	AU-50	MS-60	MS-63	PF-63
1866 . . . . .(725) . . . 744,900		$7.	$8.	$15.	$20.	$40.	$80.	$220.	$450.	$400.
1866S 994,000		7.	8.	15.	20.	40.	90.	320.	550.	
1867 . . . . .(625) . . . 449,300		9.	12.	20.	25.	50.	95.	275.	475.	400.
1867S 1,196,000		7.	8.	15.	20.	40.	80.	300.	650.	
1868 . . . . .(600) . . . 417,600		9.	14.	22.	30.	70.	120.	325.	475.	400.
1868S 1,160,000		7.	8.	15.	20.	40.	90.	325.	600.	
1869 . . . . .(600) . . . 795,300		7.	8.	15.	20.	40.	90.	275.	450.	400.
1869S 656,000		7.	8.	15.	20.	42.	90.	350.	850.	
1870 . . .(1,000) . . . 633,900		7.	8.	15.	20.	40.	80.	300.	450.	400.
1870CC 54,617		275.	450.	700.	1,600.	4,750.	9,000.			
1870S 1,004,000		7.	8.	15.	22.	45.	95.	300.	800.	
1871 . . . .(960). . 1,203,600		7.	8.	15.	22.	45.	95.	275.	450.	400.
1871CC 153,950		60.	100.	150.	275.	700.	1,300.	4,000.	16,000.	
1871S 2,178,000		7.	8.	15.	20.	42.	90.	300.	500.	
1872 . . . . .(950) . . . 880,600		7.	8.	15.	20.	40.	90.	275.	550.	400.
1872CC 257,000		25.	40.	90.	180.	400.	700.	1,900.	10,000.	
1872S 580,000		8.	9.	18.	20.	42.	120.	400.	800.	
1873 . . . . .(600) . . . 801,200		7.	8.	15.	20.	40.	95.	250.	450.	400.
1873CC 122,500		60.	100.	150.	275.	500.	1,000.	3,750.	15,000.	

Variety 5 – Arrows at Date (1873–1874)

	Mintage	G-4	VG-8	F-12	VF-20	EF-40	AU-50	MS-60	MS-63	PF-63
1873 . . . . .(550). . 1,815,150		$12.	$18.	$20.	$48.	$130.	$160.	$500.	$900.	$1,100.
1873CC 214,560		50.	90.	150.	325.	700.	1,000.	2,500.	6,000.	
1873S 228,000		17.	30.	45.	90.	175.	300.	900.	2,600.	
1874 . . . . .(700) . . 2,359,600		12.	18.	20.	48.	130.	160.	500.	900.	1,100.
1874CC 59,000		125.	200.	325.	500.	800.	1,500.	4,000.	7,500.	
1874S 394,000		15.	25.	40.	80.	140.	250.	875.	1,500.	

Variety 4 Resumed (1875–1891)

	Mintage	G-4	VG-8	F-12	VF-20	EF-40	AU-50	MS-60	MS-63	PF-63
1875 . . . . .(700). . 6,026,800		$7.	$8.	$15.	$20.	$35.	$75.	$220.	$300.	$400.
1875CC 1,008,000		7.	10.	20.	25.	45.	80.	250.	400.	
1875S 3,200,000		7.	8.	15.	20.	35.	75.	220.	300.	
1876 . . .(1,150). . 8,418,000		7.	8.	15.	20.	35.	75.	220.	300.	400.
1876CC 1,956,000		7.	8.	15.	20.	40.	80.	275.	575.	

HALF DOLLARS

	Mintage	G-4	VG-8	F-12	VF-20	EF-40	AU-50	MS-60	MS-63	PF-63
1876S 4,528,000		$7.	$8.	$15.	$20.	$35.	$75.	$220.	$300.	
1877 . . . . .(510). . 8,304,000		7.	8.	15.	20.	35.	75.	220.	300.	$400.
1877CC 1,420,000		7.	8.	15.	20.	40.	85.	260.	500.	
1877S 5,356,000		7.	8.	15.	20.	35.	75.	220.	300.	
1878 . . . . .(800). . 1,377,600		7.	8.	15.	20.	35.	75.	220.	300.	400.
1878CC 62,000		125.	190.	260.	450.	1,000.	1,300.	2,750.	9,000.	
1878S 12,000		4,000.	5,000.	6,500.	10,000.	12,000.	15,000.	18,000.	40,000.	
1879 . . .(1,100) 4,800		90.	110.	130.	170.	200.	280.	425.	500.	400.
1880 . . .(1,355) 8,400		90.	110.	130.	170.	190.	250.	375.	500.	400.
1881 . . .(975) 10,000		90.	110.	130.	170.	190.	250.	375.	500.	400.
1882 . . .(1,100) 4,400		100.	120.	180.	200.	210.	280.	425.	500.	400.
1883 . . .(1,039) 8,000		90.	110.	130.	170.	190.	245.	375.	500.	400.
1884 . . . .(875) 4,400		100.	120.	180.	200.	210.	280.	450.	525.	400.
1885 . . . .(930) 5,200		100.	120.	180.	200.	210.	260.	475.	550.	400.
1886 . . . .(886) 5,000		100.	120.	180.	200.	210.	260.	475.	550.	400.
1887 . . . .(710) 5,000		100.	120.	180.	200.	210.	260.	475.	550.	400.
1888 . . . .(832) 12,001		90.	120.	130.	170.	190.	250.	425.	500.	400.
1889 . . . .(711) 12,000		90.	110.	130.	170.	190.	250.	425.	500.	400.
1890 . . . .(590) 12,000		90.	110.	130.	170.	190.	250.	425.	500.	400.
1891 . . . . .(600) . . . 200,000		16.	22.	35.	50.	65.	80.	300.	400.	400.

BARBER OR LIBERTY HEAD (1892–1915)

Like the dime and quarter dollar, this type was designed by Charles E. Barber, whose initial B is on the truncation of the neck.

G-4 GOOD—Date and legends legible. LIBERTY worn off headband.

VG-8 VERY GOOD—Some letters legible in LIBERTY.

F-12 FINE—LIBERTY nearly completely legible, but worn.

VF-20 VERY FINE—All letters in LIBERTY evenly plain.

EF-40 EXTREMELY FINE—LIBERTY bold, and its ribbon distinct.

AU-50 ABOUT UNCIRCULATED—Slight trace of wear above forehead, leaf tips, and cheek, and on eagle's head, tail, and wing tips.

MS-60 UNCIRCULATED—No trace of wear. Light blemishes.

MS-63 CHOICE UNCIRCULATED—Some distracting contact marks or blemishes in prime focal areas. Impaired luster possible.

PF-63 CHOICE PROOF—Reflective surfaces with only a few blemishes in secondary focal places. No major flaws.

Mintmark location on reverse, below eagle.

	Mintage	G-4	VG-8	F-12	VF-20	EF-40	AU-50	MS-60	MS-63	PF-63
1892 . . .(1,245) . . . 934,000		$10.	$12.	$22.	$35.	$140.	$160.	$220.	$375.	$400.
1892O 390,000		80.	100.	140.	190.	250.	275.	460.	800.	
1892S 1,029,000		75.	90.	120.	175.	250.	300.	460.	900.	
1893 . . . . .(792). . 1,826,000		8.	12.	22.	40.	100.	150.	300.	500.	400.
1893O 1,389,000		10.	20.	32.	65.	160.	200.	310.	650.	
1893S 740,000		40.	50.	100.	160.	240.	325.	620.	1,200.	
1894 . . . . .(972). . 1,148,000		10.	20.	32.	50.	120.	150.	260.	400.	400.
1894O 2,138,000		6.	10.	30.	50.	130.	160.	260.	450.	
1894S 4,048,690		7.	12.	25.	45.	120.	150.	255.	500.	
1895 . . . . .(880). . 1,834,338		6.	10.	24.	40.	110.	150.	260.	450.	400.
1895O 1,766,000		7.	12.	28.	50.	110.	165.	275.	650.	
1895S 1,108,086		10.	14.	35.	60.	125.	175.	275.	600.	
1896 . . . . .(762) . . . 950,000		8.	10.	25.	45.	110.	150.	275.	425.	425.
1896O 924,000		10.	15.	50.	80.	175.	300.	650.	2,000.	
1896S 1,140,948		30.	40.	65.	110.	180.	240.	600.	1,500.	

Chart continues on next page.

	Mintage	G-4	VG-8	F-12	VF-20	EF-40	AU-50	MS-60	MS-63	PF-63
1897 . . . . .(731). .	2,480,000	$4.	$5.	$15.	$35.	$65.	$140.	$220.	$375.	$425.
1897O	632,000	26.	50.	140.	300.	400.	500.	800.	1,500.	
1897S	933,900	50.	75.	125.	210.	340.	450.	675.	1,500.	
1898 . . . . .(735). .	2,956,000	4.	5.	12.	30.	75.	150.	200.	375.	425.
1898O	874,000	9.	15.	50.	100.	175.	240.	450.	1,600.	
1898S	2,358,550	5.	6.	18.	40.	100.	150.	375.	1,500.	
1899 . . . . .(846). .	5,538,000	4.	5.	14.	30.	65.	140.	200.	350.	425.
1899O	1,724,000	5.	6.	22.	40.	130.	160.	325.	550.	
1899S	1,686,411	5.	6.	22.	40.	100.	150.	300.	1,000.	
1900 . . . . .(912). .	4,762,000	4.	5.	14.	35.	65.	140.	200.	375.	400.
1900O	2,744,000	5.	7.	20.	40.	125.	160.	325.	1,400.	
1900S	2,560,322	5.	7.	18.	40.	100.	150.	275.	900.	
1901 . . . . .(813). .	4,268,000	4.	5.	14.	30.	60.	150.	200.	350.	400.
1901O	1,124,000	5.	7.	25.	55.	140.	200.	675.	2,200.	
1901S	847,044	11.	18.	60.	120.	275.	425.	850.	2,200.	
1902 . . . . .(777). .	4,922,000	4.	5.	14.	30.	60.	150.	200.	350.	400.
1902O	2,526,000	5.	7.	18.	35.	90.	150.	350.	950.	
1902S	1,460,670	5.	7.	20.	45.	110.	165.	300.	850.	
1903 . . . . .(755). .	2,278,000	4.	5.	14.	35.	70.	150.	210.	500.	400.
1903O	2,100,000	5.	7.	16.	40.	90.	160.	300.	650.	
1903S	1,920,772	5.	7.	16.	40.	95.	170.	300.	850.	
1904 . . . . .(670). .	2,992,000	4.	5.	14.	30.	65.	140.	200.	500.	400.
1904O	1,117,600	6.	9.	25.	60.	150.	210.	550.	1,250.	
1904S	553,038	8.	20.	90.	200.	400.	650.	2,000.	4,500.	
1905 . . . . .(727). .	662,000	4.	5.	20.	40.	90.	140.	230.	625.	400.
1905O	505,000	6.	10.	35.	65.	135.	170.	350.	750.	
1905S	2,494,000	5.	7.	16.	38.	90.	150.	300.	875.	
1906 . . . . .(675). .	2,638,000	4.	5.	14.	30.	65.	120.	200.	350.	400.
1906D	4,028,000	5.	5.	15.	36.	75.	120.	200.	350.	
1906O	2,446,000	4.	6.	16.	35.	80.	125.	275.	525.	
1906S	1,740,154	4.	5.	18.	40.	90.	140.	275.	525.	
1907 . . . . .(575). .	2,598,000	4.	5.	14.	26.	65.	120.	200.	350.	400.
1907D	3,856,000	4.	5.	14.	32.	70.	130.	200.	350.	
1907O	3,946,600	4.	5.	14.	32.	70.	140.	220.	375.	
1907S	1,250,000	4.	5.	22.	50.	115.	275.	500.	1,750.	
1908 . . . . .(545). .	1,354,000	4.	5.	14.	30.	65.	120.	200.	350.	400.
1908D	3,280,000	4.	5.	14.	30.	65.	120.	200.	350.	
1908O	5,360,000	4.	5.	14.	30.	70.	140.	210.	425.	
1908S	1,644,828	4.	5.	20.	42.	100.	170.	350.	1,100.	
1909 . . . . .(650). .	2,368,000	4.	5.	14.	30.	65.	120.	200.	350.	400.
1909O	925,400	7.	8.	18.	45.	120.	200.	350.	800.	
1909S	1,764,000	4.	5.	14.	32.	90.	140.	260.	550.	
1910 . . . . .(551). . .	418,000	7.	9.	18.	50.	130.	145.	290.	500.	400.
1910S	1,948,000	4.	5.	14.	35.	85.	130.	250.	350.	
1911 . . . . .(543). .	1,406,000	4.	5.	14.	26.	65.	110.	180.	350.	400.
1911D	695,080	4.	5.	15.	30.	75.	125.	240.	400.	
1911S	1,272,000	4.	5.	14.	30.	75.	130.	250.	550.	
1912 . . . . .(700). .	1,550,000	4.	5.	14.	28.	70.	110.	200.	350.	400.
1912D	2,300,800	4.	5.	14.	28.	70.	110.	200.	350.	
1912S	1,370,000	4.	5.	14.	30.	75.	130.	240.	450.	
1913 . . . . .(627) . . .	188,000	15.	20.	75.	100.	175.	325.	500.	750.	500.
1913D	534,000	4.	5.	16.	35.	90.	120.	225.	400.	
1913S	604,000	4.	5.	18.	40.	90.	140.	275.	500.	
1914 . . . . .(380) . . .	124,230	40.	50.	100.	150.	250.	310.	450.	750.	700.
1914S	992,000	4.	5.	14.	30.	80.	140.	275.	450.	
1915 . . . . .(450) . . .	138,000	9.	15.	45.	90.	160.	300.	475.	1,100.	600.
1915D	1,170,400	4.	5.	11.	26.	60.	130.	200.	350.	
1915S	1,604,000	4.	5.	11.	26.	60.	130.	200.	350.	

LIBERTY WALKING (1916–1947)

This type was designed by Adolph A. Weinman. The designer's monogram AAW appears under the tip of the wing feathers. On the 1916 coins and some of the 1917 coins, the mintmark is located on the obverse below the motto.

G-4 GOOD—Rims defined. Motto IN GOD WE TRUST legible.
VG-8 VERY GOOD—Motto distinct. About half of skirt lines at left clear.
F-12 FINE—All skirt lines evident, but worn in spots. Clear details in sandal below motto.
VF-20 VERY FINE—Skirt lines sharp, including leg area. Little wear on breast and right arm.
EF-40 EXTREMELY FINE—All skirt lines bold.
AU-50 ABOUT UNCIRCULATED—Slight trace of wear on Liberty's head, knee, and breast tips and on eagle's claws and head.
MS-60 UNCIRCULATED—No trace of wear. Light blemishes.
MS-63 CHOICE UNCIRCULATED—Some distracting contact marks or blemishes in prime focal areas. Impaired luster possible.
PF-63 CHOICE PROOF—Reflective surfaces with only a few blemishes in secondary focal places. No major flaws.
PF-65 GEM PROOF—Brilliant surfaces with no noticeable blemishes or flaws. A few scattered, barely noticeable marks or hairlines possible.

1916–1917

1917–1947

Mintmark Locations

Choice Uncirculated well-struck specimens are worth more than values listed.

	Mintage	G-4	VG-8	F-12	VF-20	EF-40	AU-50	MS-60	MS-63
1916	608,000	$14.00	$20.00	$27.00	$60.	$80.	$115.	$160.	$200.
1916D, Obverse	1,014,400	13.00	17.00	20.00	45.	80.	115.	160.	250.
1916S, Obverse	508,000	40.00	50.00	75.00	175.	250.	325.	500.	1,100.
1917	12,292,000	2.10	3.00	4.50	10.	18.	30.	65.	90.
1917D, Obverse	765,400	6.00	8.00	20.00	45.	80.	125.	250.	500.
1917D, Reverse	1,940,000	4.00	5.00	17.00	35.	95.	225.	360.	725.
1917S, Obverse	952,000	9.00	11.00	25.00	140.	325.	550.	1,100.	2,100.
1917S, Reverse	5,554,000	3.00	3.50	6.00	14.	25.	70.	150.	850.
1918	6,634,000	3.00	3.50	6.00	27.	70.	120.	220.	500.
1918D	3,853,040	3.00	3.50	6.00	30.	80.	170.	500.	1,000.
1918S	10,282,000	3.00	3.50	6.00	15.	35.	80.	200.	1,000.
1919	962,000	8.00	10.00	18.00	75.	225.	275.	500.	1,400.
1919D	1,165,000	6.00	8.00	20.00	90.	250.	500.	1,400.	5,750.
1919S	1,552,000	6.00	8.00	15.00	75.	275.	675.	1,250.	2,750.
1920	6,372,000	2.00	2.50	5.00	14.	27.	55.	125.	275.
1920D	1,551,000	3.75	5.00	15.00	70.	150.	300.	600.	1,700.
1920S	4,624,000	2.00	3.00	7.50	25.	75.	160.	500.	1,200.
1921	246,000	60.00	80.00	125.00	350.	775.	1,250.	1,700.	2,500.
1921D	208,000	80.00	100.00	150.00	350.	1,000.	1,400.	1,800.	2,750.
1921S	548,000	14.00	18.00	60.00	350.	2,300.	3,300.	5,250.	12,500.
1923S	2,178,000	3.50	4.00	8.00	25.	110.	600.	950.	1,700.
1927S	2,392,000	1.75	2.00	5.00	14.	50.	150.	400.	1,000.
1928S	1,940,000	1.75	2.00	5.00	18.	55.	150.	400.	1,100.
1929D	1,001,200	1.75	2.00	4.50	9.	35.	125.	175.	350.
1929S	1,902,000	1.75	2.00	4.50	9.	40.	125.	175.	400.

Chart continues on next page.

	Mintage	G-4	VG-8	F-12	VF-20	EF-40	AU-50	MS-60	MS-63	PF-63	PF-65
1933S	1,786,000	$1.75	$2.00	$4.00	$7.00	$25.	$125.	$225.	$550.		
1934	6,964,000	1.50	1.50	1.60	2.00	4.	12.	30.	45.		
1934D	2,361,000	1.50	1.50	1.60	3.00	12.	35.	60.	90.		
1934S	3,652,000	1.50	1.50	1.60	2.25	13.	40.	150.	350.		
1935	9,162,000	1.50	1.50	1.60	2.00	3.	9.	20.	30.		
1935D	3,003,800	1.50	1.50	1.60	2.25	12.	25.	60.	100.		
1935S	3,854,000	1.50	1.50	1.60	2.25	12.	40.	90.	185.		
1936 ...(3,901)	12,614,000	1.50	1.50	1.60	2.00	3.	9.	22.	30.	$700.	$2,200.
1936D	4,252,400	1.50	1.50	1.60	2.25	7.	15.	40.	50.		
1936S	3,884,000	1.50	1.50	1.60	2.25	7.	16.	65.	75.		
1937 ...(5,728)	9,522,000	1.50	1.50	1.60	2.00	3.	8.	18.	25.	275.	650.
1937D	1,676,000	1.50	1.50	2.00	3.00	12.	30.	85.	110.		
1937S	2,090,000	1.50	1.50	1.60	2.25	7.	17.	70.	90.		
1938 ...(8,152)	4,110,000	1.50	1.50	1.60	2.00	4.	15.	27.	50.	250.	550.
1938D	491,600	20.00	25.00	30.00	40.00	55.	100.	210.	275.		
1939 ...(8,808)	6,812,000	1.50	1.50	1.60	2.00	3.	8.	18.	25.	225.	500.
1939D	4,267,800	1.50	1.50	1.60	2.00	4.	8.	20.	32.		
1939S	2,552,000	1.50	1.50	1.60	2.00	6.	20.	50.	70.		

	Mintage	VG-8	F-12	VF-20	EF-40	AU-50	MS-60	MS-63	PF-63	PF-65
1940 ..(11,279)	9,156,000	$1.50	$1.50	$1.60	$2.	$4.	$13.	$20.	$200.	$475.
1940S	4,550,000	1.50	1.50	1.60	2.	5.	15.	30.		
1941 ..(15,412)	24,192,000	1.50	1.50	1.60	2.	4.	12.	20.	175.	450.
1941D	11,248,400	1.50	1.50	1.60	2.	4.	15.	25.		
1941S	8,098,000	1.50	1.50	1.60	2.	10.	30.	50.		
1942 ..(21,120)	47,818,000	1.50	1.50	1.60	2.	4.	12.	20.	200.	500.
1942D	10,973,800	1.50	1.50	1.60	2.	4.	14.	25.		
1942S	12,708,000	1.50	1.50	1.60	2.	4.	15.	23.		
1943	53,190,000	1.50	1.50	1.60	2.	4.	12.	16.		
1943D	11,346,000	1.50	1.50	1.60	2.	4.	16.	25.		
1943S	13,450,000	1.50	1.50	1.60	2.	4.	15.	20.		
1944	28,206,000	1.50	1.50	1.60	2.	4.	12.	16.		
1944D	9,769,000	1.50	1.50	1.60	2.	4.	14.	20.		
1944S	8,904,000	1.50	1.50	1.60	2.	4.	16.	23.		
1945	3,152,000	1.50	1.50	1.60	2.	4.	12.	16.		
1945D	9,966,800	1.50	1.50	1.60	2.	4.	12.	17.		
1945S	10,156,000	1.50	1.50	1.60	2.	4.	12.	18.		
1946	12,118,000	1.50	1.50	1.60	2.	4.	12.	16.		
1946D	2,151,000	1.50	1.50	1.60	2.	4.	12.	16.		
1946S	3,724,000	1.50	1.50	1.60	2.	4.	12.	16.		
1947	4,094,000	1.50	1.50	1.60	2.	4.	12.	16.		
1947D	3,900,600	1.50	1.50	1.60	2.	4.	12.	16.		

FRANKLIN (1948-1963)

The Benjamin Franklin half dollar and the Roosevelt dime were both designed by John R. Sinnock. His initials appear below the shoulder.

VF-20 VERY FINE—At least half of the lower and upper incused lines on rim of Liberty Bell on reverse visible.
EF-40 EXTREMELY FINE—Wear spots at top of end of Franklin's curls and hair at back of ears. Wear evident at top and on lettering of Liberty Bell.
MS-60 UNCIRCULATED—No trace of wear. Light blemishes.
MS-63 CHOICE UNCIRCULATED—Some distracting contact marks or blemishes in prime focal areas. Impaired luster possible.
MS-65 GEM UNCIRCULATED—Only light, scattered contact marks that are not distracting. Strong luster, good eye appeal.
PF-63 CHOICE PROOF—Reflective surfaces with only a few blemishes in secondary focal places. No major flaws.
PF-65 GEM PROOF—Brilliant surfaces with no noticeable blemishes or flaws. A few scattered, barely noticeable marks or hairlines possible.

HALF DOLLARS

Mintmark Location

Choice, well-struck Uncirculated halves with full bell lines command higher prices.

	Mintage	VF-20	EF-40	MS-60	MS-63	MS-65	PF-63	PF-65
1948	3,006,814	$1.75	$2.00	$5.00	$8.00	$38.		
1948D	4,028,600	1.50	1.75	4.00	6.00	65.		
1949	5,614,000	1.50	2.00	15.00	20.00	70.		
1949D	4,120,600	1.50	3.00	15.00	23.00	385.		
1949S	3,744,000	1.50	5.00	25.00	35.00	60.		
1950 (51,386)	7,742,123	1.50	1.75	10.00	15.00	50.	$115.	$200.
1950D	8,031,600	1.50	1.75	9.00	15.00	225.		
1951 (57,500)	16,802,102	1.50	1.75	4.00	7.00	30.	65.	150.
1951D	9,475,200	1.50	2.00	10.00	16.00	120.		
1951S	13,696,000	1.50	1.75	9.00	15.00	50.		
1952 (81,980)	21,192,093	1.50	1.75	4.00	8.00	27.	35.	100.
1952D	25,395,600	1.50	1.75	2.75	5.00	100.		
1952S	5,526,000	1.50	2.00	15.00	20.00	55.		
1953 (128,800)	2,668,120	1.75	2.00	6.00	10.00	100.	26.	60.
1953D	20,900,400	1.50	1.50	3.00	5.00	50.		
1953S	4,148,000	1.50	2.00	7.00	10.00	30.		
1954 (233,300)	13,188,202	1.50	1.50	2.00	4.00	27.	18.	45.
1954D	25,445,580	1.50	1.50	2.50	4.50	60.		
1954S	4,993,400	1.50	1.50	3.00	4.50	25.		
1955 (378,200)	2,498,181	3.50	4.00	5.00	7.00	25.	14.	40.
1956 (669,384)	4,032,000	1.50	1.50	2.00	5.00	20.	5.	20.
1957 (1,247,952)	5,114,000	1.50	1.50	2.00	4.50	20.	5.	12.
1957D	1,966,850	1.50	1.50	2.00	4.50	20.		
1958 (875,652)	4,042,000	1.50	1.50	2.00	5.00	25.	5.	15.
1958D	23,962,412	1.50	1.50	2.00	4.50	20.		
1959 (1,149,291)	6,200,000	1.50	1.50	2.00	4.50	50.	3.50	13.
1959D	13,053,750	1.50	1.50	2.00	4.50	65.		
1960 (1,691,602)	6,024,000	1.50	1.50	1.60	4.50	65.	3.50	13.
1960D	18,215,812	1.50	1.50	2.00	6.00	225.		
1961 (3,028,244)	8,290,000	1.50	1.50	2.00	4.00	65.	2.50	17.
1961D	20,276,442	1.50	1.50	2.00	4.00	100.		
1962 (3,218,019)	9,714,000	1.50	1.50	2.00	4.00	90.	2.50	10.
1962D	35,473,281	1.50	1.50	2.00	4.00	120.		
1963 (3,075,645)	22,164,000	1.50	1.50	2.00	4.00	30.	2.50	13.
1963D	67,069,292	1.50	1.50	2.00	4.00	30.		

KENNEDY (1964 to DATE)

Gilroy Roberts, then chief engraver of the Mint, designed the obverse of this coin. His stylized initials are on the truncation of the forceful bust of President John F. Kennedy. The reverse, which uses the eagle from the Great Seal for the motif, is the work of Assistant Chief Engraver Frank Gasparro.

Mintmark Location (1964)

Mintmark Location (1968 to Date)

Silver Coinage (1964)

	Mintage	MS-63	PF-63	PF-65
1964 . . . . (3,950,762) . . . 273,304,004		$2.00	$2.50	$4.00
1964D 156,205,446		2.00		

Silver Clad Coinage (1965–1970)

	Mintage	MS-63	PF-63	PF-65		Mintage	MS-63	PF-63	PF-65
1965	65,879,366	$.75			1969D	129,881,800	$.75		
1966	108,984,932	.75			1969S	(2,934,631)		$1.00	$2.00
1967	295,046,978	.75			1970D	2,150,000	7.00		
1968D	246,951,930	.75			1970S	(2,632,810)		4.00	6.00
1968S	(3,041,506)		$1.00	$2.00					

Clad Coinage and Silver Proofs (1971 to Date)

	Mintage	MS-63	PF-63	PF-65		Mintage	MS-63	PF-63	PF-65
1971	155,164,000	$.55			1973	64,964,000	$.55		
1971D	302,097,424	.55			1973D	83,171,400	.55		
1971S	(3,220,733)		$.75	$1.25	1973S	(2,760,339)		$.75	$1.00
1972	153,180,000	.60			1974	201,596,000	.55		
1972D	141,890,000	.60			1974D	79,066,300	.55		
1972S	(3,260,996)		.75	1.25	1974S	(2,612,568)		.75	1.00

Bicentennial (1976)

	Mintage	MS-63	PF-63	PF-65		Mintage	MS-63	PF-63	PF-65
1976, Clad	234,308,000	$.55			1976S, Silver	11,000,000	$1.50		
1976D, Clad	287,565,248	.55			1976S, Silver	(4,000,000)		$2.00	$2.25
1976S, Clad	(7,059,099)		$.75	$1.00					

Eagle Reverse Resumed (1977)

	Mintage	MS-63	PF-63	PF-65
1977	43,598,000	$.60		
1977D	31,449,106	.60		
1977S	(3,251,152)		$1.00	$1.25
1978	14,350,000	.60		
1978D	13,765,799	1.00		
1978S	(3,127,781)		1.00	1.25
1979	68,312,000	.55		
1979D	15,815,422	.55		
1979S	(3,677,175)			
Filled S			1.00	1.25
Clear S			6.00	8.00
1980P	44,134,000	.55		
1980D	33,456,449	.55		
1980S	(3,554,806)		1.00	1.50
1981P	29,544,000	.75		
1981D	27,839,533	.55		
1981S	(4,063,083)		1.00	1.50
1982P	10,819,000	1.50		
1982D	13,140,102	1.50		
1982S	(3,857,479)		1.00	1.50
1983P	34,139,000	1.75		
1983D	32,472,244	1.75		
1983S	(3,279,126)		1.00	1.75
1984P	26,029,000	.75		
1984D	26,262,158	.75		
1984S	(3,065,110)		1.00	2.00
1985P	18,706,962	1.00		
1985D	19,814,034	1.25		
1985S	(3,362,821)		1.00	1.75
1986P	13,107,633	2.50		
1986D	15,336,145	2.00		
1986S	(3,010,497)		4.00	4.50
1987P	*2,890,758	1.50		
1987D	*2,890,758	1.50		
1987S	(4,227,728)		1.00	1.75
1988P	13,626,000	1.50		
1988D	1,200,096	1.00		
1988S	(3,262,948)		2.00	2.50
1989P	24,542,000	1.00		
1989D	23,000,216	.90		
1989S	(3,220,194)		1.50	3.00
1990P	22,278,000	1.00		
1990D	20,096,242	1.10		
1990S	(3,299,559)		1.50	2.00
1991P	14,874,000	.75		
1991D	15,054,678	1.25		
1991S	(2,867,787)		4.00	5.00
1992P	17,628,000	.50		
1992D	17,000,106	1.00		
1992S	(2,858,981)		3.00	3.50
1992S, Silver	(1,317,579)		4.00	5.00
1993P	15,510,000	.50		
1993D	15,000,006	$.50		
1993S	(2,633,439)		$5.	$6.
1993S, Silver	(761,353)		9.	10.
1994P	23,718,000	.50		
1994D	23,828,110	.50		
1994S	(2,484,594)		3.	4.
1994S, Silver	(785,329)		15.	15.
1995P	26,496,000	.50		
1995D	26,288,000	.50		
1995S	(2,117,496)		10.	14.
1995S, Silver	(679,985)		40.	50.
1996P	24,442,000	.50		
1996D	24,744,000	.50		
1996S	(1,750,244)		3.	4.
1996S, Silver	(775,021)		20.	25.
1997P	20,882,000	.50		
1997D	19,876,000	.50		
1997S	(2,055,000)		9.	11.
1997S, Silver	(741,678)		40.	50.
1998P	15,646,000	.50		
1998D	15,064,000	.50		
1998S	(2,086,507)		5.	7.
1998S, Silver	878,792		9.	14.
1998S, Silver, Matte Finish			125.	150.
1999P	8,900,000	.55		
1999D	10,682,000	.55		
1999S	(2,543,401)		3.	5.
1999S, Silver	(800,000)		7.	13.
2000P	22,600,000	.60		
2000D	19,466,000	.60		
2000S	(3,082,483)		2.	3.
2000S, Silver	(856,400)		4.	5.
2001P *	21,200,000	4.00		
2001D	19,504,000	.55		
2001S	(2,294,043)		4.	5.
2001S, Silver	(889,697)		5.	7.
2002P *	3,100,000	.65		
2002D *	2,500,000	.65		
2002S	(2,277,720)		2.	3.
2002S, Silver	(761,600)		5.	6.
2003P *		.65		
2003D *		.65		
2003S			2.	3.
2003S, Silver			5.	6.
2004P *		.65		
2004D *		.65		
2004S			2.	3.
2004S, Silver			5.	6.
2005P *		.65		
2005D *		.65		
2005S			2.	3.
2005S, Silver			5.	6.

* Not issued for circulation.

The silver dollar was authorized by Congress April 2, 1792. Its weight was specified at 416 grains and its fineness at .8924. The first issues appeared in 1794, and until 1804 all silver dollars had the value stamped on the edge: HUNDRED CENTS, ONE DOLLAR OR UNIT. After a lapse in coinage of the silver dollar during the period 1804 to 1835, coins were made with either plain or reeded edges and the value was placed on the reverse side.

The weight was changed by the law of January 18, 1837 to 412-1/2 grains, fineness .900. The coinage was discontinued by the Act of February 12, 1873 and reauthorized by the Act of February 28, 1878. The dollar was again discontinued after 1935, and since then copper-nickel and other base metal pieces have been coined for circulation.

FLOWING HAIR (1794–1795)

AG-3 ABOUT GOOD—Clear enough to identify.
G-4 GOOD—Date and letters legible. Main devices outlined, but lacking in detail.
VG-8 VERY GOOD—Major details discernible. Letters well formed but worn.
F-12 FINE—Hair ends distinguishable. Top hair lines visible, but otherwise worn smooth.
VF-20 VERY FINE—Some detail visible in hair in center. Other details more bold.
EF-40 EXTREMELY FINE—Hair well defined but with some wear.
AU-50 ABOUT UNCIRCULATED—Slight trace of wear on tips of highest curls; breast feathers usually weak.
MS-60 UNCIRCULATED—No trace of wear. Light blemishes.

	Mintage	AG-3	G-4	VG-8	F-12	VF-20	EF-40	AU-50	MS-60
1794	1,758	$8,000.	$14,000.	$20,000.	$25,000.	$50,000.	$90,000.	$130,000.	—
1795	160,295	400.	650.	900.	1,650.	2,500.	5,000.	8,500.	$19,500.

DRAPED BUST (1795–1804)
Small Eagle Reverse (1795–1798)

AG-3 ABOUT GOOD—Clear enough to identify.
G-4 GOOD—Bust outlined, no detail. Date legible, some leaves evident.
VG-8 VERY GOOD—Drapery worn except deepest folds. Hair lines smooth.
F-12 FINE—All drapery lines distinguishable. Some detail visible in hair lines near cheek and neck.
VF-20 VERY FINE—Left side of drapery worn smooth.
EF-40 EXTREMELY FINE—Drapery distinctly visible. Hair well outlined and detailed.
AU-50 ABOUT UNCIRCULATED—Slight trace of wear on the bust shoulder and hair to left of forehead, as well as on eagle's breast and top edges of wings.
MS-60 UNCIRCULATED—No trace of wear. Light blemishes.

	Mintage	AG-3	G-4	VG-8	F-12	VF-20	EF-40	AU-50	MS-60
1795, Bust Type	*42,738*	$325.	$500.	$700.	$1,100.	$2,000.	$3,500.	$5,000.	$17,500.
1796, All kinds	79,920	325.	500.	700.	1,100.	2,000.	3,500.	5,000.	17,500.
1797		325.	500.	700.	1,100.	2,000.	3,500.	5,000.	17,500.
1798, All kinds		325.	500.	700.	1,100.	2,000.	3,500.	5,000.	17,500.

Heraldic Eagle Reverse (1798–1804)

G-4 GOOD—Letters and date legible. E PLURIBUS UNUM illegible.
VG-8 VERY GOOD—Motto partially legible. Only deepest drapery details visible. All other lines smooth.
F-12 FINE—All drapery lines distinguishable. Some detail visible in hair lines near cheek and neck.
VF-20 VERY FINE—Left side of drapery worn smooth.
EF-40 EXTREMELY FINE—Drapery distinct. Hair well detailed.
AU-50 ABOUT UNCIRCULATED—Slight trace of wear on the bust shoulder and hair to left of forehead, as well as on eagle's breast and top edges of wings.
MS-60 UNCIRCULATED—No trace of wear. Light blemishes.

	Mintage	G-4	VG-8	F-12	VF-20	EF-40	AU-50	MS-60
1798, Heraldic Eagle		$350.	$400.	$650.	$1,000.	$1,800.	$3,000.	$8,000.
1799	423,515	350.	400.	650.	1,000.	1,800.	3,000.	8,000.
1800	220,920	350.	400.	650.	1,000.	1,800.	3,000.	8,000.
1801	54,454	350.	400.	650.	1,000.	1,800.	3,000.	8,000.
1802	41,650	350.	400.	650.	1,000.	1,800.	3,000.	8,000.
1803	85,634	350.	400.	650.	1,000.	1,800.	3,000.	8,000.
1804, Variety 1, O Above Cloud						Proof: $2,500,000.		
1804, Variety 2, O Above Space Between Cloud						Proof: $1,500,000.		

GOBRECHT DOLLARS (1836–1839)

Silver dollars of 1836, 1838, and 1839 were mostly made as patterns and restrikes, but some were made in quantities for general circulation.

	VF-20	EF-40	AU-50	PF-60
1836, C. GOBRECHT F. on base. Reverse eagle flying upward amid stars. Plain edge. Although scarce, this is the most common variety and was issued for circulation as regular coinage	$3,500.	$5,500.	$7,500.	$9,000.

Chart continues on next page.

	VF-20	EF-40	AU-50	PF-60
1838, Similar obverse, designer's name omitted, stars added around border. Reverse eagle flying left in plain field. Reeded edge	$7,000.	$9,000.	$11,000.	$12,750.
1839, Obverse as above. Reverse eagle in plain field. Reeded edge. Issued for circulation as regular coinage	7,000.	9,000.	11,000.	12,000.

LIBERTY SEATED (1840–1873)

In 1840, silver dollars were again issued for general circulation. The seated figure of Liberty device was adopted for the obverse, and a heraldic eagle for the reverse.

VG-8 VERY GOOD—Any three letters of LIBERTY at least two-thirds complete.
F-12 FINE—All seven letters of LIBERTY visible, though weak.
VF-20 VERY FINE—LIBERTY strong, but slight wear visible on its ribbon.
EF-40 EXTREMELY FINE—Horizontal lines of shield complete. Eagle's eye plain.
AU-50 ABOUT UNCIRCULATED—Traces of light wear on only the high points of the design. Half of mint luster present.
MS-60 UNCIRCULATED—No trace of wear. Light marks or blemishes.
PF-60 PROOF—Several contact marks, hairlines, or light rubs possible on surface. Luster possibly dull and eye appeal lacking.
PF-63 CHOICE PROOF—Reflective surfaces with only a few blemishes in secondary focal places. No major flaws.

No Motto (1840–1865)

Mintmark location is on reverse, below eagle.

	Mintage	VG-8	F-12	VF-20	EF-40	AU-50	MS-60	PF-60	PF-63
1840.	61,005	$75.	$100.	$150.	$225.	$300.	$900.	$5,000.	$13,000.
1841.	173,000	65.	90.	125.	200.	275.	750.	5,000.	14,000.
1842.	184,618	60.	90.	125.	200.	250.	650.	5,000.	13,500.
1843.	165,100	60.	90.	125.	200.	250.	700.	5,000.	13,500.
1844.	20,000	80.	110.		230.	350.	1,250.	5,000.	15,000.
1845.	24,500	85.	120.	160.	230.	400.	2,500.	5,250.	14,000.
1846.	110,600	60.	90.	125.	200.	250.	650.	5,000.	13,000.
1846O	59,000	80.	110.	150.	250.	350.	1,500.		
1847.	140,750	60.	90.	125.	200.	250.	650.	5,250.	12,000.
1848.	15,000	125.	200.	275.	385.	550.	1,300.	5,250.	13,000.
1849.	62,600	60.	90.	125.	200.	250.	700.	5,000.	14,000.
1850.	7,500	150.	250.	325.	500.	700.	2,300.	5,000.	13,000.
1850O	40,000	100.	125.	225.	500.	1,200.	3,000.		
1851.	1,300	1,750.	3,000.	4,500.	6,000.	7,500.	9,500.	10,500.	17,000.
1852.	1,100	1,750.	3,000.	4,500.	6,000.	7,500.	9,000.	12,000.	20,000.
1853.	46,110	80.	125.	150.	275.	450.	1,000.	6,500.	13,000.
1854.	33,140	400.	550.	800.	1,400.	1,800.	2,500.	5,000.	8,750.
1855.	26,000	300.	500.	700.	1,000.	1,200.	2,500.	5,000.	9,000.
1856.	63,500	125.	175.	225.	400.	600.	1,600.	2,500.	5,000.
1857.	94,000	125.	175.	225.	400.	600.	1,100.	2,200.	4,000.
1858. . . . . (300+)		1,200.	1,500.	2,000.	2,500.	3,000.		3,200.	5,000.
1859. . . . . (800)	255,700	100.	135.	185.	250.	300.	800.	1,000.	1,500.
1859O	360,000	60.	90.	125.	200.	250.	650.		
1859S	20,000	100.	150.	250.	500.	1,250.	4,500.		
1860 . . . . (1,330)	217,600	95.	115.	165.	225.	275.	600.	1,000.	1,500.
1860O	515,000	60.	95.	125.	150.	270.	600.		
1861 . . . . (1,000)	77,500	200.	275.	375.	500.	700.	1,200.	1,000.	1,500.

	Mintage	VG-8	F-12	VF-20	EF-40	AU-50	MS-60	PF-60	PF-63
1862	(550).... 12,090	$150.	$250.	$350.	$450.	$700.	$1,200.	$1,000.	$1,500.
1863	(460).... 27,660	125.	150.	200.	275.	450.	1,000.	950.	1,500.
1864	(470).... 31,170	90.	125.	175.	250.	425.	1,200.	1,000.	1,500.
1865	(500).... 47,000	90.	125.	150.	250.	425.	1,200.	950.	1,500.

With Motto (1866–1873)

Motto IN GOD WE TRUST on Reverse (1866–1873)

	Mintage	VG-8	F-12	VF-20	EF-40	AU-50	MS-60	PF-60	PF-63
1866	(725).... 48,900	$80.	$120.	$150.	$200.	$300.	$700.	$800.	$1,400.
1867	(625).... 46,900	80.	120.	150.	200.	300.	700.	800.	1,400.
1868	(600)... 162,100	70.	100.	150.	200.	300.	700.	800.	1,400.
1869	(600)... 423,700	70.	100.	150.	200.	300.	700.	800.	1,400.
1870	(1,000).. 415,000	70.	100.	150.	200.	250.	500.	800.	1,400.
1870CC	 11,758	175.	250.	375.	650.	1,400.	4,000.		
1870S	....		35,000.	50,000.	100,000.	200,000.	350,000.		
1871	(960) . 1,073,800	65.	100.	150.	200.	250.	500.	800.	1,400.
1871CC	 1,376	1,000.	2,000.	3,000.	4,000.	10,000.	24,000.		
1872	(950) . 1,105,500	65.	100.	150.	200.	250.	500.	800.	1,400.
1872CC	 3,150	500.	800.	1,400.	2,000.	4,000.	9,000.		
1872S	 9,000	100.	150.	275.	450.	1,000.	3,500.		
1873	(600)... 293,000	65.	100.	150.	200.	275.	500.	800.	1,400.
1873CC	 2,300	2,100.	3,000.	5,000.	7,500.	13,000.	32,000.		

TRADE DOLLARS (1873–1885)

This Trade dollar was issued for circulation in the Orient to compete with dollar-size coins of other countries. It weighed 420 grains compared to 412-1/2 grains, the weight of the regular silver dollar.

VG-8 VERY GOOD—About half of mottoes IN GOD WE TRUST (on Liberty's pedestal) and E PLURIBUS UNUM (on obverse ribbon) visible. Rim on both sides well defined.

F-12 FINE—Mottoes and liberty legible but worn.

EF-40 EXTREMELY FINE—Mottoes and liberty sharp. Only slight wear on rims.

AU-50 ABOUT UNCIRCULATED—Slight trace of wear on Liberty's left breast and left knee and on hair above ear, as well as on eagle's head, knee, and wing tips.

MS-60 UNCIRCULATED—No trace of wear. Light blemishes.

MS-63 CHOICE UNCIRCULATED—Some distracting contact marks or blemishes in prime focal areas. Impaired luster possible.

PF-63 CHOICE PROOF—Reflective surfaces with only a few blemishes in secondary focal places. No major flaws.

1875-S, S Over CC

See next page for chart.

	Mintage	VG-8	F-12	EF-40	AU-50	MS-60	MS-63	PF-63
1873 . . . .(865)	396,635	$40.	$50.	$80.	$125.	$275.	$675.	$1,100.
1873CC.	124,500	75.	100.	200.	550.	1,200.	6,500.	
1873S.	703,000	40.	50.	80.	150.	400.	800.	
1874 . . . .(700)	987,100	40.	50.	80.	125.	225.	650.	1,100.
1874CC	1,373,200	75.	100.	125.	200.	475.	2,000.	
1874S	2,549,000	40.	50.	80.	125.	200.	650.	
1875 . . . .(700)	218,200	70.	120.	225.	325.	700.	1,100.	1,100.
1875CC	1,573,700	70.	80.	125.	150.	350.	1,000.	
1875S	4,487,000	40.	50.	80.	125.	200.	650.	
1875S, S Over CC	*	80.	125.	325.	500.	1,000.	4,000.	
1876 . . . .(1,150)	455,000	40.	50.	80.	100.	225.	650.	1,100.
1876CC.	509,000	60.	85.	150.	225.	1,000.	6,000.	
1876S	5,227,000	40.	50.	80.	100.	200.	650.	
1877 . . . .(510) . .	3,039,200	40.	50.	80.	100.	225.	650.	1,100.
1877CC.	534,000	60.	90.	175.	250.	475.	2,750.	
1877S	9,519,000	40.	50.	80.	100.	200.	650.	
1878 . . . .(900).				450.				1,100.
1878CC (a).	97,000	150.	275.	825.	1,200.	4,000.	8,250.	
1878S	4,162,000	40.	50.	80.	100.	200.	650.	
1879 . . . .(1,541).								1,100.
1880 . . . .(1,987).								1,100.
1881 . . . .(960).								1,200.
1882 . . . .(1,097).								1,200.
1883 . . . .(979).								1,200.
1884 (b) . . . .(10).								130,000.
1885 (b) . . . .(5).								400,000.

* Included in number above. **a.** 44,148 Trade dollars were melted on July 19, 1878. Many of these may have been 1878-CC. **b.** The Trade dollars of 1884 and 1885 were unknown to collectors until 1908. None are listed in the Mint director's report, and numismatists believe that they are not a part of the regular Mint issue.

MORGAN (1878-1921)

George T. Morgan, formerly a pupil of William Wyon's at the Royal Mint in London, designed the new dollar. His initial M is found at the truncation of the neck, at the last tress. It also appears on the reverse on the left-hand loop of the ribbon.

Sharply struck prooflike coins have a highly reflective surface and usually command substantial premiums.

VF-20 VERY FINE—Two thirds of hair lines from top of forehead to ear visible. Ear well defined. Feathers on eagle's breast worn.

EF-40 EXTREMELY FINE—All hair lines strong and ear bold. Eagle's feathers all plain but with slight wear on breast and wing tips.

AU-50 ABOUT UNCIRCULATED—Slight trace of wear on the bust shoulder and hair left of forehead, and on eagle's breast and top edges of wings.

MS-60 UNCIRCULATED—No trace of wear. Full mint luster present, but may be noticeably marred by scuff marks or bag abrasions.

MS-63 CHOICE UNCIRCULATED—No trace of wear; full mint luster; few noticeable surface marks.

MS-64 UNCIRCULATED—A few scattered contact marks. Good eye appeal and attractive luster.

MS-65 GEM UNCIRCULATED—Only light, scattered contact marks that are not distracting. Strong luster, good eye appeal.

8 Tail Feathers, 1878, Philadelphia Only

Mintmark location on reverse, below wreath.

Most Proof Morgan dollars, where indicated in mintage records (quantity shown in parentheses), are valued approximately as follows:
Proof-60 – $400.; Proof-63 – $900.; Proof-65 – $2,200.

Most Uncirculated silver dollars have scratches or nicks because of handling of mint bags. Choice sharply struck coins with full brilliance and without blemishes are worth more than listed values.

	Mintage	VF-20	EF-40	AU-50	MS-60	MS-63	MS-65
1878, 8 Feathers ......(500) *749,500*		$10.	$14.	$17.	$50.	$75.	$600.
1878, 7 Feathers ......(250) ... *9,759,300*		8.	12.	13.	26.	40.	550.
1878, Clear Double Feathers.............*		13.	15.	23.	50.	110.	1,300.
1878CC......................2,212,000		42.	55.	60.	100.	150.	850.
1878S......................9,774,000		8.	9.	11.	20.	32.	125.
1879 ....(1,100)...14,806,000		8.	9.	11.	18.	25.	425.
1879CC, CC Over CC 756,000		60.	200.	350.	1,000.	2,300.	10,000.
1879O......................2,887,000		8.	9.	11.	30.	70.	1,250.
1879S......................9,110,000		8.		11.	18.	22.	80.
1880 ....(1,355)...12,600,000		8.	9.	11.	18.	22.	325.
1880CC......................591,000		65.	80.	100.	225.	275.	550.
1880O......................5,305,000		8.	9.	11.	26.	160.	7,000.
1880S......................8,900,000		8.	9.	11.	18.	22.	80.
1881 ....(984)....9,163,000		8.	9.	11.	18.	22.	350.
1881CC......................296,000		110.	135.	155.	185.	225.	375.
1881O......................5,708,000		8.	9.	11.	18.	22.	600.
1881S......................12,760,000		8.	9.	11.	18.	22.	80.
1882 ....(1,100)...11,100,000		8.	9.	11.	18.	22.	150.
1882CC......................1,133,000		45.	50.	55.	80.	110.	200.
1882O......................6,090,000		8.	9.	11.	18.	22.	275.
1882S......................9,250,000		8.	9.	11.	18.	22.	80.
1883 ....(1,039)...12,290,000		8.	9.	11.	18.	22.	75.
1883CC......................1,204,000		45.	50.	55.	85.	100.	200.
1883O......................8,725,000		8.	9.	11.	18.	22.	80.
1883S......................6,250,000		9.	12.	50.	240.	1,000.	7,000.
1884 ....(875)...14,070,000		8.	9.	11.	18.	22.	110.
1884CC......................1,136,000		45.	50.	60.	85.	110.	190.
1884O......................9,730,000		8.	9.	11.	18.	22.	80.
1884S......................3,200,000		9.	18.	110.	1,900.	12,000.	85,000.
1885 ....(930)...17,787,000		8.	9.	11.	18.	22.	80.
1885CC......................228,000		110.	150.	175.	225.	275.	600.
1885O......................9,185,000		8.	9.	11.	18.	22.	80.
1885S......................1,497,000		8.	16.	42.	70.	100.	550.
1886 ....(886)...19,963,000		8.	9.	11.	18.	22.	80.
1886O......................10,710,000		8.	10.	35.	225.	1,750.	85,000.
1886S......................750,000		20.	30.	45.	110.	175.	1,200.
1887 ....(710)...20,290,000		8.	9.	11.	18.	22.	80.
1887O......................11,550,000		8.	9.	11.	20.	50.	1,350.
1887S......................1,771,000		8.	9.	16.	45.	100.	1,250.
1888 ....(832)...19,183,100		8.	9.	11.	18.	22.	80.
1888O......................12,150,000		8.	9.	11.	18.	22.	175.
1888S......................657,000		27.	38.	50.	110.	165.	1,200.
1889 ....(811)...21,726,000		8.	9.	11.	18.	22.	110.
1889CC......................350,000		600.	1,400.	2,500.	8,000.	14,000.	125,000.
1889O......................11,875,000		8.	9.	17.	60.	175.	1,900.
1889S......................700,000		19.	22.	38.	100.	170.	700.

* Included in number above.

Chart continues on next page.

	Mintage	VF-20	EF-40	AU-50	MS-60	MS-63	MS-65
1890 . . . .(590). . .	16,802,000	$8.	$9.	$11.	$18.	$22.	$800.
1890CC	2,309,041	44.	55.	75.	150.	375.	2,650.
1890O	10,701,000	8.	9.	12.	26.	45.	600.
1890S	8,230,373	7.	9.	12.	22.	45.	400.
1891 . . . .(650). . .	8,693,556	8.	9.	13.	22.	70.	2,250.
1891CC	1,618,000	50.	55.	85.	180.	375.	1,900.
1891O	7,954,529	9.	11.	20.	60.	175.	3,000.
1891S	5,296,000	8.	9.	12.	27.	55.	500.
1892 . . . .(1,245). . .	1,036,000	9.	12.	32.	70.	175.	1,400.
1892CC	1,352,000	70.	150.	190.	375.	950.	3,500.
1892O	2,744,000	10.	12.	30.	70.	150.	2,000.
1892S	1,200,000	25.	90.	875.	11,000.	28,000.	73,000.
1893 . . . .(792).	378,000	55.	75.	110.	250.	600.	3,000.
1893CC	677,000	150.	600.	850.	1,500.	3,000.	22,000.
1893O	300,000	80.	150.	325.	1,000.	3,000.	90,000.
1893S	100,000	3,000.	4,250.	10,000.	35,000.	60,000.	175,000.
1894 . . . .(972).	110,000	600.	850.	1,000.	2,000.	3,000.	10,000.
1894O	1,723,000	22.	35.	90.	300.	1,750.	18,000.
1894S	1,260,000	27.	60.	150.	275.	475.	2,500.
1895 . . . .(880). . .	12,880	*14,000.	*16,000.	*20,000.	*27,500.	*35,000.
1895O	450,000	100.	150.	600.	7,000.	18,000.	82,000.
1895S	400,000	122.	250.	550.	900.	2,200.	8,000.
1896 . . . .(762). . .	9,976,000	8.	9.	11.	18.	22.	100.
1896O	4,900,000	8.	9.	60.	450.	3,800.	65,000.
1896S	5,000,000	22.	75.	200.	550.	1,100.	5,500.
1897 . . . .(731). . .	2,822,000	8.	9.	11.	18.	22.	100.
1897O	4,004,000	8.	9.	50.	300.	2,300.	20,000.
1897S	5,825,000	8.	9.	12.	27.	45.	250.
1898 . . . .(735). . .	5,884,000	8.	9.	11.	18.	22.	100.
1898O	4,440,000	8.	9.	11.	18.	22.	80.
1898S	4,102,000	8.	14.	35.	100.	175.	600.
1899 . . . .(846).	330,000	22.	28.	35.	60.	100.	275.
1899O	12,290,000	8.	9.	11.	18.	22.	80.
1899S	2,562,000	11.	17.	45.	140.	200.	600.
1900 . . . .(912). . .	8,830,000	8.	9.	11.	18.	22.	80.
1900O	12,590,000	8.	9.	11.	18.	22.	80.
1900S	3,540,000	9.	17.	30.	120.	175.	450.
1901 . . . .(813). . .	6,962,000	18.	26.	175.	900.	7,000.	80,000.
1901O	13,320,000	8.	9.	11.	18.	22.	85.
1901S	2,284,000	12.	20.	60.	160.	300.	1,350.
1902 . . . .(777). . .	7,994,000	8.	9.	11.	20.	50.	200.
1902O	8,636,000	8.	9.	11.	18.	22.	80.
1902S	1,530,000	40.	50.	100.	150.	250.	1,100.
1903 . . . .(755). . .	4,652,000	18.	25.	28.	33.	40.	110.
1903O	4,450,000	90.	100.	125.	165.	200.	300.
1903S	1,241,000	40.	130.	650.	1,700.	2,500.	2,800.
1904 . . . .(650). . .	2,788,000	8.	9.	15.	33.	110.	1,700.
1904O	3,720,000	8.	9.	11.	18.	22.	80.
1904S	2,304,000	22.	85.	275.	600.	1,100.	3,000.
1921	44,690,000	7.	8.	9.	10.	13.	70.
1921D	20,345,000	7.	8.	9.	15.	27.	125.
1921S	21,695,000	7.	8.	9.	12.	27.	575.

* Values are for Proofs.

Peace (1921–1935)

Anthony De Francisci, a medalist, designed this dollar. His monogram is located in the field of the coin under the neck of Liberty.

VF-20 VERY FINE—Hair over eye well worn. Some strands over ear well defined. Some eagle feathers on top and outside edge of right wing visible.

EF-40 EXTREMELY FINE—Hair lines over brow and ear are strong, though slightly worn. Outside wing feathers at right and those at top visible but faint.

AU-50 ABOUT UNCIRCULATED—Slight trace of wear. Most luster present, although marred by contact marks.

MS-60 UNCIRCULATED—No trace of wear. Full mint luster, but possibly noticeably marred by stains, surface marks, or bag abrasions.

MS-63 CHOICE UNCIRCULATED—Some distracting contact marks or blemishes in prime focal areas. Impaired luster possible.

MS-64 UNCIRCULATED—A few scattered contact marks. Good eye appeal and attractive luster.

MS-65 GEM UNCIRCULATED—Only light, scattered, non-distracting contact marks. Strong luster, good eye appeal.

PF-65 CHOICE PROOF—Satin surfaces, no noticeable blemishes or flaws.

Mintmark location on reverse, below ONE.

Most Uncirculated silver dollars have scratches or nicks because of handling of mint bags. Choice sharply struck coins with full brilliance and without blemishes are worth more than listed values.

	Mintage	VF-20	EF-40	AU-50	MS-60	MS-63	MS-65	PF-65
1921	1,006,473	$40.00	$45.	$55.	$100.	$150.	$800.	$16,000.
1922	51,737,000	6.50	7.	8.	10.	16.	70.	17,000.
1922D	15,063,000	6.50	7.	8.	12.	21.	150.	
1922S	17,475,000	6.50	7.	8.	12.	26.	800.	
1923	30,800,000	6.50	7.	8.	10.	16.	70.	
1923D	6,811,000	6.50	7.	9.	22.	55.	400.	
1923S	19,020,000	6.50	7.	8.	12.	35.	2,250.	
1924	11,811,000	6.50	7.	8.	10.	16.	70.	
1924S	1,728,000	8.00	10.	27.	75.	200.	3,200.	
1925	10,198,000	6.50	7.	8.	10.	16.	70.	
1925S	1,610,000	6.50	7.	12.	28.	70.	7,000.	
1926	1,939,000	6.50	7.	9.	15.	30.	150.	
1926D	2,348,700	6.50	7.	12.	25.	80.	225.	
1926S	6,980,000	6.50	7.	9.	15.	30.	300.	
1927	848,000	8.00	12.	19.	30.	70.	750.	
1927D	1,268,900	8.00	12.	40.	70.	125.	2,000.	
1927S	866,000	8.00	11.	30.	70.	140.	3,500.	
1928	360,649	150.00	175.	200.	225.	275.	1,700.	
1928S	1,632,000	10.00	12.	22.	65.	225.	8,000.	
1934	954,057	7.00	9.	15.	40.	85.	400.	
1934D	1,569,500	7.00	8.	15.	40.	135.	700.	
1934S	1,011,000	23.00	60.	225.	775.	1,500.	3,000.	
1935	1,576,000	7.00	8.	13.	30.	42.	250.	
1935S	1,964,000	7.00	9.	38.	100.	160.	425.	

EISENHOWER (1971–1978)
Eagle Reverse (1971–1974)

Honoring both President Dwight D. Eisenhower and the first landing of man on the moon, this design is the work of Chief Engraver Frank Gasparro, whose initials are on the truncation and below the eagle. The reverse is an adaptation of the official Apollo 11 insignia.

Mintmark location is above date.

	Mintage	EF-40	MS-63	PF-63	PF-65
1971, Copper-Nickel Clad	47,799,000	$1.05	$1.40		
1971D, Copper-Nickel Clad	68,587,424	1.05	1.25		
1971S, Silver Clad (4,265,234)	6,868,530		2.50	$2.50	$3.50
1972, Copper-Nickel Clad	75,890,000	1.05	1.25		
1972D, Copper-Nickel Clad	92,548,511	1.05	1.25		
1972S, Silver Clad (1,811,631)	2,193,056		2.50	3.50	6.00
1973, Copper-Nickel Clad	*2,000,056	1.50	6.00		
1973D, Copper-Nickel Clad	*2,000,000	1.50	6.00		
1973S, Copper-Nickel Clad (2,760,339)				3.00	7.00
1973S, Silver Clad (1,013,646)	1,883,140		3.50	10.00	16.00
1974, Copper-Nickel Clad	27,366,000	1.05	1.30		
1974D, Copper-Nickel Clad	45,517,000	1.05	1.30		
1974S, Copper-Nickel Clad (2,612,568)				2.50	3.50
1974S, Silver Clad (1,306,579)	1,900,156		3.00	3.00	4.00

* 1,769,258 of each sold only in sets and not released for circulation. Unissued coins destroyed at mint.

Bicentennial Coinage Dated 1776–1976

Obverse   Reverse Variety 2   Reverse Variety 1

Variety 1: Design in low relief, bold lettering on reverse.
Variety 2: Sharp design, delicate lettering on reverse.

SILVER AND RELATED DOLLARS

	Mintage	EF-40	MS-63	PF-63	PF-65
1776–1976, Copper-Nickel Clad, Variety 1	4,019,000	$1.10	$2.50		
1776–1976, Copper-Nickel Clad, Variety 2	113,318,000	1.10	1.20		
1776–1976D, Copper-Nickel Clad, Variety 1	21,048,710	1.10	1.40		
1776–1976D, Copper-Nickel Clad, Variety 2	82,179,564	1.10	1.20		
1776–1976S, Copper-Nickel Clad, Variety 1	(2,845,450)			$2.50	$5.00
1776–1976S, Copper-Nickel Clad, Variety 2	(4,149,730)			2.50	3.50
1776–1976S, Silver Clad, Variety 1	11,000,000		4.00		
1776–1976S, Silver Clad, Variety 2	(4,000,000)			5.00	10.00

Eagle Reverse Resumed (1977–1978)

	Mintage	EF-40	MS-63	PF-63	PF-65
1977, Copper-Nickel Clad	12,596,000	$1.05	$1.50		
1977D, Copper-Nickel Clad	32,983,006	1.05	1.25		
1977S, Copper-Nickel Clad	(3,251,152)			$2.50	$4.00
1978, Copper-Nickel Clad	25,702,000	1.05	1.25		
1978D, Copper-Nickel Clad	33,012,890	1.05	1.25		
1978S, Copper-Nickel Clad	(3,127,781)			2.50	5.00

SUSAN B. ANTHONY (1979–1999)

Clear S   Filled S

	Mintage	MS-63	PF-63	PF-65		Mintage	MS-63	PF-63	PF-65
1979P, Narrow Rim	360,222,000	$1.00			1980S, Proof	(3,554,806)		$2.50	$5.
1979P, Wide Rim	*	2.50			1981P	3,000,000	$2.00		
1979D	288,015,744	1.00			1981D	3,250,000	2.00		
1979S	109,576,000	1.00			1981S	3,492,000	2.00		
Proof, Filled S			$2.50	$5.	1981S, Proof	(4,063,083)		2.50	4.
Proof, Clear S			35.00	50.	1981S, Proof, Clear S			80.00	115.
1980P	27,610,000	1.00			1999P	29,592,000	1.10		
1980D	41,628,708	1.00			1999P, Proof			4.00	9.
1980S	20,422,000	1.00			1999D	11,776,000	1.15		

* Included in number above.

SACAGAWEA (2000 TO DATE)

The design of this coin was selected in national competition from among 120 submissions that were considered by a panel appointed by Treasury Secretary Robert Rubin. The adopted motif depicts Sacagawea, a young Native American Shoshone, as rendered by artist Glenna Goodacre. On her back she carries Jean Baptiste, her infant son. The reverse shows an eagle in flight, designed by Mint engraver Thomas D. Rogers, Sr.

The composition exemplifies the spirit of Liberty, Peace, and Freedom shown by Sacagawea in her conduct as interpreter and guide to explorers Meriwether Louis and William Clark during their famed journey westward from the great northern plains to the Pacific.

These coins have a distinctive golden color and a plain edge to distinguish them from other denominations or coins of a similar size. The change in composition and appearance was mandated under the United States Dollar Coin Act of 1997.

Several distinctive finishes can be identified on the Sacagawea dollars as a result of the mint attempting to adjust the dies, blanks, strikes, or finishing to produce coins with minimal spotting and a better surface color. One group of 5,000 pieces dated 2000, with a special finish were presented to sculptor Glenna Goodacre in payment for the obverse design. Unexplained error coins made from mismatched dies (a state quarter obverse combined with a Sacagawea dollar reverse) are extremely rare.

	Mintage	MS-63	PF-63	PF-65
2000P	767,140,000	$1.00		
2000D	518,916,000	1.00		
2000S	(3,082,483)		$3.00	$6.00
2001P	62,468,000	1.00		
2001D	70,939,500	1.00		
2001S	(2,294,043)		6.00	20.00
2002P	3,865,610	1.10		
2002D	3,732,000	1.10		
2002S	(2,277,720)		3.50	15.00
2003P	3,080,000	1.10		
2003D	3,080,000	1.10		
2003S			3.00	10.00
2004P	2,660,000	1.10		
2004D	2,660,000	1.10		
2004S			3.00	11.00
2005P		1.10		
2005D		1.10		
2005S			3.00	8.00

GOLD DOLLARS

Coinage of the gold dollar was authorized by the Act of March 3, 1849. The weight was 25.8 grains, fineness .900. The first type, struck until 1854, is known as the Liberty Head type.

In 1854, the piece was made larger in diameter and thinner. The design was changed to a feather headdress on a female, generally referred to as the Indian Princess Head type. In 1856 the type was changed slightly by enlarging the size of the head.

LIBERTY HEAD (1849–1854)

VF-20 VERY FINE—LIBERTY on headband complete and legible. Knobs on coronet defined.
EF-40 EXTREMELY FINE—Slight wear on Liberty's hair. Knobs on coronet sharp.
AU-50 ABOUT UNCIRCULATED—Trace of wear on headband. Nearly full luster.
AU-55 CHOICE ABOUT UNCIRCULATED—Evidence of friction on design high points.
MS-60 UNCIRCULATED—No trace of wear. Light marks and blemishes.
MS-63 CHOICE UNCIRCULATED—Some distracting contact marks or blemishes in prime focal areas. Impaired luster possible.

	Mintage	VF-20	EF-40	AU-50	AU-55	MS-60	MS-63
1849	688,567	$100.	$140.	$170.	$190.	$280.	$1,200.
1849, Small Head, No L	*	100.	140.	175.	200.	300.	1,300.
1849C	11,634	650.	950.	1,400.	2,500.	6,000.	14,000.
1849D	21,588	850.	1,150.	1,450.	2,250.	3,750.	9,000.
1849O	21,500	110.	175.	230.	375.	500.	2,250.
1850	481,953	100.	140.	150.	165.	260.	800.
1850C	6,966	700.	975.	1,750.	3,250.	5,800.	18,000.
1850D	8,382	850.	1,200.	2,000.	3,500.	7,000.	20,000.
1850O	14,000	185.	270.	550.	1,100.	2,200.	4,500.
1851	3,317,671	100.	140.	150.	165.	190.	800.
1851C	41,267	750.	1,000.	1,200.	1,500.	2,000.	4,500.
1851D	9,882	900.	1,200.	1,550.	2,400.	4,500.	12,000.
1851O	290,000	120.	155.	175.	225.	550.	1,800.
1852	2,045,351	100.	145.	155.	165.	200.	800.
1852C	9,434	725.	950.	1,200.	1,700.	3,000.	8,000.
1852D	6,360	900.	1,300.	1,700.	3,200.	7,000.	22,000.
1852O	140,000	105.	175.	240.	450.	850.	4,600.
1853	4,076,051	100.	145.	155.	165.	200.	800.
1853C	11,515	750.	1,000.	1,500.	2,200.	3,900.	10,000.
1853D	6,583	900.	1,200.	1,800.	3,250.	7,000.	22,000.
1853O	290,000	115.	155.	170.	225.	450.	1,500.
1854	855,502	100.	145.	155.	165.	200.	800.
1854D	2,935	900.	1,550.	4,250.	5,500.	9,000.	27,000.
1854S	14,632	225.	310.	500.	900.	1,700.	3,200.

* Included in number above.

INDIAN PRINCESS HEAD,
SMALL HEAD (1854–1856)

VF-20 VERY FINE—Feather-curl tips on headdress outlined but details worn.
EF-40 EXTREMELY FINE—Slight wear on tips of feather curls on headdress.
AU-50 ABOUT UNCIRCULATED—Trace of wear on feathers, nearly full luster.
AU-55 CHOICE ABOUT UNCIRCULATED—Evidence of friction on design high points. Most of original mint luster present.
MS-60 UNCIRCULATED—No trace of wear. Light marks and blemishes.
MS-63 CHOICE UNCIRCULATED—Some distracting contact marks or blemishes in prime focal areas. Impaired luster possible.
PF-63 CHOICE PROOF—Reflective surfaces with only a few blemishes in secondary focal areas. No major flaws.

	Mintage	VF-20	EF-40	AU-50	AU-55	MS-60	MS-63	PF-63
1854	783,943	$210.	$325.	$400.	$900.	$2,700.	$12,000.	$65,000.
1855	758,269	210.	325.	400.	900.	2,700.	12,000.	57,500.
1855C	9,803	900.	2,500.	4,000.	7,000.	17,000.		
1855D	1,811	3,250.	6,500.	17,000.	22,500.	37,500.	70,000.	
1855O	55,000	300.	400.	975.	2,000.	5,250.	17,500.	
1856S	24,600	575.	950.	1,700.	2,750.	6,000.	24,000.	

INDIAN PRINCESS HEAD,
LARGE HEAD (1856–1889)

VF-20 VERY FINE—Slight detail in curled feathers in headdress. Details worn smooth at eyebrow, hair below headdress, and behind ear and bottom curl.
EF-40 EXTREMELY FINE—Slight wear above and to right of eye and on top of curled feathers.
AU-50 ABOUT UNCIRCULATED—Trace of wear on feathers, nearly full luster.
AU-55 CHOICE ABOUT UNCIRCULATED—Evidence of friction on design high points. Most of original mint luster present.
MS-60 UNCIRCULATED—No trace of wear. Light marks and blemishes.
MS-63 CHOICE UNCIRCULATED—Some distracting contact marks or blemishes in prime focal areas. Impaired luster possible.
PF-63 CHOICE PROOF—Reflective surfaces with only a few blemishes in secondary focal places. No major flaws.

	Mintage	VF-20	EF-40	AU-50	AU-55	MS-60	MS-63	PF-63
1856	1,762,936	$105.	$150.	$160.	$185.	$200.	$750.	$15,000.
1856D	1,460	2,700.	4,250.	5,250.	8,500.	23,000.		
1857	774,789	100.	145.	160.	185.	200.	750.	8,000.
1857C	13,280	800.	1,100.	2,200.	3,700.	8,500.	23,000.	
1857D	3,533	900.	1,375.	2,800.	3,700.	8,500.	26,000.	
1857S	10,000	375.	450.	825.	1,250.	4,350.	16,000.	
1858	117,995	100.	145.	165.	175.	200.	750.	4,750.
1858D	3,477	900.	1,200.	2,350.	4,000.	7,250.	20,000.	
1858S	10,000	275.	375.	950.	1,200.	4,000.	12,000.	
1859	(80)... 168,244	100.	145.	165.	175.	200.	750.	3,500.

GOLD DOLLARS

	Mintage	VF-20	EF-40	AU-50	AU-55	MS-60	MS-63	PF-63
1859C	5,235	$750.	$1,000.	$2,400.	$3,750.	$7,500.	$24,000.	
1859D	4,952	900.	1,200.	2,250.	3,250.	8,000.	17,000.	
1859S	15,000	175.	375.	775.	1,250.	4,000.	12,000.	
1860	(154) 36,514	100.	145.	165.	175.	260.	850.	$3,350.
1860D	1,566	1,800.	2,850.	4,750.	6,000.	11,500.	40,000.	
1860S	13,000	250.	360.	525.	700.	1,750.	4,000.	
1861	(349) 527,150	100.	145.	165.	175.	210.	725.	3,900.
1861D		5,000.	7,250.	13,000.	15,000.	22,500.	43,000.	
1862	(35) 1,361,355	100.	145.	165.	175.	200.	725.	4,100.
1863	(50) 6,200	325.	625.	1,200.	1,450.	2,850.	5,000.	4,000.
1864	(50) 5,900	270.	350.	575.	625.	725.	2,000.	5,500.
1865	3,725	270.	350.	550.	625.	1,050.	2,350.	3,900.
1866	(30) 7,100	270.	350.	500.	550.	725.	1,500.	4,000.
1867	(50) 5,200	310.	375.	475.	575.	850.	1,500.	4,000.
1868	(25) 10,500	210.	300.	360.	425.	725.	1,500.	4,500.
1869	(25) 5,900	260.	375.	475.	525.	800.	1,500.	4,750.
1870	(35) 6,300	210.	300.	360.	400.	725.	1,500.	4,850.
1870S	3,000	350.	550.	850.	1,100.	1,700.	5,000.	
1871	(30) 3,900	210.	275.	350.	400.	600.	1,500.	3,600.
1872	(30) 3,500	215.	260.	325.	375.	700.	1,600.	5,250.
1873, Close 3	(25) 1,800	300.	575.	675.	725.	1,200.	2,750.	11,500.
1873, Open 3	123,300	100.	145.	160.	170.	200.	725.	
1874	(20) 198,800	100.	145.	160.	170.	200.	725.	5,750.
1875	(20) 400	1,400.	2,800.	3,700.	3,900.	5,250.	8,000.	12,000.
1876	(45) 3,200	210.	260.	340.	360.	475.	775.	3,800.
1877	(20) 3,900	125.	250.	340.	360.	475.	775.	4,600.
1878	(20) 3,000	150.	260.	340.	360.	475.	775.	3,800.
1879	(30) 3,000	135.	200.	235.	250.	375.	775.	4,000.
1880	(36) 1,600	115.	150.	170.	190.	300.	700.	3,650.
1881	(87) 7,620	115.	150.	170.	190.	300.	700.	3,600.
1882	(125) 5,000	125.	150.	170.	190.	300.	750.	3,250.
1883	(207) 10,800	120.	150.	170.	190.	300.	750.	3,250.
1884	(1,006) 5,230	120.	150.	170.	190.	300.	750.	3,250.
1885	(1,105) 11,156	120.	150.	170.	190.	300.	750.	3,250.
1886	(1,016) 5,000	120.	150.	170.	190.	300.	750.	3,250.
1887	(1,043) 7,500	120.	150.	170.	190.	300.	750.	3,250.
1888	(1,079) 15,501	120.	150.	170.	190.	300.	750.	3,250.
1889	(1,779) 28,950	120.	150.	170.	190.	300.	750.	3,250.

Although authorized by the Act of April 2, 1792, coinage of quarter eagles was not begun until 1796.

CAPPED BUST TO RIGHT (1796–1807)

F-12 FINE—Hair worn smooth on high spots. E PLURIBUS UNUM on ribbon weak but legible.
VF-20 VERY FINE—Some wear on high spots.
EF-40 EXTREMELY FINE—Only slight wear on Liberty's hair and cheek.
AU-50 ABOUT UNCIRCULATED—Trace of wear on cap, hair, cheek, and drapery.
AU-55 CHOICE ABOUT UNCIRCULATED—Evidence of friction on design high points. Some original mint luster present.
MS-60 UNCIRCULATED—No trace of wear. Light blemishes.

No Stars on Obverse (1796)   **Stars on Obverse (1796–1807)**

	Mintage	F-12	VF-20	EF-40	AU-50	AU-55	MS-60
1796, No Stars on Obverse	963	$19,000.	$27,500.	$50,000.	$60,000.	$70,000.	$120,000.
1796, Stars on Obverse	432	16,000.	25,000.	45,000.	55,000.	65,000.	110,000.
1797	427	10,000.	12,500.	20,000.	35,000.	40,000.	80,000.
1798	1,094	3,250.	5,250.	7,000.	15,000.	20,000.	40,000.
1802, 2 Over 1	3,035	3,250.	5,250.	6,000.	8,000.	10,000.	16,000.
1804, 13-Star Reverse	3,327	18,000.	23,000.	50,000.	85,000.	100,000.	150,000.
1804, 14-Star Reverse	*	3,250.	5,000.	6,500.	8,000.	10,000.	16,000.
1805	1,781	3,250.	5,000.	6,500.	8,000.	10,500.	17,000.
1806, 6 Over 4, 8 Stars Left, 5 R	1,136	3,500.	5,250.	6,750.	8,500.	12,000.	18,000.
1806, 6 Over 5, 7 Stars Left, 6 R	480	4,500.	6,500.	9,000.	15,000.	22,000.	50,000.
1807	6,812	3,250.	4,800.	5,750.	8,500.	10,000.	15,000.

* Included in number above.

CAPPED BUST TO LEFT, LARGE SIZE (1808)

F-12 FINE—E PLURIBUS UNUM on reverse, and LIBERTY on headband, legible but weak.
VF-20 VERY FINE—Motto and LIBERTY clear.
EF-40 EXTREMELY FINE—All details of hair plain.
AU-50 ABOUT UNCIRCULATED—Trace of wear above eye, on top of cap, and on cheek and hair.
AU-55 CHOICE ABOUT UNCIRCULATED—Evidence of friction on design high points. Some original mint luster present.
MS-60 UNCIRCULATED—No trace of wear. Light blemishes.

	Mintage	F-12	VF-20	EF-40	AU-50	AU-55	MS-60
1808	2,710	$16,000.	$22,000.	$27,500.	$55,000.	$60,000.	$85,000.

CAPPED HEAD TO LEFT (1821–1834)

Those dated 1829 to 1834 are smaller in diameter than the 1821 to 1827 pieces.

	Mintage	F-12	VF-20	EF-40	AU-50	AU-55	MS-60
1821	6,448	$3,500.	$4,750.	$6,000.	$7,500.	$8,500.	$17,500.
1824, 4 Over 1	2,600	3,500.	4,750.	6,000.	7,500.	8,500.	15,000.
1825	4,434	3,500.	4,750.	6,000.	7,500.	8,500.	13,000.
1826, 6 Over 5	760	4,000.	5,000.	6,250.	7,750.	9,000.	25,000.
1827	2,800	4,200.	5,250.	7,000.	8,000.	10,000.	15,000.
1829	3,403	3,500.	4,250.	5,000.	6,500.	8,000.	10,000.
1830	4,540	3,500.	4,250.	5,000.	6,500.	8,000.	10,000.
1831	4,520	3,500.	4,250.	5,000.	6,500.	8,000.	10,000.
1832	4,400	3,500.	4,250.	5,000.	6,500.	8,000.	11,000.
1833	4,160	3,500.	4,250.	5,250.	6,750.	8,000.	12,000.
1834, With Motto	4,000	5,000.	7,500.	12,000.	15,000.	18,000.	27,000.

CLASSIC HEAD, NO MOTTO ON REVERSE (1834–1839)

In 1834, the quarter eagle was redesigned. A ribbon binding the hair, bearing the word LIBERTY, replaces the Liberty cap. The motto was omitted from the reverse.

F-12 FINE—LIBERTY on headband legible and complete. Curl under ear outlined but no detail.
VF-20 VERY FINE—LIBERTY plain; detail in hair curl.
EF-40 EXTREMELY FINE—Small amount of wear on top of hair and below L in LIBERTY. Wear evident on wing.
AU-50 ABOUT UNCIRCULATED—Trace of wear on coronet and hair above ear.
AU-55 CHOICE ABOUT UNCIRCULATED—Evidence of friction on design high points. Some of original mint luster present.
MS-60 UNCIRCULATED—No trace of wear. Light blemishes.
MS-63 CHOICE UNCIRCULATED—Some distracting contact marks or blemishes in prime focal areas. Impaired luster possible.

Mintmark location.

	Mintage	F-12	VF-20	EF-40	AU-50	AU-55	MS-60	MS-63
1834, No Motto	112,234	$185.	$240.	$350.	$500.	$700.	$1,600.	$4,250.
1835	131,402	185.	240.	350.	500.	700.	1,700.	5,000.
1836	547,986	185.	240.	350.	500.	700.	1,600.	4,500.
1837	45,080	200.	240.	350.	650.	800.	2,200.	7,500.
1838	47,030	200.	240.	350.	675.	900.	1,600.	5,000.
1838C	7,880	750.	1,000.	1,700.	4,500.	6,000.	17,500.	27,500.
1839	27,021	200.	275.	500.	1,200.	1,500.	3,250.	12,500.
1839C	18,140	700.	950.	1,500.	2,500.	4,500.	14,000.	32,000.
1839D	13,674	700.	975.	2,000.	4,000.	6,000.	15,000.	35,000.
18390	17,781	300.	350.	700.	1,100.	1,700.	4,200.	16,000.

LIBERTY HEAD (1840–1907)

4 Plain 4

4 Crosslet 4

Mintmark location.

	Mintage	VF-20	EF-40	AU-50	AU-55	MS-60	MS-63	PF-63
1840	18,859	$135.	$650.	$2,000.	$2,350.	$4,750.	$9,000.	
1840C	12,822	850.	1,200.	3,100.	4,300.	9,000.	25,000.	
1840D	3,532	2,100.	6,250.	10,000.	16,000.	28,000.		
18400	33,580	185.	600.	1,400.	2,500.	8,000.	19,500.	
1841	36,000	75,000.	80,000.	85,000.	110,000.			$110,000.
1841C	10,281	850.	1,200.	2,500.	5,500.	13,000.	32,500.	
1841D	4,164	1,250.	3,100.	7,750.	10,000.	20,000.	42,500.	

Chart continues on next page.

	Mintage	VF-20	EF-40	AU-50	AU-55	MS-60	MS-63	PF-63
1842	2,823	$700.	$1,850.	$4,750.	$7,000.	$15,000.	$37,500.	$42,500.
1842C	6,729	1,000.	2,300.	5,250.	7,500.	20,000.	36,000.	
1842D	4,643	1,250.	2,750.	8,250.	12,500.	25,000.	40,000.	
1842O	19,800	260.	800.	1,650.	3,250.	8,250.	22,500.	
1843	100,546	125.	200.	300.	600.	1,500.	3,500.	42,500.
1843C	26,064	850.	1,200.	2,100.	3,250.	6,250.	15,000.	
1843D	36,209	1,000.	1,450.	2,100.	5,500.	7,250.	21,500.	
1843O	364,002	135.	180.	265.	550.	1,500.	6,000.	
1844	6,784	275.	650.	1,450.	3,250.	5,500.	16,500.	42,500.
1844C	11,622	900.	1,550.	5,000.	7,250.	14,000.	34,000.	
1844D	17,332	1,000.	1,400.	2,000.	3,500.	5,100.	20,000.	
1845	91,051	190.	230.	275.	375.	875.	3,500.	42,500.
1845D	19,460	1,000.	1,400.	2,600.	5,000.	10,000.	26,000.	
1845O	4,000	725.	1,650.	4,500.	5,250.	14,000.	37,500.	
1846	21,598	200.	375.	650.	1,500.	4,000.	17,500.	42,500.
1846C	4,808	975.	1,850.	6,500.	8,500.	13,000.	27,000.	
1846D	19,303	1,000.	1,400.	2,000.	3,500.	8,000.	20,000.	
1846O	62,000	220.	300.	800.	1,500.	4,750.	14,500.	
1847	29,814	170.	275.	625.	850.	2,650.	6,500.	
1847C	23,226	850.	1,200.	1,800.	2,500.	4,800.	11,000.	
1847D	15,784	975.	1,425.	2,000.	3,500.	7,500.	18,500.	
1847O	124,000	165.	275.	750.	1,250.	3,000.	13,500.	
1848	6,500	375.	650.	1,350.	2,250.	4,500.	12,000.	42,500.

CAL. Gold Quarter Eagle (1848)

In 1848, about 230 ounces of gold were sent to Secretary of War Marcy by Col. R.B. Mason, Military Governor of California. The gold was turned over to the Mint and made into quarter eagles. The distinguishing mark "CAL." was punched above the eagle on the reverse side, while the coins were in the die.

CAL. Above Eagle on Reverse (1848)

	Mintage	VF-20	EF-40	AU-50	AU-55	MS-60	MS-63
1848, CAL. Above Eagle	1,389	$10,000.	$20,000.	$25,000.	$30,000.	$35,000.	$50,000.
1848C	16,788	850.	1,250.	2,350.	4,000.	11,000.	28,000.
1848D	13,771	1,000.	1,450.	2,250.	4,000.	8,000.	25,000.
1849	23,294	215.	360.	650.	975.	1,900.	6,000.
1849C	10,220	850.	1,300.	3,750.	6,000.	17,500.	40,000.
1849D	10,945	1,000.	1,400.	2,750.	4,250.	12,000.	25,000.
1850	252,923	130.	165.	275.	375.	800.	2,900.
1850C	9,148	850.	1,200.	2,650.	5,000.	13,500.	30,000.
1850D	12,148	975.	1,200.	2,450.	4,750.	11,000.	35,000.
1850O	84,000	160.	350.	900.	1,350.	3,750.	11,750.
1851	1,372,748	130.	155.	175.	190.	240.	925.
1851C	14,923	850.	1,200.	3,500.	4,500.	9,250.	27,500.
1851D	11,264	1,000.	1,500.	3,000.	4,750.	9,000.	23,500.
1851O	148,000	140.	160.	650.	1,250.	3,500.	11,000.
1852	1,159,681	130.	155.	175.	190.	250.	925.
1852C	9,772	850.	1,300.	3,350.	5,000.	13,500.	26,000.
1852D	4,078	1,000.	1,950.	5,500.	6,250.	12,500.	37,500.
1852O	140,000	140.	230.	700.	1,200.	3,750.	9,250.
1853	1,404,668	130.	155.	175.	195.	275.	900.
1853D	3,178	1,300.	2,450.	3,800.	5,500.	12,500.	37,500.

QUARTER EAGLES

	Mintage	VF-20	EF-40	AU-50	AU-55	MS-60	MS-63	PF-63
1854	596,258	$130.	$155.	$175.	$195.	$275.	$1,175.	
1854C	7,295	850.	1,550.	3,900.	5,250.	11,000.	31,000.	
1854D	1,760	2,100.	4,000.	8,500.	12,500.	20,000.	60,000.	
1854O	153,000	130.	165.	325.	550.	1,200.	2,750.	
1854S	246	35,000.	70,000.	150,000.	—	—		
1855	235,480	130.	155.	175.	195.	280.	1,250.	
1855C	3,677	1,050.	2,350.	4,650.	6,500.	19,500.	37,000.	
1855D	1,123	2,500.	5,750.	13,500.	20,000.	38,000.	62,500.	
1856	384,240	130.	155.	175.	200.	300.	1,200.	$32,500.
1856C	7,913	900.	1,750.	3,000.	5,000.	11,500.	24,500.	
1856D	874	5,000.	9,000.	19,000.	25,000.	55,000.	95,000.	
1856O	21,100	155.	525.	925.	2,400.	4,000.	23,500.	
1856S	72,120	150.	275.	675.	1,200.	3,350.	9,750.	
1857	214,130	130.	155.	175.	210.	300.	1,300.	30,000.
1857D	2,364	1,000.	1,950.	2,950.	4,750.	9,750.	24,500.	
1857O	34,000	150.	275.	750.	1,250.	3,250.	9,500.	
1857S	69,200	150.	260.	650.	2,000.	4,250.	12,000.	
1858	47,377	130.	185.	265.	350.	950.	2,500.	21,000.
1858C	9,056	850.	1,200.	2,250.	2,600.	7,520.	26,000.	
1859	(80) 39,364	130.	190.	300.	400.	925.	2,400.	14,000.
1859D	2,244	1,250.	2,250.	3,600.	5,000.	14,500.	50,000.	
1859S	15,200	235.	700.	1,900.	2,600.	5,000.	13,000.	
1860	(112) 22,563	130.	190.	350.	400.	850.	2,000.	13,500.
1860C	7,469	850.	1,400.	2,800.	6,000.	16,500.	29,000.	
1860S	35,600	165.	500.	850.	1,200.	3,000.	7,500.	
1861	(90) 1,283,788	135.	155.	180.	195.	250.	775.	14,500.
1861S	24,000	260.	675.	2,250.	3,100.	5,800.	14,000.	
1862, 2 Over 1	*	650.	1,300.	2,600.	3,200.	6,250.		
1862	(35) 98,508	150.	235.	375.	450.	925.	2,850.	12,500.
1862S	8,000	650.	1,600.	3,300.	4,750.	13,500.	28,500.	
1863, Proof only	(30)							35,000.
1863S	10,800	360.	1,100.	2,400.	4,000.	10,500.	20,000.	
1864	(50) 2,824	4,250.	8,500.	17,500.	20,000.	30,000.		9,000.
1865	(25) 1,520	3,600.	5,500.	14,500.	16,000.	29,500.	35,000.	11,500.
1865S	23,376	160.	475.	1,100.	1,500.	3,350.	7,500.	
1866	(30) 3,080	950.	2,650.	4,250.	5,500.	9,000.	20,000.	8,000.
1866S	38,960	210.	475.	1,100.	1,650.	4,750.	15,500.	
1867	(50) 3,200	275.	600.	875.	1,250.	3,750.	7,000.	8,000.
1867S	28,000	180.	475.	1,250.	1,500.	3,100.	11,000.	
1868	(25) 3,600	170.	300.	500.	650.	1,175.	5,500.	9,000.
1868S	34,000	140.	225.	825.	1,200.	3,000.	11,000.	
1869	(25) 4,320	180.	250.	550.	900.	2,400.	3,750.	6,500.
1869S	29,500	165.	360.	625.	1,250.	3,400.	6,750.	
1870	(35) 4,520	175.	325.	575.	950.	2,850.	6,000.	6,750.
1870S	16,000	140.	325.	600.	1,250.	3,500.	12,000.	
1871	(30) 5,320	180.	250.	450.	625.	1,750.	3,000.	6,750.
1871S	22,000	140.	210.	415.	575.	1,725.	3,600.	
1872	(30) 3,000	280.	600.	825.	1,750.	3,600.	10,500.	5,750.
1872S	18,000	140.	280.	700.	1,200.	3,450.	9,000.	
1873	(25) 178,000	125.	155.	185.	200.	220.	625.	5,500.
1873S	27,000	160.	280.	675.	800.	2,100.	6,250.	
1874	(20) 3,920	185.	280.	550.	725.	1,650.	4,500.	7,500.
1875	(20) 400	2,750.	4,000.	7,000.	8,500.	12,500.	20,000.	9,000.
1875S	11,600	125.	225.	600.	900.	3,350.	6,750.	
1876	(45) 4,176	215.	500.	700.	1,250.	2,600.	4,600.	5,500.
1876S	5,000	175.	400.	725.	1,500.	2,600.	7,250.	
1877	(20) 1,632	280.	600.	825.	1,150.	2,350.	7,500.	6,000.
1877S	35,400	125.	150.	180.	210.	475.	1,800.	
1878	(20) 286,240	125.	150.	180.	200.	300.	650.	8,750.
1878S	178,000	125.	150.	180.	200.	260.	1,500.	
1879	(30) 88,960	125.	150.	175.	190.	260.	675.	6,250.
1879S	43,500	150.	210.	375.	725.	1,700.	4,000.	
1880	(36) 2,960	135.	260.	475.	625.	1,000.	2,800.	6,250.

* Included in number below.

Chart continues on next page.

	Mintage	VF-20	EF-40	AU-50	AU-55	MS-60	MS-63	PF-63
1881 . . . . (51) 640		$1,500.	$2,400.	$3,500.	$4,200.	$7,000.	$14,000.	$5,500.
1882 . . . . (67) 4,000		150.	225.	310.	390.	525.	2,000.	4,500.
1883 . . . . (82) 1,920		150.	300.	750.	975.	2,000.	4,750.	4,500.
1884 . . . . (73) 1,950		150.	300.	450.	600.	1,200.	2,250.	4,500.
1885 . . . . (87) 800		475.	1,300.	1,800.	2,000.	3,500.	6,000.	4,750.
1886 . . . . (88) 4,000		140.	200.	325.	375.	850.	2,200.	4,750.
1887 . . . . (122) 6,160		135.	190.	260.	300.	525.	2,000.	4,350.
1888 . . . . (97) 16,001		125.	170.	210.	220.	240.	650.	4,350.
1889 . . . . (48) 17,600		125.	160.	200.	210.	250.	650.	5,250.
1890 . . . . (93) 8,720		135.	175.	220.	240.	375.	950.	4,500.
1891 . . . . (80) 10,960		125.	155.	180.	200.	310.	675.	4,250.
1892 . . . . (105) 2,440		130.	180.	250.	290.	575.	1,950.	4,250.
1893 . . . . (106) . . . 30,000		125.	150.	170.	190.	225.	600.	4,250.
1894 . . . . (122) 4,000		130.	170.	240.	260.	600.	1,250.	4,250.
1895 . . . . (119) 6,000		125.	160.	210.	225.	300.	675.	4,250.
1896 . . . . (132) . . . 19,070		125.	150.	175.	190.	220.	625.	4,250.
1897 . . . . (136) . . . 29,768		125.	150.	175.	190.	220.	625.	4,100.
1898 . . . . (165) . . . 24,000		125.	150.	175.	190.	220.	625.	4,250.
1899 . . . . (150) . . . 27,200		125.	150.	175.	190.	220.	625.	4,100.
1900 . . . . (205) . . . 67,000		125.	160.	200.	210.	220.	625.	4,100.
1901 . . . . (223) . . . 91,100		125.	150.	175.	190.	220.	625.	4,100.
1902 . . . . (193) . . . 133,540		125.	150.	175.	190.	220.	625.	4,100.
1903 . . . . (197) . . . 201,060		125.	150.	175.	190.	220.	625.	4,100.
1904 . . . . (170) . . . 160,790		125.	150.	175.	190.	220.	625.	4,100.
1905 . . . . (144) . . . 217,800		125.	150.	175.	190.	220.	625.	4,100.
1906 . . . . (160) . . . 176,330		125.	150.	175.	190.	220.	625.	4,100.
1907 . . . . (154) . . . 336,294		125.	150.	175.	190.	220.	625.	4,100.

INDIAN HEAD (1908–1929)

Bela Lyon Pratt designed this coin and the similar $5 gold piece.

VF-20 VERY FINE—Hair-cord knot distinct. Feathers at top of head clear. Cheekbone worn.
EF-40 EXTREMELY FINE—Cheekbone, war bonnet, and headband feathers slightly worn.
AU-50 ABOUT UNCIRCULATED—Trace of wear on cheekbone and headdress.
MS-60 UNCIRCULATED—No trace of wear. Light blemishes.
MS-63 CHOICE UNCIRCULATED—Some distracting contact marks or blemishes in prime focal areas. Impaired luster possible.
MS-64 UNCIRCULATED—A few scattered contact marks visible. Good eye appeal and attractive luster.
MATTE PF-63 CHOICE PROOF—Few blemishes in secondary focal areas. No major flaws. Matte surfaces.

Mintmark location is on reverse, to left of arrows.

	Mintage	VF-20	EF-40	AU-50	MS-60	MS-63	MS-64	MATTE PF-63
1908 . . . . (236) . . . 564,821		$125.	$135.	$140.	$210.	$1,200.	$1,600.	$5,500.
1909 . . . . (139) . . . 441,760		125.	135.	140.	200.	1,600.	2,100.	5,500.
1910 . . . . (682) . . . 492,000		125.	135.	140.	200.	1,500.	2,500.	5,500.
1911 . . . . (191) . . . 704,000		125.	135.	140.	200.	1,200.	1,800.	5,500.
1911D 55,680		1,000.	1,600.	2,000.	5,000.	18,500.	25,000.	
1912 . . . . (197) . . . 616,000		125.	135.	140.	210.	1,800.	2,700.	5,500.
1913 . . . . (165) . . . 722,000		125.	135.	140.	210.	1,100.	1,900.	5,750.
1914 . . . . (117) . . . 240,000		135.	150.	160.	300.	5,200.	7,500.	5,750.
1914D 448,000		125.	135.	140.	210.	1,700.	4,000.	
1915 . . . . (100) . . . 606,000		125.	135.	140.	190.	1,000.	1,750.	6,000.
1925D 578,000		125.	130.	140.	185.	900.	1,300.	
1926 446,000		125.	130.	140.	185.	900.	1,300.	
1927 388,000		125.	130.	140.	185.	900.	1,300.	
1928 416,000		125.	130.	140.	185.	900.	1,300.	
1929 532,000		125.	130.	140.	185.	900.	1,300.	

The three-dollar gold piece was authorized by the Act of February 21, 1853. Coinage was struck beginning in 1854. It was never popular and saw very little circulation.

VF-20 VERY FINE—Eyebrow, hair about forehead and ear, and bottom curl all worn smooth. Faint details visible on curled feather-ends of headdress.

EF-40 EXTREMELY FINE—Light wear above and to right of eye, and on top of curled feathers.

AU-50 ABOUT UNCIRCULATED—Trace of wear on top of curled feathers and in hair above and to right of eye.

AU-55 CHOICE ABOUT UNCIRCULATED—Evidence of friction on design high points. Much of original mint luster present.

MS-60 UNCIRCULATED—No trace of wear. Light blemishes.

MS-63 CHOICE UNCIRCULATED—Some distracting contact marks or blemishes in prime focal areas. Impaired luster possible.

PF-63 CHOICE PROOF—Reflective surfaces with only a few blemishes in secondary focal places. No major flaws.

Mintmark location is on reverse, below wreath.

	Mintage	VF-20	EF-40	AU-50	AU-55	MS-60	MS-63	PF-63
1854	138,618	$550.	$750.	$1,100.	$1,300.	$2,000.	$4,750.	$47,500.
1854D	1,120	6,750.	12,000.	22,000.	32,500.	53,000.		
1854O	24,000	750.	1,500.	2,500.	5,700.	13,500.	22,000.	
1855	50,555	550.	750.	1,100.	1,300.	2,000.	5,250.	27,500.
1855S	6,600	800.	1,700.	4,500.	6,250.	19,000.	65,000.	
1856	26,010	550.	800.	1,100.	1,300.	2,100.	5,750.	15,000.
1856S	34,500	600.	1,000.	1,800.	3,700.	7,500.	17,000.	
1857	20,891	550.	800.	1,100.	1,350.	2,250.	7,500.	13,000.
1857S	14,000	650.	1,500.	3,750.	5,000.	13,000.		
1858	2,133	700.	1,200.	1,800.	3,000.	5,800.	13,000.	15,000.
1859	(80)...15,558	600.	750.	1,100.	1,350.	2,000.	5,300.	11,000.
1860	(119)...7,036	600.	800.	1,100.	1,500.	2,200.	5,250.	7,500.
1860S	7,000	650.	1,350.	4,000.	6,500.	12,000.	30,000.	
1861	(113)...5,959	600.	850.	1,300.	1,500.	2,700.	6,500.	11,000.
1862	(35)...5,750	600.	850.	1,300.	1,500.	2,700.	6,500.	8,000.
1863	(39)...5,000	650.	950.	1,300.	1,600.	2,900.	6,000.	9,000.
1864	(50)...2,630	650.	950.	1,300.	1,600.	2,900.	6,250.	9,500.
1865	(25)...1,140	850.	1,800.	3,750.	4,500.	6,750.	12,000.	14,000.
1866	(30)...4,000	650.	800.	1,100.	1,500.	2,700.	7,000.	9,500.
1867	(50)...2,600	650.	825.	1,100.	1,600.	2,700.	7,000.	9,500.
1868	(25)...4,850	600.	800.	1,200.	1,450.	2,250.	5,500.	10,000.
1869	(25)...2,500	625.	825.	1,300.	1,600.	3,000.	7,500.	10,000.
1870	(35)...3,500	600.	900.	1,400.	1,700.	3,100.	7,750.	8,000.
1870S *(unique)*		—						
1871	(30)...1,300	650.	875.	1,250.	1,500.	3,000.	6,750.	8,750.
1872	(30)...2,000	600.	825.	1,200.	1,400.	2,700.	7,000.	10,500.
1873, Open 3 (Original)...	(25)	2,350.	3,500.	6,500.	9,500.			16,000.
1873, Close 3		2,200.	3,500.	6,600.	10,000.	20,000.	30,000.	
1874	(20)...41,800	600.	800.	1,000.	1,300.	1,900.	4,800.	12,500.
1875, Proof Only	(20)	15,500.	22,000.	36,000.	40,000.			65,000.
1876, Proof Only	(45)	4,500.	8,000.	10,500.	15,000.			22,000.
1877	(20)...1,468	1,000.	2,500.	4,500.	6,000.	9,000.	25,000.	14,000.
1878	(20)...82,304	525.	575.	1,000.	1,300.	2,000.	4,500.	12,500.
1879	(30)...3,000	550.	800.	1,000.	1,400.	2,100.	4,750.	10,500.
1880	(36)...1,000	600.	1,400.	1,700.	1,825.	2,500.	5,000.	10,000.
1881	(54)...500	1,000.	2,000.	3,400.	4,000.	5,200.	8,500.	8,000.
1882	(76)...1,500	675.	850.	1,300.	1,500.	2,500.	5,000.	8,000.
1883	(89)...900	650.	1,100.	1,675.	2,000.	2,700.	5,000.	8,000.
1884	(106)...1,000	650.	1,300.	1,750.	2,000.	2,700.	5,250.	8,000.
1885	(109)...801	650.	1,300.	1,700.	2,100.	2,800.	5,400.	8,000.
1886	(142)...1,000	625.	1,100.	1,750.	2,000.	3,200.	5,900.	8,000.
1887	(160)...6,000	575.	625.	1,300.	1,450.	2,500.	4,700.	8,000.
1888	(291)...5,000	575.	625.	1,100.	1,400.	2,100.	4,650.	8,000.
1889	(129)...2,300	575.	675.	1,000.	1,300.	2,200.	4,650.	8,000.

STELLA (1879–1880)

These pattern coins were first suggested by the Hon. John A. Kasson, then U.S. Envoy Extraordinary and Minister Plenipotentiary to Austria-Hungary. It was through the efforts of Dr. W.W. Hubbell, who patented the alloy goloid (used in making another pattern piece, the goloid metric dollar) that we have these beautiful and interesting coins.

The $4 Stella—so called because of the five-pointed star on the reverse—was envisioned by Kasson as America's answer to various foreign gold coins popular in the international market. The British sovereign, Italy's 20 lire, and the 20 pesetas of Spain were three such coins: each smaller than a U.S. $5 gold piece, they were used widely in international trade.

The Stella was one of many proposals made to Congress for an international trade coin, and one of only several that made it to pattern coin form (others include the 1868 $5 and 1874 Bickford $10).

Odds were stacked against the Stella from the start. The denomination of four U.S. dollars didn't match any of the coin's European counterparts, and at any rate the U.S. double eagle ($20 coin)—already used in international commerce—was a more convenient medium of exchange. The Stella was never minted in quantities for circulation.

There are two distinct types in both years of issue. Charles E. Barber designed the Flowing Hair type, and George T. Morgan the Coiled Hair. They were struck as patterns in gold, aluminum, copper, and white metal. Only those struck in gold are listed.

	Mintage	EF-40	AU-50	PF-60	PF-63	PF-65
1879, Flowing Hair. . . . . (425)		$35,000.	$45,000.	$60,000.	$95,000.	$125,000.
1879, Coiled Hair *(12 known)*.		75,000.	95,000.	110,000.	175,000.	350,000.
1880, Flowing Hair *(17 known)*		60,000.	65,000.	75,000.	125,000.	220,000.
1880, Coiled Hair *(8 known)*.		115,000.	150,000.	190,000.	300,000.	400,000.

The half eagle was the first gold coin struck for the United States. The $5 piece was authorized to be coined by the Act of April 2, 1792, and the first type weighed 135 grains, of .91667 fineness. The weight was changed by the Act of June 28, 1834 to 129 grains, of .899225 fineness. Fineness became .900 by the Act of January 18, 1837.

CAPPED BUST TO RIGHT (1795–1807)

F-12 FINE—Liberty's hair worn smooth but with distinct outline. For heraldic type, E PLURIBUS UNUM faint but legible.
VF-20 VERY FINE—Slight to noticeable wear on high spots such as hair, turban, and eagle's head and wings.
EF-40 EXTREMELY FINE—Slight wear on hair and highest part of cheek.
AU-50 ABOUT UNCIRCULATED—Trace of wear on cap, hair, cheek, and drapery.
MS-60 UNCIRCULATED—No trace of wear. Light blemishes.
MS-63 CHOICE UNCIRCULATED—Some distracting contact marks or blemishes in prime focal areas. Impaired luster possible.

Small Eagle (1795–1798)

	Mintage	F-12	VF-20	EF-40	AU-50	AU-55	MS-60	MS-63
1795, Small Eagle	8,707	$8,000.	$11,000.	$14,000.	$19,000.	$22,000.	$30,000.	$100,000.

1796, 6 Over 5   **1797, 15 Stars**   **1797, 16 Stars**

	Mintage	F-12	VF-20	EF-40	AU-50	AU-55	MS-60	MS-63
1796, 6 Over 5	6,196	$8,500.	$12,000.	$17,000.	$22,000.	$24,000.	$45,000.	$110,000.
1797, 15 Stars	3,609	9,500.	13,000.	23,000.	45,000.	60,000.	90,000.	
1797, 16 Stars	3,609	9,500.	13,000.	21,000.	40,000.	50,000.	85,000.	
1798, Small Eagle (7 known)			70,000.	110,000.	190,000.	300,000.		

Heraldic Eagle (1795–1807)

	Mintage	F-12	VF-20	EF-40	AU-50	AU-55	MS-60	MS-63
1795, Heraldic Eagle		$6,000.	$9,000.	$15,000.	$27,500.	$35,000.	$55,000.	$115,000.
1797, 7 Over 5		6,000.	9,000.	16,500.	35,000.	42,500.	100,000.	
1798, Large 8, 13-Star Reverse	24,867	1,700.	2,300.	3,200.	6,500.	7,500.	12,500.	
1798, Large 8, 14-Star Reverse	*	2,000.	2,700.	4,500.	10,000.	13,000.	24,000.	
1799	7,451	1,800.	2,400.	3,000.	5,500.	6,000.	12,000.	37,000.

* Included in number above.

Chart continues on next page.

	Mintage	F-12	VF-20	EF-40	AU-50	AU-55	MS-60	MS-63
1800	37,628	$1,750.	$2,200.	$2,600.	$4,700.	$5,200.	$7,000.	$15,000.
1802, 2 Over 1	53,176	1,750.	2,200.	2,600.	4,500.	4,700.	6,500.	13,000.
1803, 3 Over 2	33,506	1,750.	2,200.	2,600.	4,500.	4,700.	6,500.	13,000.
1804	30,475	1,750.	2,200.	2,600.	4,500.	4,700.	6,500.	13,000.
1805	33,183	1,750.	2,200.	2,600.	4,500.	4,700.	6,500.	13,000.
1806	64,093	1,750.	2,200.	2,600.	4,500.	4,700.	6,500.	13,000.
1807	32,488	1,750.	2,200.	2,600.	4,500.	4,700.	6,500.	13,000.

CAPPED BUST TO LEFT (1807–1812)

F-12 FINE—LIBERTY on cap legible but partly weak.
VF-20 VERY FINE—Headband edges slightly worn. LIBERTY bold.
EF-40 EXTREMELY FINE—Slight wear on highest portions of hair; 80% of major curls plain.
AU-50 ABOUT UNCIRCULATED—Trace of wear above eye and on top of cap, cheek, and hair.
AU-55 CHOICE ABOUT UNCIRCULATED—Evidence of friction on design high points. Some mint luster present.
MS-60 UNCIRCULATED—No trace of wear. Light blemishes.
MS-63 CHOICE UNCIRCULATED—Some distracting contact marks or blemishes in prime focal areas. Impaired luster possible.

	Mintage	F-12	VF-20	EF-40	AU-50	AU-55	MS-60	MS-63
1807	51,605	$1,300.	$1,600.	$2,200.	$3,300.	$4,000.	$5,000.	$9,500.
1808, 8 Over 7	55,578	1,500.	2,200.	2,500.	4,000.	5,250.	7,500.	17,500.
1808	*	1,300.	1,600.	2,200.	3,300.	4,000.	5,000.	10,000.
1809, 9 Over 8	33,875	1,300.	1,600.	2,200.	3,300.	4,000.	5,000.	10,000.
1810, All kinds	100,287	1,300.	1,600.	2,200.	3,300.	4,000.	5,000.	9,500.
1811	99,581	1,300.	1,600.	2,200.	3,300.	4,000.	5,000.	9,500.
1812	58,087	1,300.	1,600.	2,200.	3,300.	4,000.	5,000.	9,500.

* Included in number above.

CAPPED HEAD TO LEFT (1813–1834)
Large Diameter (1813–1829)

	Mintage	F-12	VF-20	EF-40	AU-50	AU-55	MS-60	MS-63
1813	95,428	$1,500.	$1,900.	$2,500.	$3,500.	$4,000.	$5,500.	$10,000.
1814, 4 Over 3	15,454	1,750.	2,000.	2,750.	4,000.	4,750.	6,500.	17,000.
1815	635	25,000.	35,000.	50,000.	75,000.	85,000.	110,000.	150,000.
1818, All kinds	48,588	1,800.	2,000.	2,500.	4,000.	4,750.	6,500.	13,500.
1819	51,723	7,500.	12,500.	17,500.	25,000.	30,000.	40,000.	65,000.
1820, All kinds	263,806	1,800.	2,000.	2,500.	4,000.	4,750.	7,500.	17,000.
1821	34,641	4,000.	8,500.	13,500.	20,000.	25,000.	45,000.	100,000.
1822 *(3 known)*	17,796			2,000,000.				
1823	14,485	1,800.	2,500.	3,500.	5,000.	6,500.	13,000.	22,500.
1824	17,340	3,500.	7,500.	10,500.	15,000.	17,500.	25,000.	42,500.
1825, 5 Over 1	29,060	3,500.	5,500.	8,000.	12,500.	15,000.	25,000.	45,000.
1825, 5 Over 4 *(2 known)*	*			225,000.				
1826	18,069	2,700.	5,000.	6,500.	10,000.	12,500.	17,500.	35,000.
1827	24,913	4,000.	6,500.	8,500.	12,500.	15,000.	25,000.	45,000.
1828, 8 Over 7 *(5 known)*	28,029	10,000.	15,000.	27,500.	40,000.	45,000.	80,000.	125,000.
1828	*	4,000.	8,000.	12,500.	20,000.	25,000.	45,000.	65,000.
1829, Large Date	57,442	10,000.	18,000.	25,000.	40,000.	45,000.	75,000.	125,000.

* Included in number above.

Reduced Diameter (1829-1834)

	Mintage	F-12	VF-20	EF-40	AU-50	AU-55	MS-60	MS-63
1829, Small Date . . . . *		$25,000.	$35,000.	$60,000.	$80,000.	$95,000.	$125,000.	$175,000.
1830	126,351	9,000.	12,500.	13,500.	15,500.	17,500.	25,000.	45,000.
1831	140,594	9,000.	12,500.	13,500.	15,500.	17,500.	25,000.	45,000.
1832, Curved-Base 2, 12 Stars *(5 known)*.	157,487	25,000.	35,000.	70,000.	90,000.			
1832, Sq.-Base 2, 13 Stars . . . . . . *		9,000.	12,500.	13,500.	15,500.	17,500.	25,000.	45,000.
1833	193,630	9,000.	12,500.	13,500.	15,500.	17,500.	25,000.	45,000.
1834	50,141	9,000.	12,500.	13,500.	15,500.	17,500.	27,500.	47,500.

* Included in number above.

CLASSIC HEAD (1834-1838)

	Mintage	F-12	VF-20	EF-40	AU-50	AU-55	MS-60	MS-63
1834	657,460	$185.	$275.	$400.	$700.	$950.	$2,200.	$5,500.
1835	371,534	185.	275.	400.	700.	950.	2,200.	5,500.
1836	553,147	185.	275.	400.	700.	950.	2,200.	5,500.
1837	207,121	200.	300.	450.	700.	1,100.	2,500.	9,000.
1838	286,588	200.	300.	450.	725.	1,100.	2,500.	9,000.
1838C	17,179	800.	1,400.	3,000.	7,500.	9,500.	18,000.	45,000.
1838D	20,583	750.	1,400.	3,000.	6,000.	8,500.	17,000.	25,000.

LIBERTY HEAD (1839-1908)
Variety 1 - No Motto Above Eagle (1839-1866)

VF-20 VERY FINE—LIBERTY on coronet bold. Major lines show in curls on neck.
EF-40 EXTREMELY FINE—Details clear in curls on neck. Slight wear on top and lower part of coronet and on hair.
AU-50 ABOUT UNCIRCULATED—Trace of wear on coronet and hair above eye.
AU-55 CHOICE ABOUT UNCIRCULATED—Evidence of friction on design high points. Some original mint luster.
MS-60 UNCIRCULATED—No trace of wear. Light blemishes.
MS-63 CHOICE UNCIRCULATED—Some distracting contact marks or blemishes in prime focal areas. Impaired luster possible.
PF-63 CHOICE PROOF—Attractive reflective surfaces with only a few blemishes in secondary focal places. No major flaws.

Mintmark: 1839, above date; 1840-1908, below eagle.

	Mintage	VF-20	EF-40	AU-50	AU-55	MS-60	MS-63
1839	118,143	$185.	$325.	$800.	$1,250.	$2,750.	$16,000.
1839C	17,205	1,000.	1,875.	4,000.	5,750.	15,000.	45,000.

Chart continues on next page.

	Mintage	VF-20	EF-40	AU-50	AU-55	MS-60	MS-63	PF-63
1839D	18,939	$1,000.	$1,500.	$3,650.	$5,500.	$13,000.		
1840	137,382	160.	250.	875.	1,375.	2,600.	$7,500.	
1840C	18,992	1,000.	1,750.	4,750.	8,000.	17,500.	47,500.	
1840D	22,896	1,000.	1,450.	4,750.	5,250.	10,500.	33,500.	
1840O	40,120	220.	575.	1,275.	2,250.	7,000.	17,500.	
1841	15,833	260.	625.	1,250.	1,550.	3,550.	7,750.	$47,500.
1841C	21,467	950.	1,300.	2,150.	4,000.	11,500.	32,500.	
1841D	29,392	1,000.	1,300.	2,250.	4,000.	10,000.	19,000.	

1842, Large Date

Large Letters

Small Letters

	Mintage	VF-20	EF-40	AU-50	AU-55	MS-60	MS-63	PF-63
1842, Small Letters	27,578	$230.	$750.	$2,200.	$3,750.	$9,500.	$16,750.	$57,500.
1842, Large Letters	*	475.	1,400.	2,000.	3,250.	7,750.	17,500.	
1842C, Small Date	27,432	7,250.	16,500.	30,000.	40,000.	77,500.		
1842C, Large Date	*	950.	1,400.	2,350.	4,750.	12,000.	27,500.	
1842D, Small Date	59,608	1,000.	1,350.	2,200.	3,750.	10,500.	25,000.	
1842D, Large Date	*	1,675.	4,250.	10,000.	14,000.	34,000.		
1842O	16,400	700.	2,100.	6,750.	8,000.	16,000.	30,000.	
1843	611,205	150.	180.	250.	375.	1,200.	7,250.	
1843C	44,277	950.	1,300.	2,650.	3,750.	8,000.	24,000.	
1843D	98,452	1,000.	1,300.	2,250.	3,750.	8,000.	18,000.	
1843O, Small Letters	19,075	375.	1,000.	1,650.	3,250.	13,500.	28,000.	
1843O, Large Letters	82,000	200.	775.	1,375.	3,000.	8,500.	20,000.	
1844	340,330	150.	165.	260.	350.	1,400.	6,500.	
1844C	23,631	950.	2,100.	4,500.	6,000.	15,500.	30,000.	
1844D	88,982	1,000.	1,550.	2,450.	3,500.	7,500.	18,000.	
1844O	364,600	180.	265.	410.	1,000.	3,000.	10,000.	
1845	417,099	150.	165.	250.	425.	1,450.	6,500.	
1845D	90,629	1,000.	1,300.	2,250.	3,250.	8,250.	19,000.	
1845O	41,000	275.	475.	1,900.	3,000.	7,000.	19,500.	
1846, Large Date	395,942	150.	165.	250.	425.	1,750.	9,500.	
1846, Small Date	*	150.	165.	250.	425.	1,750.	9,500.	
1846C	12,995	1,000.	2,000.	4,500.	5,500.	16,000.	50,000.	
1846D	80,294	1,000.	1,450.	2,500.	3,250.	9,000.	16,500.	
1846O	58,000	265.	675.	2,200.	3,250.	8,250.	20,000.	
1847	915,981	150.	170.	230.	325.	1,000.	5,250.	
1847C	84,151	950.	1,350.	2,400.	3,000.	9,250.	19,500.	
1847D	64,405	1,000.	1,350.	2,200.	3,250.	7,250.	13,500.	
1847O	12,000	1,300.	5,000.	6,750.	9,000.	18,000.	26,500.	
1848	260,775	155.	190.	290.	400.	1,050.	8,500.	
1848C	64,472	950.	1,350.	2,500.	4,750.	14,000.	36,000.	
1848D	47,465	1,000.	1,350.	2,200.	3,750.	10,000.	21,000.	
1849	133,070	150.	185.	500.	800.	1,900.	9,500.	
1849C	64,823	950.	1,350.	2,100.	4,000.	9,500.	20,000.	
1849D	39,036	1,000.	1,350.	2,300.	3,500.	9,500.	22,000.	
1850	64,491	190.	425.	750.	850.	2,600.	13,500.	
1850C	63,591	950.	1,350.	2,100.	2,500.	8,500.	17,000.	
1850D	43,984	1,000.	1,300.	2,800.	5,500.	22,000.		

* Included in number above.

	Mintage	VF-20	EF-40	AU-50	AU-55	MS-60	MS-63	PF-63
1851	377,505	$150.	$165.	$250.	$500.	$2,000.	$7,250.	
1851C	49,176	950.	1,300.	2,250.	4,750.	11,000.	37,500.	
1851D	62,710	1,000.	1,300.	2,200.	4,250.	10,000.	19,500.	
1851O	41,000	400.	1,000.	2,750.	4,250.	9,500.	14,000.	
1852	573,901	150.	170.	230.	375.	850.	5,000.	
1852C	72,574	950.	1,350.	2,100.	2,400.	5,000.	17,000.	
1852D	91,584	1,000.	1,350.	2,200.	3,750.	9,000.	21,500.	
1853	305,770	150.	170.	250.	375.	1,000.	6,750.	
1853C	65,571	950.	1,350.	2,200.	3,100.	6,000.	20,000.	
1853D	89,678	1,000.	1,350.	2,200.	3,200.	7,250.	18,000.	
1854	160,675	150.	170.	360.	800.	1,450.	6,000.	
1854C	39,283	950.	1,350.	2,700.	3,500.	10,000.	35,000.	
1854D	56,413	1,000.	1,350.	2,200.	3,500.	7,500.	22,500.	
1854O	46,000	210.	370.	975.	1,650.	5,750.	14,500.	
1854S	268	—	—	250,000.	—			
1855	117,098	150.	165.	250.	400.	1,250.	6,200.	
1855C	39,788	950.	1,400.	2,300.	3,500.	11,000.	28,000.	
1855D	22,432	1,000.	1,350.	2,250.	3,500.	12,000.	31,000.	
1855O	11,100	425.	1,500.	3,250.	4,500.	14,500.		
1855S	61,000	275.	650.	1,550.	3,750.	11,000.		
1856	197,990	150.	170.	230.	400.	1,600.	8,000.	
1856C	28,457	950.	1,300.	2,300.	4,100.	14,500.		
1856D	19,786	1,000.	1,300.	2,600.	3,750.	7,750.	28,500.	
1856O	10,000	450.	850.	3,250.	4,500.	8,750.		
1856S	105,100	215.	425.	875.	1,750.	4,750.	21,500.	
1857	98,188	150.	170.	275.	400.	1,100.	5,500.	
1857C	31,360	950.	1,300.	2,250.	3,500.	6,250.	24,000.	
1857D	17,046	1,000.	1,300.	2,500.	3,500.	9,250.	30,000.	
1857O	13,000	450.	975.	3,250.	4,250.	10,000.	39,000.	
1857S	87,000	215.	375.	800.	2,000.	6,750.	13,500.	
1858	15,136	170.	375.	500.	950.	2,750.	6,500.	
1858C	38,856	950.	1,350.	2,200.	3,250.	7,250.	27,500.	
1858D	15,362	1,000.	1,350.	2,200.	3,750.	8,750.	30,000.	
1858S	18,600	475.	1,600.	3,850.	8,000.	21,500.		
1859 (80)	16,734	225.	425.	575.	1,200.	5,000.	8,000.	$28,000.
1859C	31,847	950.	1,350.	2,650.	3,750.	10,500.	35,000.	
1859D	10,366	1,000.	1,350.	2,250.	4,250.	10,000.	29,000.	
1859S	13,220	875.	2,500.	3,750.	5,750.	20,000.		
1860 (62)	19,763	190.	400.	775.	950.	2,800.	11,500.	22,000.
1860C	14,813	950.	1,500.	2,300.	4,000.	9,250.	20,000.	
1860D	14,635	1,000.	1,450.	2,500.	5,000.	12,000.	36,000.	
1860S	21,200	750.	1,500.	4,000.	7,250.	18,000.		
1861 (66)	688,084	150.	175.	255.	375.	850.	2,150.	21,000.
1861C	6,879	1,400.	2,800.	5,500.	8,000.	17,000.	70,000.	
1861D	1,597	3,500.	6,000.	13,000.	19,000.	38,000.	95,000.	
1861S	18,000	600.	3,000.	4,000.	5,500.	22,500.		
1862 (35)	4,430	350.	1,000.	2,000.	2,750.	10,000.	25,000.	21,000.
1862S	9,500	2,000.	4,500.	10,000.	16,000.	40,000.		
1863 (30)	2,442	750.	2,500.	4,000.	5,500.	15,000.		21,000.
1863S	17,000	850.	2,500.	6,500.	8,000.	18,000.		
1864 (50)	4,170	400.	1,250.	2,750.	3,500.	8,000.		21,000.
1864S	3,888	3,500.	9,000.	2,000.	25,000.	40,000.		
1865 (25)	1,270	750.	1,500.	5,500.	6,750.	10,000.		18,000.
1865S	27,612	650.	1,500.	2,500.	3,500.	10,000.	15,000.	
1866S	9,000	1,000.	2,200.	6,500.	9,000.	22,500.		

Variety 2 – Motto Above Eagle (1866–1908)

VF-20 VERY FINE—Half of hair lines above coronet missing. Hair curls under ear evident, but worn. Motto and its ribbon sharp.

EF-40 EXTREMELY FINE—Small amount of wear on top of hair and below L in LIBERTY. Wear evident on wing tips and neck of eagle.

AU-50 ABOUT UNCIRCULATED—Trace of wear on tip of coronet and hair above eye.

AU-55 CHOICE ABOUT UNCIRCULATED—Evidence of friction on design high points. Some original mint luster present.

MS-60 UNCIRCULATED—No trace of wear. Light blemishes.

MS-63 CHOICE UNCIRCULATED—Some distracting contact marks or blemishes in prime focal areas. Impaired luster possible.

PF-63 CHOICE PROOF—Reflective surfaces with only a few blemishes in secondary focal places. No major flaws.

	Mintage	VF-20	EF-40	AU-50	AU-55	MS-60	MS-63	PF-63
1866 . . . .(30)	6,700	$400.	$900.	$2,000.	$2,500.	$8,000.		$13,000.
1866S	34,920	500.	1,500.	4,500.	5,500.	14,000.		
1867 . . . .(50)	6,870	250.	900.	2,000.	2,500.	6,500.		12,500.
1867S	29,000	750.	1,550.	4,500.	6,000.	15,000.		
1868 . . . .(25)	5,700	400.	650.	1,500.	2,000.	6,000.		13,000.
1868S	52,000	250.	1,000.	1,900.	2,500.	10,000.		
1869 . . . .(25)	1,760	500.	1,250.	1,700.	2,200.	8,500.		13,000.
1869S	31,000	300.	1,000.	1,700.	2,500.	15,000.		
1870 . . . .(35)	4,000	400.	1,200.	1,200.	1,800.	8,500.		13,000.
1870CC	7,675	3,000.	9,000.	17,500.	22,000.			
1870S	17,000	450.	1,500.	4,500.	6,000.	18,000.		
1871 . . . .(30)	3,200	500.	850.	1,850.	2,500.	8,000.		12,000.
1871CC	20,770	750.	2,250.	8,000.	12,000.	40,000.		
1871S	25,000	250.	500.	1,500.	2,000.	7,500.		
1872 . . . .(30)	1,660	450.	1,000.	1,500.	2,000.	7,500.	$10,000.	12,000.
1872CC	16,980	850.	3,200.	13,000.	18,000.	40,000.		
1872S	36,400	250.	350.	1,500.	1,850.	7,500.		
1873 . . . .(25) . . .	112.505	115.	150.	200.	225.	450.	2,200.	12,000.
1873CC	7,416	1,500.	8,000.	16,000.	23,000.	40,000.		
1873S	31,000	250.	750.	1,850.	2,150.	10,000.		
1874 . . . .(20)	3,488	300.	850.	1,250.	1,500.	6,500.	12,500.	12,000.
1874CC	21,198	500.	1,200.	6,000.	7,500.	25,000.		
1874S	16,000	300.	1,200.	2,500.	3,000.	11,000.		
1875 . . . .(20)	200	22,000.	30,000.	40,000.	50,000.			45,000.
1875CC	11,828	900.	2,500.	7,500.	11,000.	35,000.		
1875S	9,000	300.	1,100.	2,800.	4,200.	12,000.		
1876 . . . .(45)	1,432	675.	1,300.	2,000.	3,000.	6,500.	13,000.	10,000.
1876CC	6,887	800.	3,500.	8,500.	10,500.	27,500.		
1876S	4,000	850.	1,800.	5,000.	6,000.	12,500.		
1877 . . . .(20)	1,132	500.	1,500.	2,000.	2,750.	7,000.	15,000.	13,000.
1877CC	8,680	600.	2,000.	6,500.	8,500.	30,000.		
1877S	26,700	200.	250.	700.	800.	4,000.	10,000.	
1878 . . . .(20) . . .	131,720	100.	115.	150.	160.	225.	1,000.	15,000.
1878CC	9,054	1,700.	5,200.	13,000.	17,000.	40,000.		
1878S	144,700	100.	120.	155.	165.	300.	2,000.	
1879 . . . .(30) . . .	301,920	100.	115.	145.	160.	225.	1,000.	12,000.
1879CC	17,281	300.	950.	2,250.	3,500.	14,000.		
1879S	426,200	100.	115.	145.	160.	400.	1,500.	
1880 . . . .(36) . .	3,166,400	100.	115.	125.	135.	160.	600.	10,000.
1880CC	51,017	300.	500.	1,000.	2,000.	6,500.		
1880S	1,348,900	100.	120.	125.	130.	150.	525.	
1881 . . . .(42) . .	5,708,760	100.	120.	125.	130.	150.	525.	9,500.
1881CC	13,886	350.	850.	4,000.	5,500.	17,000.	40,000.	

HALF EAGLES

	Mintage	VF-20	EF-40	AU-50	AU-55	MS-60	MS-63	PF-63
1881S	969,000	$100.	$120.	$125.	$130.	$150.	$525.	
1882	(48)...2,514,520	100.	120.	125.	130.	150.	525.	$9,500.
1882CC	82,817	250.	400.	500.	650.	5,000.	25,000.	
1882S	969,000	100.	120.	125.	130.	150.	525.	
1883	(61)....233,400	100.	120.	125.	130.	150.	800.	9,500.
1883CC	12,598	300.	750.	2,000.	3,000.	11,000.		
1883S	83,200	100.	120.	150.	175.	450.	1,500.	
1884	(48)....191,030	100.	120.	125.	160.	400.	1,480.	9,500.
1884CC	16,402	350.	600.	1,800.	2,500.	11,000.		
1884S	177,000	100.	120.	125.	135.	180.	1,260.	
1885	(66)....601,440	100.	120.	125.	130.	150.	525.	9,500.
1885S	1,211,500	100.	120.	125.	130.	150.	500.	
1886	(72)....388,360	100.	120.	125.	130.	150.	650.	9,200.
1886S	3,268,000	100.	120.	125.	130.	150.	500.	
1887, Proof Only	(87)							32,500.
1887S	1,912,000	100.	120.	125.	130.	150.	525.	
1888	(95)....18,201	100.	120.	125.	130.	160.	800.	7,500.
1888S	293,900	100.	130.	185.	225.	750.	2,500.	
1889	(45)......7,520	160.	220.	285.	320.	750.	1,300.	8,500.
1890	(88)......4,240	240.	265.	340.	500.	1,250.	4,000.	8,500.
1890CC	53,800	180.	210.	320.	350.	750.	3,500.	
1891	(53)....61,360	100.	130.	150.	185.	280.	1,000.	8,500.
1891CC	208,000	175.	210.	325.	340.	425.	2,100.	
1892	(92)....753,480	100.	115.	120.	125.	150.	500.	8,500.
1892CC	82,968	175.	210.	360.	420.	1,000.	3,500.	
1892O	10,000	280.	580.	800.	1,000.	2,200.	7,000.	
1892S	298,400	100.	115.	150.	175.	285.	2,000.	
1893	(77)...1,528,120	100.	115.	120.	125.	150.	500.	8,500.
1893CC	60,000	160.	250.	400.	485.	850.	4,000.	
1893O	110,000	135.	180.	285.	350.	600.	3,800.	
1893S	224,000	100.	115.	120.	130.	150.	600.	
1894	(75)....957,880	100.	115.	120.	125.	150.	500.	8,500.
1894O	16,600	120.	200.	310.	375.	820.	3,250.	
1894S	55,900	150.	215.	315.	380.	1,800.	6,400.	
1895	(81)...1,345,855	100.	110.	120.	125.	150.	500.	7,200.
1895S	112,000	120.	150.	235.	310.	2,000.	3,750.	
1896	(103)....58,960	100.	110.	120.	125.	150.	600.	7,200.
1896S	155,400	120.	145.	175.	240.	685.	3,600.	
1897	(83)....867,800	100.	110.	115.	120.	150.	500.	7,200.
1897S	354,000	110.	125.	145.	200.	550.	3,300.	
1898	(75)....633,420	100.	110.	115.	120.	150.	500.	7,200.
1898S	1,397,400	100.	115.	125.	130.	160.	600.	
1899	(99)...1,710,630	100.	110.	115.	120.	150.	500.	7,200.
1899S	1,545,000	100.	110.	120.	125.	160.	600.	
1900	(230)...1,405,500	100.	110.	115.	120.	150.	500.	7,200.
1900S	329,000	100.	110.	120.	130.	160.	550.	
1901	(140)....615,900	100.	110.	115.	120.	150.	500.	7,200.
1901S, 1 Over 0	3,648,000	110.	125.	140.	160.	200.	550.	
1901S	*	100.	110.	120.	125.	150.	500.	
1902	(162)....172,400	100.	110.	120.	125.	150.	500.	7,200.
1902S	939,000	100.	110.	120.	125.	150.	500.	
1903	(154)....226,870	100.	110.	120.	125.	150.	500.	7,200.
1903S	1,855,000	100.	110.	120.	125.	150.	500.	
1904	(136)....392,000	100.	110.	120.	125.	150.	500.	7,200.
1904S	97,000	100.	130.	160.	200.	600.	2,500.	
1905	(108)....302,200	100.	110.	120.	125.	150.	500.	7,200.
1905S	880,700	100.	120.	135.	175.	350.	950.	
1906	(85)....348,735	100.	110.	115.	120.	150.	500.	7,200.
1906D	320,000	100.	110.	115.	120.	150.	500.	
1906S	598,000	100.	110.	120.	125.	160.	600.	
1907	(92)....626,100	100.	110.	115.	120.	150.	500.	7,200.
1907D	888,000	100.	110.	115.	120.	150.	500.	
1908	421,874	100.	110.	115.	120.	150.	500.	

* Included in number above.

INDIAN HEAD (1908–1929)

This type conforms in design to the quarter eagle of the same date. The incuse designs and lettering make the Indian Head a unique series, along with the quarter eagle, in United States coinage.

VF-20 VERY FINE—Noticeable wear on large middle feathers and tip of eagle's wing.
EF-40 EXTREMELY FINE—Cheekbone, war bonnet, and headband feathers slightly worn. Feathers on eagle's upper wing show considerable wear.
AU-50 ABOUT UNCIRCULATED—Trace of wear on cheekbone and headdress.
AU-55 CHOICE ABOUT UNCIRCULATED—Evidence of friction on design high points. Much of original mint luster present.
MS-60 UNCIRCULATED—No trace of wear. Light blemishes.
MS-63 CHOICE UNCIRCULATED—Some distracting contact marks or blemishes in prime focal areas. Impaired luster possible.
MATTE PF-63—Matte surfaces with only a few blemishes in secondary focal places. No major flaws.

Mintmark Location

Scarcer coins with well struck mintmarks command higher prices.

	Mintage	VF-20	EF-40	AU-50	AU-55	MS-60	MS-63	MATTE PF-63
1908 . . . .(167) . . .	577,845	$125.	$135.	$150.	$160.	$235.	$1,400.	$7,000.
1908D	148,000	125.	135.	150.	160.	235.	1,400.	
1908S	82,000	200.	240.	260.	285.	750.	1,800.	
1909 . . . .(78) . . .	627,060	125.	135.	150.	160.	235.	1,400.	7,500.
1909D	3,423,560	125.	135.	150.	160.	235.	1,400.	
1909O	34,200	975.	1,300.	1,900.	2,200.	6,500.	32,000.	
1909S	297,200	150.	160.	185.	220.	800.	7,000.	
1910 . . . .(250) . . .	604,000	125.	135.	150.	160.	235.	1,400.	7,500.
1910D	193,600	135.	145.	165.	175.	250.	1,800.	
1910S	770,200	165.	180.	195.	220.	600.	3,500.	
1911 . . . .(139) . . .	915,000	125.	135.	150.	160.	235.	1,400.	7,200.
1911D	72,500	260.	285.	350.	480.	2,400.	23,000.	
1911S	1,416,000	160.	170.	185.	200.	375.	1,800.	
1912 . . . .(144) . . .	790,000	125.	135.	150.	160.	235.	1,400.	7,200.
1912S	392,000	185.	200.	220.	300.	1,100.	9,400.	
1913 . . . .(99) . . .	915,901	125.	135.	150.	160.	235.	1,400.	7,200.
1913S	408,000	165.	180.	250.	280.	850.	9,000.	
1914 . . . .(125) . . .	247,000	125.	135.	150.	160.	235.	1,400.	7,200.
1914D	247,000	130.	140.	160.	170.	245.	1,900.	
1914S	263,000	185.	200.	220.	250.	725.	8,500.	
1915 . . . .(75) . . .	588,000	125.	135.	150.	160.	235.	1,400.	10,000.
1915S	164,000	175.	220.	245.	360.	1,275.	11,500.	
1916S	240,000	180.	195.	210.	225.	380.	1,740.	
1929	662,000	3,500.	4,000.	4,400.	4,500.	5,000.	7,000.	

Coinage authority including specified weights and fineness of the eagle conforms to that of the half eagle. The small eagle reverse was used until 1797, when the large, heraldic eagle replaced it.

CAPPED BUST TO RIGHT (1795–1804)

F-12 FINE—Details on turban and head obliterated.
VF-20 VERY FINE—Hair lines in curls on neck and details under turban and over forehead worn but distinguishable.
EF-40 EXTREMELY FINE—Definite wear on hair to left of eye and strand of hair across and around turban, as well as on eagle's wing tips.
AU-50 ABOUT UNCIRCULATED—Trace of wear on cap, hair, cheek, and drapery
AU-55 CHOICE ABOUT UNCIRCULATED—Evidence of friction on design high points. Most of original mint luster present.
MS-60 UNCIRCULATED—No trace of wear. Light blemishes.
MS-63 CHOICE UNCIRCULATED—Some distracting contact marks or blemishes in prime focal areas. Impaired luster possible.

Small Eagle (1795–1797)

	Mintage	F-12	VF-20	EF-40	AU-50	AU-55	MS-60	MS-63
1795	5,583	$10,000.	$14,000.	$16,000.	$25,000.	$30,000.	$45,000.	$75,000.
1796	4,146	11,000.	16,000.	20,000.	27,000.	32,000.	50,000.	90,000.
1797, Small Eagle	3,615	17,000.	20,000.	25,000.	50,000.	65,000.	135,000.	

Heraldic Eagle (1797–1804)

	Mintage	F-12	VF-20	EF-40	AU-50	AU-55	MS-60	MS-63
1797, Large Eagle	10,940	$5,000.	$6,500.	$7,500.	$13,000.	$16,000.	$21,000.	$45,000.
1798, 8/7, 9 Stars Left, 4 Rt	900	6,000.	9,000.	17,000.	25,000.	32,000.	6,000.	165,000.
1798, 8/7, 7 Stars Left, 6 Rt	842	11,000.	19,000.	40,000.	85,000.	100,000.	150,000.	
1799	37,449	4,500.	6,000.	6,500.	9,000.	12,000.	15,000.	22,000.
1800	5,999	4,500.	6,000.	6,500.	9,500.	13,000.	19,000.	42,000.

See next page for chart.

	Mintage	F-12	VF-20	EF-40	AU-50	AU-55	MS-60	MS-63
1801	44,344	$4,500.	$6,000.	$6,500.	$9,000.	$12,000.	$15,000.	$22,000.
1803	15,017	4,500.	6,000.	6,500.	10,000.	12,500.	16,000.	35,000.
1804	3,757	5,000.	6,500.	7,000.	15,000.	17,000.	25,000.	75,000.

LIBERTY HEAD, NO MOTTO ABOVE EAGLE (1838–1866)

In 1838 the weight and diameter of the eagle were reduced and the obverse and reverse were redesigned. Liberty now faced left and the word LIBERTY was placed on the coronet.

VF-20 VERY FINE—Hair lines above coronet partly worn. Curls under ear worn but defined.

EF-40 EXTREMELY FINE—Small amount of wear on top of hair and below L in LIBERTY. Wear evident on wing tips and neck of eagle.

AU-50 ABOUT UNCIRCULATED—Trace of wear on tip of coronet and hair above eye.

AU-55 CHOICE ABOUT UNCIRCULATED—Evidence of friction on design high points. Some of original mint luster present.

MS-60 UNCIRCULATED—No trace of wear. Light blemishes.

MS-63 CHOICE UNCIRCULATED—Some distracting contact marks or blemishes in prime focal areas. Impaired luster possible.

PF-63 CHOICE PROOF—Attractive reflective surfaces with only a few blemishes in secondary focal places. No major flaws.

Mintmark is on reverse, below eagle.

	Mintage	VF-20	EF-40	AU-50	AU-55	MS-60	MS-63	PF-63
1838	7,200	$560.	$1,575.	$3,400.	$4,800.	$22,000.	$60,000.	
1839, Large Letters	25,801	560.	1,075.	3,000.	4,000.	20,000.	36,000.	
1839, Small Letters	12,447	775.	1,950.	4,000.	5,200.	22,000.	64,000.	
1840	47,338	225.	350.	800.	1,000.	6,800.		
1841	63,131	225.	340.	640.	800.	5,000.	18,000.	
1841O	2,500	1,120.	2,700.	7,200.	9,600.	22,000.		
1842	81,507	225.	290.	700.	1,000.	6,800.	18,000.	
1842O	27,400	225.	340.	1,400.	2,000.	11,700.		
1843	75,462	225.	340.	800.	1,200.	7,500.		
1843O	175,162	225.	320.	620.	800.	7,200.		
1844	6,361	580.	1,640.	3,200.	4,000.	10,800.		
1844O	118,700	225.	340.	1,040.	1,240.	9,800.		
1845	26,153	360.	440.	1,260.	1,500.	10,000.		
1845O	47,500	250.	425.	1,120.	1,400.	9,400.	30,000.	
1846	20,095	385.	560.	3,200.	4,200.	15,800.		
1846O	81,780	280.	400.	2,000.	2,520.	10,800.	27,000.	
1847	862,258	225.	290.	320.	400.	2,100.	16,500.	
1847O	571,500	225.	290.	340.	420.	3,750.	14,000.	
1848	145,484	225.	300.	480.	580.	3,420.	18,000.	$135,000.
1848O	35,850	400.	750.	2,000.	2,480.	9,400.	20,000.	
1849	653,618	225.	300.	340.	400.	2,400.	9,200.	
1849O	23,900	275.	1,360.	3,200.	3,980.	15,800.		
1850	291,451	250.	270.	340.	425.	2,650.	12,600.	
1850O	57,500	275.	450.	1,960.	2,420.	11,300.		
1851	176,328	250.	285.	350.	460.	3,160.	21,200.	
1851O	263,000	240.	280.	560.	680.	4,160.	15,600.	
1852	263,106	225.	270.	335.	460.	3,160.	18,000.	
1852O	18,000	400.	620.	2,280.	4,000.	11,000.		
1853, 3 Over 2	201,253	350.	460.	1,100.	1,380.	10,400.		
1853	*	225.	270.	340.	420.	2,600.	13,100.	
1853O	51,000	240.	285.	600.	985.	9,100.		
1854	54,250	230.	310.	440.	560.	4,360.		
1854O	52,500	225.	425.	960.	1,160.	6,260.	25,000.	
1854S	123,826	230.	270.	495.	680.	7,160.	28,000.	

* Included in number above.

EAGLES

	Mintage	VF-20	EF-40	AU-50	AU-55	MS-60	MS-63	PF-63
1855	121,701	$225.	$275.	$340.	$425.	$2,660.	$12,300.	
1855O	18,000	400.	800.	3,400.	4,020.	15,600.		
1855S	9,000	900.	1,360.	4,460.	5,340.	22,400.		
1856	60,490	225.	300.	350.	425.	2,650.	9,100.	
1856O	14,500	450.	800.	2,300.	2,800.	11,500.		
1856S	68,000	230.	450.	640.	785.	6,680.		
1857	16,606	275.	600.	1,160.	1,385.	9,280.		
1857O	5,500	500.	1,140.	1,975.	2,380.	13,800.		
1857S	26,000	300.	500.	1,260.	1,340.	7,725.	10,800.	
1858	2,521	3,200.	4,500.	6,500.	8,000.	27,000.		
1858O	20,000	225.	460.	1,020.	1,235.	6,185.		
1858S	11,800	900.	1,875.	3,320.	4,020.	19,800.		
1859	(80)....16,013	225.	390.	625.	780.	5,880.		$39,000.
1859O	2,300	3,000.	4,500.	8,900.	10,000.	33,000.		
1859S	7,000	1,200.	3,000.	7,500.	9,000.	30,000.		
1860	(50)....15,055	270.	410.	720.	900.	5,200.	11,300.	28,000.
1860O	11,100	350.	800.	1,380.	1,680.	8,800.		
1860S	5,000	1,500.	3,200.	9,200.	10,800.	28,000.		
1861	(69)...113,164	225.	270.	310.	360.	1,920.		26,000.
1861S	15,500	900.	2,000.	3,480.	4,200.	22,000.		
1862	(35)....10,960	350.	650.	1,325.	1,485.	7,600.		26,000.
1862S	12,500	1,000.	1,910.	3,080.	3,720.	24,000.		
1863	(30)....1,218	2,500.	5,000.	10,000.	12,000.	33,000.	60,000.	28,000.
1863S	10,000	900.	2,060.	4,985.	5,260.	15,600.		
1864	(50)....3,530	1,200.	2,200.	4,420.	5,280.	9,200.		28,000.
1864S	2,500	3,000.	6,590.	15,800.	17,800.	36,000.		
1865	(25)....3,980	1,100.	1,900.	4,500.	5,000.	25,000.		28,000.
1865S	16,700	2,000.	5,125.	9,600.	11,400.	31,000.		
1866S	8,500	1,100.	2,300.	7,500.	9,000.	30,000.		

LIBERTY HEAD, MOTTO ABOVE EAGLE (1866–1907)

VF-20 VERY FINE—Half of hair lines over coronet visible. Curls under ear worn but defined. IN GOD WE TRUST and its ribbon sharp.

EF-40 EXTREMELY FINE—Small amount of wear on top of hair and below L in LIBERTY. Wear evident on wing tips and neck of eagle.

AU-50 ABOUT UNCIRCULATED—Trace of wear on hair above eye and on coronet.

AU-55 CHOICE ABOUT UNCIRCULATED—Evidence of friction on design high points. Some of original mint luster present.

MS-60 UNCIRCULATED—No trace of wear. Light blemishes.

MS-63 CHOICE UNCIRCULATED—Some distracting contact marks or blemishes in prime focal areas. Impaired luster possible.

PF-63 CHOICE PROOF—Reflective surfaces with only a few blemishes in secondary focal areas. No major flaws.

Mintmark is on reverse, below eagle.

	Mintage	VF-20	EF-40	AU-50	AU-55	MS-60	MS-63	PF-63
1866	(30)....3,750	$500.	$1,020.	$2,720.	$3,260.	$14,500.		$21,500.
1866S	11,500	900.	2,025.	4,085.	4,900.	16,500.		
1867	(50)....3,090	1,000.	1,475.	2,920.	3,600.	19,000.		22,500.
1867S	9,000	1,500.	3,490.	5,100.	6,200.	29,750.		
1868	(25)...10,630	350.	500.	945.	1,120.	9,100.		23,800.
1868S	13,500	900.	1,275.	2,200.	3,450.	17,000.		
1869	(25)....1,830	1,000.	1,600.	2,880.	3,460.	23,400.		21,500.
1869S	6,430	900.	1,500.	3,385.	4,025.	16,000.		
1870	(35)....3,990	600.	700.	1,250.	1,460.	12,300.		21,500.
1870CC	5,908	5,500.	16,000.	30,000.	35,000.	70,000.	$112,000.	
1870S	8,000	600.	1,500.	3,620.	4,200.	24,600.		

Chart continues on next page.

	Mintage	VF-20	EF-40	AU-50	AU-55	MS-60	MS-63	PF-63
1871 . . . .(30) 1,790		$900.	$1,700.	$2,485.	$2,750.	$12,750.		$22,800.
1871CC. 8,085		1,300.	3,200.	9,500.	11,260.	42,900.	$54,000.	
1871S. 16,500		625.	925.	3,425.	4,040.	18,800.		
1872 . . . .(30) 1,620		1,500.	2,100.	6,000.	7,250.	10,200.	23,000.	21,500.
1872CC. 4,600		1,400.	5,000.	14,000.	16,900.	43,000.	54,000.	
1872S. 17,300		400.	550.	1,060.	1,260.	14,400.		
1873 . . . .(25) 800		3,000.	6,500.	10,000.	12,000.	35,000.		
1873CC. 4,543		2,200.	6,400.	14,500.	18,000.	45,000.	54,000.	
1873S. 12,000		600.	1,000.	2,700.	3,500.	20,000.		
1874 . . . .(20) 53,140		210.	240.	250.	270.	1,200.	5,000.	23,800.
1874CC. 16,767		575.	1,500.	4,800.	5,800.	30,000.	53,000.	
1874S. 10,000		750.	2,100.	4,000.	5,600.	30,000.		
1875 . . . .(20) 100		27,000.	32,000.	42,000.				80,000.
1875CC. 7,715		2,200.	5,500.	14,000.	16,750.	47,000.	63,000.	
1876 . . . .(45). 687		1,900.	4,000.	7,600.	8,900.	38,000.		19,000.
1876CC. 4,696		2,000.	4,200.	11,200.	13,000.	38,000.	50,000.	
1876S. 5,000		850.	1,000.	3,225.	3,800.	27,600.		
1877 . . . .(20). 797		1,500.	3,000.	4,500.	5,300.	20,400.		19,000.
1877CC. 3,332		1,500.	3,000.	8,000.	9,860.	34,000.		
1877S. 17,000		350.	550.	1,160.	1,380.	16,600.		
1878 . . . .(20). 73,780		225.	245.	260.	290.	575.	3,400.	19,000.
1878CC. 3,244		2,000.	5,500.	11,200.	14,500.	34,000.		
1878S. 26,100		325.	400.	965.	1,125.	8,500.	20,000.	
1879 . . . .(30) 384,740		210.	240.	250.	275.	375.	2,680.	16,600.
1879CC. 1,762		3,500.	7,500.	14,000.	16,600.	47,000.		
1879O. 1,500		1,200.	2,750.	5,125.	6,200.	21,750.		
1879S. 224,000		210.	225.	235.	250.	675.	3,960.	
1880 . . . .(36) . . . 1,644,840		210.	220.	230.	240.	250.	2,000.	15,200.
1880CC. 11,190		325.	500.	925.	1,085.	8,920.		
1880O. 9,200		250.	450.	820.	975.	5,100.		
1880S. 506,250		200.	210.	220.	230.	260.	2,500.	
1881 . . . .(40) . . . 3,877,220		200.	210.	220.	230.	240.	800.	15,200.
1881CC. 24,015		300.	400.	580.	685.	3,900.	14,400.	
1881O. 8,350		250.	430.	675.	800.	4,700.		
1881S. 970,000		200.	210.	220.	230.	240.	2,400.	
1882 . . . .(40) . . . 2,324,440		200.	210.	220.	230.	240.	700.	13,300.
1882CC. 6,764		400.	640.	1,800.	2,100.	9,900.	18,000.	
1882O. 10,820		275.	375.	720.	850.	3,900.	12,900.	
1882S. 132,000		200.	210.	225.	245.	350.	1,800.	
1883 . . . .(40) 208,700		200.	210.	220.	230.	240.	1,650.	13,300.
1883CC. 12,000		350.	550.	1,320.	1,460.	8,900.	27,000.	
1883O. 800		1,600.	4,750.	6,500.	7,500.	22,500.		
1883S. 38,000		200.	240.	250.	270.	600.	7,200.	
1884 . . . .(45) 76,860		200.	210.	220.	230.	290.	2,500.	13,300.
1884CC. 9,925		350.	600.	1,350.	1,575.	7,860.	25,000.	
1884S. 124,250		200.	210.	220.	230.	320.	3,380.	
1885 . . . .(65) 253,462		200.	210.	220.	230.	250.	2,650.	11,400.
1885S. 228,000		200.	210.	220.	230.	250.	2,800.	
1886 . . . .(60) 236,100		200.	210.	220.	230.	250.	1,700.	10,900.
1886S. 826,000		200.	210.	220.	230.	250.	900.	
1887 . . . .(80) 53,600		200.	210.	220.	230.	425.	2,600.	10,900.
1887S. 817,000		200.	210.	220.	230.	240.	1,600.	
1888 . . . .(75) 132,921		200.	210.	220.	240.	400.	3,160.	10,500.
1888O. 21,335		200.	210.	220.	240.	400.	3,160.	
1888S. 648,700		200.	210.	220.	240.	250.	1,980.	
1889 . . . .(45) 4,440		290.	350.	600.	800.	1,600.	5,000.	10,500.
1889S. 425,400		200.	210.	220.	230.	240.	1,400.	
1890 . . . .(63) 57,980		200.	210.	230.	250.	450.	3,200.	8,500.
1890CC. 17,500		335.	360.	380.	550.	1,250.	9,000.	
1891 . . . .(48) 91,820		200.	210.	230.	230.	240.	2,650.	8,500.
1891CC. 103,732		235.	270.	340.	375.	475.	3,160.	
1892 . . . .(72) 797,480		200.	210.	230.	230.	235.	1,125.	8,500.
1892CC. 40,000		235.	280.	400.	485.	2,125.	5,860.	
1892O. 28,688		200.	210.	230.	240.	255.	3,600.	
1892S. 115,500		200.	210.	220.	230.	250.	2,600.	
1893 . . . .(55) . . . 1,840,840		200.	210.	220.	230.	235.	720.	8,500.

	Mintage	VF-20	EF-40	AU-50	AU-55	MS-60	MS-63	PF-63
1893CC	14,000	$325.	$500.	$900.	$1,450.	$3,500.	$11,250.	
1893O	17,000	200.	210.	260.	285.	410.	3,750.	
1893S	141,350	200.	210.	230.	235.	240.	3,000.	
1894 ....(43)	2,470,735	200.	210.	230.	235.	240.	700.	$8,500.
1894O	107,500	200.	210.	230.	230.	575.	3,500.	
1894S	25,000	200.	225.	460.	540.	2,340.	8,000.	
1895 ....(56)	567,770	200.	210.	230.	240.	250.	750.	8,500.
1895O	98,000	200.	210.	220.	245.	370.	2,750.	
1895S	49,000	200.	210.	300.	325.	1,530.	7,000.	
1896 ....(78)	76,270	200.	210.	220.	230.	270.	1,400.	8,500.
1896S	123,750	200.	210.	300.	375.	1,500.	7,500.	
1897 ....(69)	1,000,090	200.	210.	220.	230.	250.	700.	8,500.
1897O	42,500	200.	210.	220.	240.	550.	2,675.	
1897S	234,750	200.	210.	220.	240.	550.	2,500.	
1898 ....(67)	812,130	200.	210.	220.	230.	240.	1,120.	8,300.
1898S	473,600	200.	210.	220.	230.	240.	2,700.	
1899 ....(86)	1,262,219	200.	210.	220.	230.	240.	740.	8,300.
1899O	37,047	200.	210.	220.	240.	390.	3,000.	
1899S	841,000	200.	210.	220.	230.	260.	1,650.	
1900 ....(120)	293,840	200.	210.	220.	230.	260.	740.	8,300.
1900S	81,000	200.	210.	240.	280.	550.	3,100.	
1901 ....(85)	1,718,740	200.	210.	220.	230.	250.	700.	8,300.
1901O	72,041	200.	210.	220.	230.	240.	1,950.	
1901S	2,812,750	200.	210.	220.	230.	240.	700.	
1902 ....(113)	82,400	200.	210.	220.	230.	240.	700.	8,300.
1902S	469,500	200.	210.	220.	230.	240.	700.	
1903 ....(96)	125,830	200.	210.	220.	230.	240.	700.	8,300.
1903O	112,771	200.	210.	220.	250.	350.	2,400.	
1903S	538,000	200.	210.	220.	230.	240.	775.	
1904 ....(108)	161,930	200.	210.	220.	230.	240.	700.	8,300.
1904O	108,950	200.	210.	220.	230.	250.	2,040.	
1905 ....(86)	200,992	200.	210.	220.	230.	250.	860.	8,300.
1905S	369,250	200.	210.	230.	240.	650.	3,000.	
1906 ....(77)	165,420	200.	210.	220.	230.	240.	1,000.	8,300.
1906D	981,000	200.	210.	230.	240.	240.	750.	
1906O	86,895	200.	210.	230.	240.	250.	2,200.	
1906S	457,000	200.	210.	230.	250.	350.	2,500.	
1907 ....(74)	1,203,899	200.	210.	220.	230.	240.	700.	8,300.
1907D	1,030,000	200.	210.	220.	230.	240.	1,000.	
1907S	210,500	200.	210.	220.	250.	350.	2,400.	

INDIAN HEAD (1907–1933)

VF-20 VERY FINE—Bonnet feathers worn near band. Wear visible on high points of hair.

EF-40 EXTREMELY FINE—Slight wear on cheekbone and headdress feathers. Slight wear visible on eagle's eye and left wing.

AU-50 ABOUT UNCIRCULATED—Trace of wear on hair above eye and on forehead.

AU-55 CHOICE ABOUT UNCIRCULATED—Evidence of friction on design high points. Much of original mint luster present.

MS-60 UNCIRCULATED—No trace of wear. Light blemishes.

MS-63 CHOICE UNCIRCULATED—Some distracting contact marks or blemishes in prime focal areas. Impaired luster possible.

MATTE PF-63—Matte surfaces with only a few blemishes in secondary focal places. No major flaws.

No Motto
Mintmark is above left tip of branch on 1908-D No Motto.

See next page for chart.

With Motto IN GOD WE TRUST
Mintmark is at left of arrow points.

Gem Uncirculated (MS-65) coins are rare and worth substantial premiums.

	Mintage	VF-20	EF-40	AU-50	AU-55	MS-60	MS-63
1907, Wire Rim, Periods 500		$8,200.	$9,000.	$10,000.	$12,500.	$12,000.	$17,500.
1907, Rounded Rim, Periods Before							
and After E PLURIBUS UNUM 42		15,000.	17,000.	18,000.	19,000.	23,000.	39,000.
1907, No Periods................ 239,406		260.	270.	290.	300.	335.	1,700.
1908, No Motto 33,500		270.	280.	300.	310.	560.	2,700.
1908D, No Motto................ 210,000		260.	270.	290.	300.	510.	3,900.

Variety 2 – Motto on Reverse (1908–1933)

	Mintage	VF-20	EF-40	AU-50	AU-55	MS-60	MS-63	MATTE PF-63
1908 ....(116)... 341,370		$240.	$250.	$285.	$295.	$350.	$1,200.	$11,000.
1908D..................... 836,500		240.	250.	300.	320.	500.	4,050.	
1908S..................... 59,850		270.	280.	350.	385.	1,000.	5,600.	
1909 ....(74)... 184,789		240.	250.	285.	295.	350.	1,500.	11,000.
1909D..................... 121,540		240.	250.	285.	295.	360.	2,340.	
1909S..................... 292,350		240.	250.	285.	295.	410.	2,600.	
1910 ....(204)... 318,500		240.	250.	285.	295.	350.	760.	11,000.
1910D 2,356,640		240.	250.	285.	295.	350.	740.	
1910S 811,000		240.	250.	285.	295.	400.	1,200.	
1911 ....(95)... 505,500		240.	250.	285.	295.	350.	775.	11,000.
1911D..................... 30,100		400.	500.	560.	675.	2,400.	11,000.	
1911S..................... 51,000		360.	375.	435.	460.	725.	4,500.	
1912 ....(83)... 405,000		240.	250.	285.	295.	350.	750.	11,000.
1912S..................... 300,000		240.	250.	285.	300.	500.	3,500.	
1913 ....(71)... 442,000		240.	250.	285.	295.	350.	700.	11,000.
1913S..................... 66,000		400.	425.	560.	700.	2,300.	17,500.	
1914 ....(50)... 151,000		240.	250.	285.	300.	375.	1,260.	11,000.
1914D..................... 343,500		240.	250.	285.	300.	385.	1,280.	
1914S..................... 208,000		240.	250.	285.	305.	450.	1,400.	
1915 ....(75)... 351,000		240.	250.	285.	300.	385.	840.	11,000.
1915S..................... 59,000		375.	485.	560.	625.	1,900.	6,300.	
1916S..................... 138,500		240.	250.	300.	320.	495.	2,700.	
1920S..................... 126,500		4,000.	5,000.	5,500.	6,500.	12,000.	37,000.	
1926 1,014,000		240.	250.	285.	295.	350.	700.	
1930S..................... 96,000		3,200.	4,500.	5,500.	6,250.	7,000.	12,500.	
1932 4,463,000		240.	250.	285.	295.	350.	700.	
1933..................... 312,500		35,000.	45,000.	35,000.	65,000.	70,000.	125,000.	

This largest denomination of all regular United States issues was authorized to be coined by the Act of March 3, 1849. The coin's weight was set at 516 grains, and its fineness at .900. A single pattern of 1849 resides in the Smithsonian.

LIBERTY HEAD (1849–1907)

VF-20 VERY FINE—LIBERTY on crown bold; prongs on crown defined; lower half worn flat. Hair worn about ear.
EF-40 EXTREMELY FINE—Trace of wear on rounded prongs of crown and down hair curls. Minor bagmarks.
AU-50 ABOUT UNCIRCULATED—Trace of wear on hair over eye and on coronet.
AU-55 CHOICE ABOUT UNCIRCULATED—Evidence of friction on design high points. Some of original mint luster present.
MS-60 UNCIRCULATED—No trace of wear. Light blemishes.
MS-63 CHOICE UNCIRCULATED—Some distracting contact marks or blemishes in prime focal areas. Impaired luster possible.
PF-63 CHOICE PROOF—Reflective surfaces with only a few blemishes in secondary focal areas. No major flaws.

Without Motto on Reverse (1849–1866)

Mintmark is below eagle.

	Mintage	VF-20	EF-40	AU-50	AU-55	MS-60	MS-63	PF-63
1850	1,170,261	$450.	$635.	$1,525.	$1,800.	$4,100.	$30,000.	
1850O	141,000	470.	775.	4,400.	5,250.	20,000.		
1851	2,087,155	410.	420.	540.	650.	1,950.	12,500.	
1851O	315,000	420.	500.	960.	1,150.	10,600.		
1852	2,053,026	410.	420.	520.	635.	2,000.	8,600.	
1852O	190,000	420.	500.	1,075.	1,250.	10,000.		
1853	1,261,326	410.	420.	540.	640.	2,700.	13,800.	
1853O	71,000	415.	650.	1,500.	1,780.	16,000.		
1854	757,899	410.	420.	540.	680.	3,600.	13,800.	
1854O	3,250	20,000.	42,000.	65,000.	80,000.	160,000.		
1854S	141,468	415.	450.	710.	850.	2,200.	7,400.	
1855	364,666	410.	420.	635.	800.	4,800.		
1855O	8,000	1,275.	3,150.	9,600.	10,800.	44,000.		
1855S	879,675	410.	420.	600.	790.	4,250.	8,000.	
1856	329,878	410.	420.	610.	825.	5,200.	14,000.	
1856O	2,250	25,000.	50,000.	70,000.	80,000.	150,000.	300,000.	
1856S	1,189,750	410.	420.	650.	785.	3,400.	7,400.	
1857	439,375	410.	420.	540.	675.	2,000.	16,100.	
1857O	30,000	600.	1,000.	2,500.	3,000.	17,000.	75,000.	
1857S	970,500	400.	425.	575.	800.	2,600.	5,000.	
1858	211,714	450.	500.	680.	780.	2,900.	22,000.	
1858O	35,250	850.	1,200.	2,700.	3,100.	16,000.		
1858S	846,710	410.	450.	550.	780.	5,600.		
1859	(80) 43,597	525.	1,160.	2,300.	2,800.	18,000.		$55,000.
1859O	9,100	2,000.	4,200.	10,000.	12,000.	50,000.		
1859S	636,445	410.	450.	560.	760.	2,900.		
1860	(59) 577,670	410.	450.	535.	585.	2,260.	12,000.	45,000.
1860O	6,600	1,750.	3,200.	9,600.	11,000.	55,000.		
1860S	544,950	410.	420.	575.	680.	3,750.	12,300.	
1861	(66) 2,976,453	410.	420.	535.	625.	1,450.	5,800.	45,000.
1861O	17,741	1,300.	2,400.	7,600.	9,000.	52,000.		
1861S	768,000	410.	420.	880.	975.	4,900.	19,000.	
1862	(35) 92,133	500.	800.	1,600.	1,760.	9,200.	20,600.	38,000.

DOUBLE EAGLES

	Mintage	VF-20	EF-40	AU-50	AU-55	MS-60	MS-63	PF-63
1862S	854,173	$410.	$450.	$880.	$940.	$6,200.		
1863	(30)...142,790	450.	485.	1,020.	1,100.	10,000.	$22,000.	
1863S	966,570	415.	430.	750.	860.	4,500.	19,000.	
1864	(50)...204,235	425.	565.	1,000.	1,160.	8,000.		$38,000.
1864S	793,660	410.	420.	920.	1,000.	3,800.	13,600.	
1865	(25)...351,175	410.	420.	525.	585.	3,600.	15,800.	38,000.
1865S	1,042,500	410.	420.	525.	580.	3,200.	3,800.	
1866S	12,000	900.	1,600.	6,000.	7,400.	27,000.		

Motto Above Eagle
Value TWENTY D. (1866–1876)

	Mintage	VF-20	EF-40	AU-50	AU-55	MS-60	MS-63	PF-63
1866	(30)...698,745	$375.	$460.	$700.	$800.	$2,900.	$18,000.	$38,000.
1866S	842,250	410.	420.	690.	850.	9,500.		
1867	(50)...251,015	410.	420.	500.	575.	1,600.	12,400.	38,000.
1867S	920,750	410.	450.	880.	960.	9,000.		
1868	(25)...98,575	500.	640.	1,080.	1,200.	6,200.	24,700.	30,000.
1868S	837,500	410.	420.	675.	760.	5,500.		
1869	(25)...175,130	415.	525.	690.	820.	4,000.	13,200.	30,000.
1869S	686,750	410.	420.	600.	800.	3,500.	19,000.	
1870	(35)...155,150	410.	535.	925.	1,020.	5,750.		30,000.
1870CC	3,789	55,000.	70,000.	135,000.	200,000.	250,000.		
1870S	982,000	410.	420.	500.	650.	3,000.	18,000.	
1871	(30)...80,120	410.	535.	860.	980.	2,400.	16,000.	29,000.
1871CC	17,387	2,800.	4,500.	11,000.	13,400.	30,000.		
1871S	928,000	410.	420.	430.	480.	2,600.	13,600.	
1872	(30)...251,850	410.	420.	430.	460.	1,700.	15,800.	29,000.
1872CC	26,900	1,000.	1,300.	3,000.	4,200.	16,000.		
1872S	780,000	410.	420.	430.	460.	1,800.	15,200.	
1873	(25).1,709,800	410.	420.	430.	440.	600.	7,250.	29,000.
1873CC	22,410	1,250.	2,200.	3,600.	4,260.	19,000.	66,000.	
1873S	1,040,600	410.	420.	430.	445.	1,000.	13,200.	
1874	(20)...366,780	410.	420.	430.	440.	700.	12,300.	29,000.
1874CC	115,085	600.	825.	1,300.	1,420.	5,200.		
1874S	1,214,000	410.	420.	430.	440.	850.	16,000.	
1875	(20)...295,720	410.	420.	430.	440.	600.	6,800.	60,000.
1875CC	111,151	600.	700.	860.	925.	1,350.	11,000.	
1875S	1,230,000	410.	420.	430.	440.	600.	10,000.	
1876	(45)...583,860	410.	420.	430.	440.	600.	7,300.	28,000.
1876CC	138,441	600.	700.	900.	980.	2,700.	22,000.	
1876S	1,597,000	410.	420.	430.	450.	625.	7,500.	

Value TWENTY DOLLARS (1877–1907)

	Mintage	VF-20	EF-40	AU-50	AU-55	MS-60	MS-63	PF-63
1877 . . . .(20). . .	397,650	$410.	$420.	$430.	$440.	$500.	$3,400.	$22,000.
1877CC.	42,565	695.	860.	1,300.	1,380.	9,600.		
1877S	1,735,000	410.	420.	430.	440.	450.	7,750.	
1878 . . . .(20). . .	543,625	410.	420.	430.	440.	450.	3,500.	23,500.
1878CC.	13,180	1,080.	1,600.	2,500.	2,800.	15,000.		
1878S	1,739,000	410.	420.	430.	440.	450.	13,750.	
1879 . . . .(30). . .	207,600	410.	420.	430.	440.	600.	7,950.	28,000.
1879CC.	10,708	1,200.	2,000.	3,400.	4,500.	19,000.		
1879O.	2,325	3,000.	4,500.	9,000.	13,000.	50,000.	75,000.	
1879S	1,223,800	410.	420.	430.	440.	800.		
1880 . . . .(36). . . .	51,420	410.	420.	430.	500.	1,780.	10,400.	23,500.
1880S.	836,000	410.	420.	430.	440.	600.	9,400.	
1881 . . . .(61).	2,199	3,000.	4,000.	8,000.	10,000.	29,000.		23,500.
1881S	727,000	410.	420.	430.	440.	550.	11,000.	
1882 . . . .(59)	571	4,200.	12,000.	16,000.	23,000.	45,000.	85,000.	23,500.
1882CC.	39,140	700.	850.	1,060.	1,400.	4,250.		
1882S	1,125,000	400.	430.	450.	475.	500.	9,500.	
1883, Proof only . . . .(92)								40,000.
1883CC.	59,962	700.	800.	950.	1,200.	2,600.	13,000.	
1883S	1,189,000	410.	420.	430.	440.	450.	5,300.	
1884, Proof only . . . .(71)								40,000.
1884CC.	81,139	600.	710.	880.	975.	1,600.		
1884S.	916,000	410.	420.	430.	440.	450.	4,260.	
1885 . . . .(77)	751	3,700.	4,750.	6,200.	7,060.	21,000.	39,000.	23,500.
1885CC.	9,450	1,175.	1,680.	3,000.	3,260.	6,100.		
1885S	683,500	410.	420.	430.	440.	450.	4,200.	
1886 . . . .(106).	1,000	6,000.	9,500.	18,000.	22,000.	30,000.	47,000.	20,000.
1887, Proof only . . . . . .(121)								38,000.
1887S.	283,000	410.	420.	430.	440.	450.	8,900.	
1888 . . . .(105). . .	226,161	410.	420.	430.	440.	450.	2,975.	17,000.
1888S.	859,600	410.	420.	430.	440.	450.	3,400.	
1889 . . . .(41). . . .	44,070	410.	420.	430.	440.	450.	6,860.	16,700.
1889CC.	30,945	650.	800.	1,150.	1,220.	2,000.	9,800.	
1889S.	774,700	410.	420.	430.	440.	450.	4,260.	
1890 . . . .(55). . .	75,940	410.	420.	430.	440.	450.	3,480.	16,000.
1890CC.	91,209	600.	650.	760.	825.	1,350.	17,000.	
1890S.	802,750	410.	420.	430.	440.	450.	5,340.	

DOUBLE EAGLES

	Mintage	VF-20	EF-40	AU-50	AU-55	MS-60	MS-63	PF-63
1891 ....(52)......1,390		$1,800.	$2,800.	$4,900.	$5,600.	$21,000.		$16,000.
1891CC......................5,000		2,400.	5,000.	5,500.	7,000.	12,000.	$28,000.	
1891S 1,288,125		410.	420.	430.	440.	450.	2,080.	
1892 ....(93)......4,430		625.	900.	1,420.	1,540.	3,500.	12,000.	15,500.
1892CC.....................27,265		635.	750.	1,080.	1,160.	2,200.	15,750.	
1892S....................930,150		410.	420.	430.	440.	450.	2,500.	
1893 ....(59)....344,280		410.	420.	430.	440.	450.	1,500.	15,800.
1893CC.....................18,402		750.	900.	1,020.	1,100.	1,750.	9,400.	
1893S...................996,175		410.	420.	430.	440.	450.	2,400.	
1894 ....(50)...1,368,940		410.	420.	430.	440.	450.	980.	15,500.
1894S 1,048,550		410.	420.	430.	440.	450.	1,500.	
1895 ....(51)...1,114,605		410.	420.	430.	440.	450.	810.	15,500.
1895S 1,143,500		410.	420.	430.	440.	450.	1,500.	
1896 ....(128)....792,535		410.	420.	430.	440.	450.	1,260.	15,500.
1896S 1,403,925		410.	420.	430.	440.	450.	1,400.	
1897 ....(86)...1,383,175		410.	420.	430.	440.	450.	850.	15,500.
1897S 1,470,250		410.	420.	430.	440.	450.	920.	
1898 ....(75)....170,395		410.	420.	430.	440.	450.	3,000.	15,500.
1898S 2,575,175		410.	420.	430.	440.	450.	830.	
1899 ....(84)...1,669,300		410.	420.	430.	440.	450.	640.	15,500.
1899S 2,010,300		410.	420.	430.	440.	450.	1,150.	
1900 ....(124)...1,874,460		410.	420.	430.	440.	450.	550.	15,500.
1900S 2,459,500		410.	420.	430.	440.	450.	1,450.	
1901 ....(96).....111,430		410.	420.	430.	440.	450.	600.	15,500.
1901S 1,596,000		410.	420.	430.	440.	450.	2,400.	
1902 ....(114)......31,140		410.	420.	430.	440.	450.	6,500.	15,500.
1902S 1,753,625		410.	420.	430.	440.	450.	2,400.	
1903 ....(158)....287,270		410.	420.	430.	440.	450.	550.	15,500.
1903S...................954,000		410.	420.	430.	440.	450.	1,120.	
1904 ....(98)...6,256,699		410.	420.	430.	440.	450.	550.	15,500.
1904S 5,134,175		410.	420.	430.	440.	450.	600.	
1905 ....(92).....58,919		410.	420.	430.	440.	600.	9,100.	15,500.
1905S 1,813,000		410.	420.	430.	440.	450.	2,380.	
1906 ....(94).....69,596		410.	420.	430.	440.	450.	4,000.	15,500.
1906D...................620,250		410.	420.	430.	440.	450.	1,200.	
1906S 2,065,750		410.	420.	430.	440.	450.	1,450.	
1907 ....(78)...1,451,786		410.	420.	430.	440.	450.	580.	15,500.
1907D...................842,250		410.	420.	430.	440.	450.	1,275.	
1907S 2,165,800		410.	420.	430.	440.	450.	1,460.	

SAINT-GAUDENS (1907–1933)

The $20 gold piece designed by Augustus Saint-Gaudens is considered by many to be the most beautiful United States coin. The first coins issued were 11,250 high-relief pieces struck for general circulation. The relief is much higher than that of later issues and the date 1907 is in Roman numerals. A few of the Proof coins were made using the lettered-edge collar from the extremely high relief version. These can be distinguished by a pronounced bottom left serif on the N in UNUM, and other minor differences. Flat-relief double eagles were issued later in 1907 with Arabic numerals, and continued through 1933.

The field of the rare, ultra high-relief experimental pieces is excessively concave and connects directly with the edge without any border, giving it a sharp knifelike appearance. Liberty's skirt shows two folds on the side of her right leg; the Capitol building in the background at left is very small; the sun, on the reverse side, has 14 rays, as opposed to the regular high-relief coins, which have only 13 rays extending from the sun. High-relief Proofs are trial or experimental pieces.

VF-20 VERY FINE—Minor wear on Liberty's legs and toes. Eagle's left wing and breast feathers worn.
EF-40 EXTREMELY FINE—Drapery lines on chest visible. Wear on left breast, knee, and below. Eagle's feathers on breast and right wing bold.
AU-50 ABOUT UNCIRCULATED—Trace of wear on nose, breast, and knee. Wear visible on eagle's wings.
AU-55 CHOICE ABOUT UNCIRCULATED—Evidence of friction on design high points. Most of mint luster remains.
MS-60 UNCIRCULATED—No trace of wear. Light marks or blemishes.
MS-63 SELECT UNCIRCULATED—Some distracting contact marks or blemishes in prime focal areas. Impaired luster possible.
MATTE PF-63—Matte surfaces with only a few blemishes in secondary focal places. No major flaws.

Ultra High Relief Pattern, MCMVII (1907)

	PF
1907, Ultra High Relief, Plain Edge *(unique)*	—
1907, Ultra High Relief, Lettered Edge	—

Without Motto IN GOD WE TRUST (1907–1908)
High Relief, MCMVII (1907)

	Mintage	VF-20	EF-40	AU-50	AU-55	MS-60	MS-63	PF
1907 High Relief, Roman Numerals (MCMVII), Wire Rim	12,367	$4,000.	$5,000.	$5,750.	$7,000.	$8,250.	$16,500.	—

Arabic Numerals, No Motto (1907–1908)

	No Motto	**Motto IN GOD WE TRUST**
	Mintmark is on obverse, above date.	**(1908–1933)**

	Mintage	VF-20	EF-40	AU-50	AU-55	MS-60	MS-63	MATTE PF-63
1907	361,667	$425.	$440.	$445.	$450.	$485.	$625.	
1908	4,271,551	425.	440.	445.	450.	485.	550.	
1908D	663,750	425.	440.	475.	500.	525.	650.	
1908, With Motto ....(101)	156,359	425.	440.	445.	450.	475.	1,000.	$16,000.
1908D, With Motto	349,500	425.	440.	475.	490.	525.	900.	
1908S, With Motto	22,000	800.	1,100.	1,200.	1,400.	3,200.	9,500.	

DOUBLE EAGLES

1909, 9 Over 8

	Mintage	VF-20	EF-40	AU-50	AU-55	MS-60	MS-63	MATTE PF-63
1909, 9 Over 8 . . . . *		$425.	$440.	$500.	$600.	$700.	$4,500.	
1909 . . . .(67). . .	161,282	425.	440.	475.	480.	510.	2,200.	$16,000.
1909D	52,500	425.	440.	600.	650.	900.	5,500.	
1909S	2,774,925	425.	440.	475.	480.	525.	600.	
1910 . . . .(167).	482,000	425.	440.	475.	480.	500.	550.	16,000.
1910D	429,000	425.	440.	475.	480.	500.	600.	
1910S	2,128,250	425.	440.	475.	480.	510.	650.	
1911 . . . .(100). . . .	197,250	425.	440.	475.	480.	510.	1,360.	16,000.
1911D	846,500	425.	440.	475.	480.	500.	550.	
1911S	775,750	425.	440.	475.	480.	500.	550.	
1912 . . . .(74).	149,750	425.	440.	475.	480.	500.	900.	16,000.
1913 . . . .(58).	168,780	425.	440.	475.	480.	500.	2,000.	16,000.
1913D	393,500	425.	440.	475.	480.	500.	650.	
1913S	34,000	425.	440.	625.	650.	850.	2,600.	
1914 . . . .(70).	95,250	425.	440.	475.	480.	500.	1,200.	16,000.
1914D	453,000	425.	440.	475.	480.	500.	550.	
1914S	1,498,000	425.	440.	475.	480.	500.	550.	
1915 . . . .(50).	152,000	425.	440.	475.	480.	500.	1,500.	16,000.
1915S	567,500	425.	440.	475.	480.	500.	550.	
1916S	796,000	425.	440.	475.	480.	500.	650.	
1920	228,250	425.	440.	475.	480.	500.	620.	
1920S	558,000	7,000.	9,500.	11,000.	13,000.	20,000.	40,000.	
1921	528,500	9,000.	14,000.	15,000.	18,000.	28,000.	89,000.	
1922	1,375,500	425.	440.	450.	455.	475.	550.	
1922S	2,658,000	440.	500.	525.	700.	800.	1,500.	
1923	566,000	425.	440.	450.	460.	475.	550.	
1923D	1,702,250	425.	440.	480.	485.	500.	550.	
1924	4,323,500	425.	440.	450.	460.	475.	525.	
1924D	3,049,500	725.	950.	1,000.	1,100.	1,400.	5,000.	
1924S	2,927,500	725.	950.	1,000.	1,100.	1,400.	5,000.	
1925	2,831,750	425.	440.	450.	455.	475.	525.	
1925D	2,938,500	800.	1,000.	1,360.	1,500.	2,200.	6,250.	
1925S	3,776,500	725.	1,000.	1,240.	1,400.	4,000.	15,000.	
1926	816,750	425.	440.	450.	455.	475.	525.	
1926D	481,000	1,400.	2,000.	2,500.	3,000.	6,000.	16,000.	
1926S	2,041,500	560.	900.	1,080.	1,100.	1,200.	3,000.	
1927	2,946,750	425.	440.	450.	455.	475.	525.	
1927D	180,000	95,000.	150,000.	160,000.	175,000.	200,000.	300,000.	
1927S	3,107,000	2,750.	4,400.	4,750.	5,200.	8,000.	38,000.	
1928	8,816,000	425.	440.	450.	455.	475.	525.	
1929	1,779,750	4,000.	6,000.	6,500.	7,000.	7,750.	15,000.	
1930S	74,000	9,000.	14,000.	15,000.	16,000.	18,000.	35,000.	
1931	2,938,250	5,000.	8,000.	8,500.	9,250.	12,500.	21,000.	
1931D	106,500	5,200.	8,200.	9,000.	9,800.	18,000.	24,000.	
1932	1,101,750	5,000.	9,500.	10,500.	11,000.	12,000.	20,000.	
1933	445,500	*None placed in circulation*						

* Included in number below.

Collecting United States commemorative coins is like gathering snapshots for an album of important events, places, and people in the nation's history. Because they represent so many different aspects of America—from wars and Olympic games to presidents, state parks, and historical landmarks, every collector can assemble a set with its own special significance.

All U.S. commemorative coins are issued as legal tender, though in most cases the precious metal of the coins surpasses their face values. The weight and fineness for commemoratives follow those of standard-issue gold, silver, and clad coins.

CLASSIC COMMEMORATIVE SILVER AND GOLD

(1892–1893) World's Columbian Exposition

	Mintage	AU-50	MS-60	MS-63	MS-65
1892, Columbian Exposition	950,000	$9.	$15.	$35.	$375.
1893, Same type	1,550,405	8.	15.	35.	425.

(1893) World's Columbian Exposition, Isabella Quarter

	Mintage	AU-50	MS-60	MS-63	MS-65
1893, Columbian Exposition, Chicago	24,214	$270.	$350.	$400.	$1,500.

(1900) Lafayette Dollar

	Mintage	AU-50	MS-60	MS-63	MS-65
1900, Lafayette Dollar	36,026	$225.	$350.	$900.	$4,500.

(1903) Louisiana Purchase Exposition

	Mintage	AU-50	MS-60	MS-63	MS-65
1903, Louisiana Purchase/Thomas Jefferson 17,500		$175.	$200.	$400.	$1,500.
1903, Louisiana Purchase/William McKinley 17,500		175.	200.	400.	1,700.

(1904–1905) Lewis and Clark Exposition

	Mintage	AU-50	MS-60	MS-63	MS-65
1904, Lewis and Clark Exposition 10,025		$275.	$350.	$1,000.	$4,500.
1905, Lewis and Clark Exposition 10,041		300.	400.	1,500.	8,000.

(1915) Panama-Pacific Exposition

	Mintage	AU-50	MS-60	MS-63	MS-65
1915S, Panama-Pacific Exposition 27,134		$150.	$225.	$400.	$1,200.
1915S, Panama-Pacific Exposition, $1 15,000		150.	175.	350.	1,000.
1915S, Panama-Pacific Exposition, $2.50 6,749		600.	700.	1,500.	2,700.
1915S, Panama-Pacific, $50, Round 483		17,500.	20,000.	35,000.	80,000.

167

(1915) Panama-Pacific Exposition

	Mintage	AU-50	MS-60	MS-63	MS-65
1915S, Panama-Pacific, $50, Octagonal	645	$16,000.	$18,000.	$30,000.	$75,000.

(1916–1917) McKinley Memorial

	Mintage	AU-50	MS-60	MS-63	MS-65
1916, McKinley Memorial Dollar	15,000	$150.	$175.	$350.	$1,000.
1917, McKinley Memorial Dollar	5,000	175.	275.	600.	2,000.

(1918) Illinois Centennial

	Mintage	AU-50	MS-60	MS-63	MS-65
1918, Illinois Centennial...................	100,058	$40.	$50.	$90.	$225.

(1920) Maine Centennial

	Mintage	AU-50	MS-60	MS-63	MS-65
1920, Maine Centennial....................	50,028	$40.	$75.	$90.	$300.

COMMEMORATIVES

	Mintage	AU-50	MS-60	MS-63	MS-65
(1920–1921) Pilgrim Tercentenary				**With 1921 in Field on Obverse**	
1920, Pilgrim Tercentenary 152,112	$30.	$40.	$50.	$200.
1921, Same, With Date Added in Field. 20,053	40.	50.	70.	275.

(1920–1921) Pilgrim Tercentenary — With 1921 in Field on Obverse

	Mintage	AU-50	MS-60	MS-63	MS-65
(1921) Alabama Centennial				**Without 2x2 in Field**	
1921, Alabama Centennial, With "2X2" in Field of Obverse. 6,006	$125.	$175.	$225.	$1,000.
1921, Alabama Centennial, no "2X2". 59,038	75.	110.	200.	950.

(1921) Alabama Centennial — Without 2x2 in Field

	Mintage	AU-50	MS-60	MS-63	MS-65
(1921) Missouri Centennial				**With 2★4 in Field**	
1921, Missouri Centennial, "2★4" in Field 5,000	$225.	$250.	$500.	$2,750.
1921, Missouri Centennial, No "2★4". 5,428	125.	200.	450.	2,750.

(1921) Missouri Centennial — With 2★4 in Field

(1922) Grant Memorial

	Mintage	AU-50	MS-60	MS-63	MS-65
1922, Grant Memorial, Star in Obverse Field * 4,256	$350.	$750.	$900.	$3,750.
1922, Same type, No Star in Field 67,405	35.	60.	90.	400.
1922, Grant Memorial Dollar, With Star * 5,016	500.	600.	900.	1,700.
1922, Grant Memorial Dollar, No Star 5,000	450.	575.	900.	1,700.

* Fake stars usually have a flattened spot on the reverse.

(1923) Monroe Doctrine Centennial

	Mintage	AU-50	MS-60	MS-63	MS-65
1923S, Monroe Doctrine Centennial 274,077	$10.	$25.	$65.	$1,300.

(1924) Huguenot-Walloon Tercentenary

	Mintage	AU-50	MS-60	MS-63	MS-65
1924, Huguenot-Walloon Tercentenary 142,080	$50.	$70.	$100.	$300.

(1925) California Diamond Jubilee

	Mintage	AU-50	MS-60	MS-63	MS-65
1925S, California Diamond Jubilee	86,394	$75.	$100.	$125.	$600.

(1925) Fort Vancouver Centennial

	Mintage	AU-50	MS-60	MS-63	MS-65
1925, Fort Vancouver Centennial	14,994	$125.	$150.	$180.	$700.

(1925) Lexington-Concord Sesquicentennial

	Mintage	AU-50	MS-60	MS-63	MS-65
1925, Lexington-Concord Sesquicentennial	162,013	$30.	$50.	$70.	$310.

(1925) Stone Mountain Memorial

	Mintage	AU-50	MS-60	MS-63	MS-65
1925, Stone Mountain Memorial	1,314,709	$20.	$30.	$40.	$125.

(1926–1939) Oregon Trail Memorial

	Mintage	AU-50	MS-60	MS-65
1926, Oregon Trail Memorial	47,955		$75.	$150.
1926S, Same type, S mint	83,055		75.	150.
1928, Oregon Trail Memorial (same as 1926)	6,028		90.	175.
1933D, Oregon Trail Memorial	5,008		125.	275.
1934D, Oregon Trail Memorial	7,006		85.	165.
1936, Oregon Trail Memorial	10,006		75.	150.
1936S, Same type, S mint	5,006		75.	175.
1937D, Oregon Trail Memorial	12,008		75.	150.
1938, Oregon Trail Memorial (same as 1926)	6,006			
1938D, Same type, D mint	6,005	*Set*	275.	450.
1938S, Same type, S mint	6,006			
1939, Oregon Trail Memorial (same as 1926)	3,004			
1939D, Same type, D mint	3,004	*Set*	550.	1,100.
1939S, Same type, S mint	3,005			
Oregon Trail Memorial, single type coin		60.	75.	150.

(1926) Sesquicentennial of American Independence

	Mintage	AU-50	MS-60	MS-63	MS-65
1926, Sesquicentennial of American Independence	141,120	$25.	$40.	$75.	$2,100.
1926, American Independence, $2.50	46,019	135.	175.	300.	2,700.

COMMEMORATIVES

(1927) Vermont Sesquicentennial

	Mintage	AU-50	MS-60	MS-63	MS-65
1927, Vermont Sesquicentennial (Battle of Bennington)	28,142	$70.	$100.	$125.	$475.

(1928) Hawaiian Sesquicentennial

	Mintage	AU-50	MS-60	MS-63	MS-65
1928, Hawaiian Sesquicentennial.	9,958	$700.	$1,000.	$1,250.	$3,500.
1928, Hawaiian Sesquicentennial Sandblast Proof Presentation Piece	50				

(1934–1938) Daniel Boone Bicentennial   **1934 Added on Reverse**

	Mintage	AU-50	MS-60	MS-63	MS-65
1934, Daniel Boone Bicentennial	10,007	$50.	$65.	$70.	$110
1935, Same type	10,010				
1935D, Same type, D mint.	5,005	*Set*	150.	175.	300.
1935S, Same type, S mint.	5,005				
1935, Same as 1934, but 1934 on Reverse.	10,008				
1935D, Same type, D mint.	2,003	*Set*	325.	350.	850.
1935S, Same type, S mint.	2,004				
1936, Daniel Boone (same as above).	12,012				
1936D, Same type, D mint.	5,005	*Set*	145.	170.	300.
1936S, Same type, S mint.	5,006				
1937, Daniel Boone (same as above).	9,810				
1937D, Same type, D mint.	2,506	*Set*	275.	320.	550.
1937S, Same type, S mint.	2,506				

Chart continues on next page.

	Mintage	AU-50	MS-60	MS-63	MS-65
1938, Daniel Boone (same as previous page) 2,100					
1938D, Same type, D mint. 2,100		*Set*	$390.	$470.	$800.
1938S, Same type, S mint 2,100					
Daniel Boone Bicentennial, single type coin		$50.	65.	70.	110.

(1934) Maryland Tercentenary

	Mintage	AU-50	MS-60	MS-63	MS-65
1934, Maryland Tercentenary. 25,015		$50.	$75.	$100.	$175.

(1934–1938) Texas Independence Centennial

	Mintage	AU-50	MS-60	MS-63	MS-65
1934, Texas Independence Centennial 61,463		$40.	$45.	$50.	$100.
1935, Texas Centennial (same as 1934) 9,996					
1935D, Same type, D mint. 10,007		*Set*	150.	175.	275.
1935S, Same type, S mint 10,008					
1936, Texas Centennial (same as 1934) 8,911					
1936D, Same type, D mint. 9,039		*Set*	150.	175.	275.
1936S, Same type, S mint 9,055					
1937, Texas Centennial (same as 1934) 6,571					
1937D, Same type, D mint. 6,605		*Set*	150.	175.	275.
1937S, Same type, S mint 6,637					
1938, Texas Centennial (same as 1934) 3,780					
1938D, Same type, D mint. 3,775		*Set*	260.	320.	650.
1938S, Same type, S mint 3,814					
Texas Centennial, single type coin		40.	45.	50.	100.

(1935–1939) Arkansas Centennial

	Mintage	AU-50	MS-60	MS-63	MS-65
1935, Arkansas Centennial	13,012				
1935D, Same type, D mint	5,505	*Set*	$150.	$200.	$375.
1935S, Same type, S mint	5,506				
1936, Arkansas Centennial (same as 1935;					
date 1936 on reverse)	9,660				
1936D, Same type, D mint	9,660	*Set*	150.	200.	375.
1936S, Same type, S mint	9,660				
1937, Arkansas Centennial (same as 1935)	5,505				
1937D, Same type, D mint	5,505	*Set*	150.	200.	450.
1937S, Same type, S mint	5,505				
1938, Arkansas Centennial (same as 1935)	3,156				
1938D, Same type, D mint	3,155	*Set*	150.	225.	750.
1938S, Same type, S mint	3,155				
1939, Arkansas Centennial (same as 1935)	2,104				
1939D, Same type, D mint	2,104	*Set*	350.	400.	1,500.
1939S, Same type, S mint	2,105				
Arkansas Centennial, single type coin		$35.	50.	65.	125.

(1935–1936) California–Pacific International Exposition

	Mintage	AU-50	MS-60	MS-63	MS-65
1935S, California-Pacific Exposition	70,132	$25.	$40.	$50.	$65.
1936D, California-Pacific Exposition	30,092	27.	50.	55.	70.

(1935) Connecticut Tercentenary

	Mintage	AU-50	MS-60	MS-63	MS-65
1935, Connecticut Tercentenary	25,018	$100.	$130.	$150.	$300.

(1935) Hudson, New York, Sesquicentennial

	Mintage	AU-50	MS-60	MS-63	MS-65
1935, Hudson, NY, Sesquicentennial	10,008	$250.	$300.	$325.	$750.

(1935) Old Spanish Trail

	Mintage	AU-50	MS-60	MS-63	MS-65
1935, Old Spanish Trail	10,008	$360.	$425.	$500.	$700.

(1936) Albany, New York, Charter

	Mintage	AU-50	MS-60	MS-63	MS-65
1936, Albany, New York, Charter	17,671	$125.	$150.	$170.	$225.

COMMEMORATIVES

(1936) Arkansas Centennial – Robinson

	Mintage	AU-50	MS-60	MS-63	MS-65
1936, Arkansas Centennial (Robinson) 25,265		$50.	$60.	$80.	$175.

(1936) Battle of Gettysburg Anniversary

	Mintage	AU-50	MS-60	MS-63	MS-65
1936, Battle of Gettysburg Anniversary 26,928		$130.	$160.	$185.	$350.

(1936) Bridgeport, Connecticut, Centennial

	Mintage	AU-50	MS-60	MS-63	MS-65
1936, Bridgeport, Connecticut, Centennial 25,015		$70.	$100.	$110.	$130.

(1936) Cincinnati Music Center Centennial

	Mintage	AU-50	MS-60	MS-63	MS-65
1936, Cincinnati Music Center Centennial 5,005					
1936D, Same type, D mint. 5,005		*Set*	$340.	$360.	$1,300.
1936S, Same type, S mint. 5,006					
Cincinnati Music Center, single type coin		$100.	115.	120.	350.

(1936) Cleveland Centennial/Great Lakes Exposition

	Mintage	AU-50	MS-60	MS-63	MS-65
1936, Cleveland, Great Lakes Exposition	50,030	$40.	$50.	$60.	$110.

(1936) Columbia, South Carolina, Sesquicentennial

	Mintage	AU-50	MS-60	MS-63	MS-65
1936, Columbia, SC, Sesquicentennial.	9,007				
1936D, Same type, D mint.	8,009	Set	$360.	$410.	$500.
1936S, Same type, S mint.	8,007				
Columbia, SC, Sesqui, single type coin.		$110.	120.	140.	175.

(1936) Delaware Tercentenary

	Mintage	AU-50	MS-60	MS-63	MS-65
1936, Delaware Tercentenary.	20,993	$112.	$145.	$170.	$200.

(1936) Elgin, Illinois, Centennial

	Mintage	AU-50	MS-60	MS-63	MS-65
1936, Elgin, Illinois, Centennial	20,015	$90.	$125.	$130.	$150.

(1936) Long Island Tercentenary

	Mintage	AU-50	MS-60	MS-63	MS-65
1936, Long Island Tercentenary.............. 81,826		$35.	$45.	$60.	$200.

(1936) Lynchburg, Virginia, Sesquicentennial

	Mintage	AU-50	MS-60	MS-63	MS-65
1936, Lynchburg, VA, Sesquicentennial......... 20,013		$90.	$100.	$110.	$170.

(1936) Norfolk, Virginia, Bicentennial

	Mintage	AU-50	MS-60	MS-63	MS-65
1936, Norfolk, VA, Bicentennial 16,936		$175.	$185.	$200.	$235.

(1936) Providence, Rhode Island, Tercentenary

	Mintage	AU-50	MS-60	MS-63	MS-65
1936, Rhode Island Tercentenary.............. 20,013					
1936D, Same type, D mint................... 15,010		*Set*	$120.	$140.	$350.
1936S, Same type, S mint................... 15,011					
Rhode Island Tercentenary, single type coin...........		$30.	40.	55.	125.

(1936) San Francisco – Oakland Bay Bridge Opening

	Mintage	AU-50	MS-60	MS-63	MS-65
1936S, San Francisco – Oakland Bay Bridge 71,424		$65.	$70.	$75.	$150.

(1936) Wisconsin Territorial Centennial

	Mintage	AU-50	MS-60	MS-63	MS-65
1936, Wisconsin Territorial Centennial. 25,015		$65.	$75.	$95.	$130.

(1936) York County, Maine, Tercentenary

	Mintage	AU-50	MS-60	MS-63	MS-65
1936, York County, Maine, Tercentenary 25,015		$65.	$75.	$85.	$115.

(1937) Battle of Antietam Anniversary

COMMEMORATIVES

	Mintage	AU-50	MS-60	MS-63	MS-65
1937, Battle of Antietam Anniversary 18,028		$225.	$300.	$375.	$400.

(1937) Roanoke Island, North Carolina, 350th Anniversary

	Mintage	AU-50	MS-60	MS-63	MS-65
1937, Roanoke Island, NC, 350th Anniversary . . . 29,030		$80.	$120.	$130.	$150.

(1938) New Rochelle, New York, 250th Anniversary

	Mintage	AU-50	MS-60	MS-63	MS-65
1938, New Rochelle, NY, 250th Anniversary 15,266		$120.	$200.	$210.	$225.

(1946) Iowa Centennial

	Mintage	AU-50	MS-60	MS-63	MS-65
1946, Iowa Centennial 100,057		$35.	$45.	$60.	$90.

(1946–1951) Booker T. Washington Memorial

	Mintage		MS-60	MS-65
1946, Booker T. Washington Memorial **(a)**	1,000,546			
1946D, Same type, D mint	200,113	Set	$30.	$75.
1946S, Same type, S mint	500,279			
1947, Same type as 1946	100,017			
1947D, Same type, D mint	100,017	Set	35.	125.
1947S, Same type, S mint	100,017			
1948, Same type as 1946	8,005			
1948D, Same type, D mint	8,005	Set	65.	100.
1948S, Same type, S mint	8,005			
1949, Same type as 1946	6,004			
1949D, Same type, D mint	6,004	Set	100.	160.
1949S, Same type, S mint	6,004			
1950, Same type as 1946	6,004			
1950D, Same type, D mint	6,004	Set	55.	90.
1950S, Same type, S mint	512,091			
1951, Same type as 1946	510,082			
1951D, Same type, D mint	7,004	Set	45.	85.
1951S, Same type, S mint	7,004			
Booker T. Washington Memorial, single type coin			8.	20.

a. Minted; quantity melted unknown.

(1951–1954) Carver/Washington Commemorative

	Mintage		MS-60	MS-63	MS-65
1951, Carver/Washington	110,018				
1951D, Same type, D mint	10,004	Set	$35.	$60.	$240.
1951S, Same type, S mint	10,004				
1952, Same type as 1951	2,006,292				
1952D, Same type, D mint	8,006	Set	32.	55.	200.
1952S, Same type, S mint	8,006				
1953, Same type as 1951	8,003				
1953D, Same type, D mint	8,003	Set	32.	60.	240.
1953S, Same type, S mint	108,020				

COMMEMORATIVES

	Mintage	AU-50	MS-60	MS-63	MS-65
1954, Same type as 1951	12,006				
1954D, Same type, D mint	12,006	*Set*	$32.	$55.	$210.
1954S, Same type, S mint	122,024				
Carver/Washington, single type coin		$9.	10.	12.	22.

MODERN COMMEMORATIVES

(1982) George Washington 250th Anniversary

	Mintage	MS-67	PF-67
1982D, George Washington 250th Anniversary	2,210,458	$3.50	
1982S, Same, Proof	(4,894,044)		$3.00

(1983–1984) Los Angeles Olympiad

	Mintage	MS-67	PF-67
1983P, Discus Thrower silver dollar	294,543	$5.00	
1983D, Same type, D mint	174,014	5.00	
1983S, Same type, S mint	(1,577,025) ... 174,014	5.00	$5.50
1984P, Olympic Coliseum silver dollar	217,954	6.50	
1984D, Same type, D mint	116,675	13.00	
1984S, Same type, S mint	(1,801,210) ... 116,675	11.00	6.00

(1983–1984) Los Angeles Olympiad

	Mintage	MS-67	PF-67
1984P, Olympic gold $10	(33,309)		$220.00
1984D, Olympic gold $10	(34,533)		220.00
1984S, Olympic gold $10	(48,551)		210.00
1984W, Olympic gold $10	(381,085) 75,886	$200.00	210.00

(1986) Statue of Liberty

	Mintage	MS-67	PF-67
1986D, Statue of Liberty half dollar	928,008	$3.75	
1986S, Same type, S mint, Proof	(6,925,627)		$3.90
1986P, Statue of Liberty silver dollar	723,635	7.00	
1986S, Same type, S mint, Proof	(6,414,638)		10.00
1986W, Statue of Liberty gold $5	(404,013) 95,248	105.00	105.00

(1987) U.S. Constitution Bicentennial

	Mintage	MS-67	PF-67
1987P, U.S. Constitution Bicentennial silver dollar.................... 451,629		$6.	
1987S, Same type, S mint, Proof.................... (2,747,116).........			$6.
1987W, U.S. Constitution gold $5 .... (651,659) ... 214,225		105.	105.

(1988) Seoul Olympiad

	Mintage	MS-67	PF-67
1988D, Olympiad silver dollar................................... 191,368		$6.	
1988S, Same type, S mint, Proof.................... (1,359,366).........			$6.
1988W, Olympiad gold $5 .... (281,465) 62,913		110.	110.

(1989) Congress Bicentennial

	Mintage	MS-67	PF-67
1989D, Congress Bicentennial half dollar	163,753	$4.50	
1989S, Congress Bicentennial half dollar	(767,897)		$4.50
1989D, Congress silver dollar	135,203	9.00	
1989S, Congress silver dollar	(762,198)		11.00
1989W, Congress Bicentennial gold $5	(164,690) 46,899	105.00	105.00

(1990) Eisenhower Centennial

	Mintage	MS-67	PF-67
1990W, Eisenhower Centennial silver dollar	241,669	$10.	
1990P, Same type, P mint, Proof	(1,144,461)		$13.

(1991) Korean War Memorial

	Mintage	MS-67	PF-67
1991D, Korean War Memorial silver dollar........................ 213,049		$9.	
1991P, Same type, P mint, Proof...................... (618,488).........			$11.

(1991) Mount Rushmore Golden Anniversary

	Mintage	MS-67	PF-67
1991D, Mount Rushmore Golden Anniversary half dollar 172,754		$10.	
1991S, Same type, S mint, Proof..................... (753,257)........			$10.
1991P, Mount Rushmore silver dollar 133,139		18.	
1991S, Same type, S mint, Proof..................... (738,419).........			20.
1991W, Mount Rushmore gold $5...................... (111,991).... 31,959		110.	105.

(1991) United Service Organizations

	Mintage	MS-67	PF-67
1991D, U.S.O. silver dollar	124,958	$9.	
1991S, Same type, S mint, Proof.	(321,275)		$10.

(1992) XXV Olympiad

	Mintage	MS-67	PF-67
1992P, Olympic clad half dollar	161,619	$5.	
1992S, Same type, S mint, Proof.	(519,699).		$5.
1992D, Olympic silver dollar.	187,562	15.	
1992S, Same type, S mint, Proof.	(504,544).		16.
1992W, Olympic gold $5	(77,313) 27,732	105.	105.

(1992) Christopher Columbus Quincentenary

	Mintage	MS-67	PF-67
1992D, Columbus Quincentenary half dollar	135,718	$6.	
1992S, Same type, S mint, Proof	(390,255)		$6.
1992D, Columbus silver dollar	106,962	15.	
1992P, Same type, P mint, Proof	(385,290)		20.
1992W, Columbus gold $5	(79,734) 24,331	$120.	$110.

(1992) White House 200th Anniversary

	Mintage	MS-67	PF-67
1992D, White House 200th Anniversary silver dollar	123,803	$18.	
1992W, Same type, W mint, Proof	(375,849)		$20.

(1993) Bill of Rights

	Mintage	MS-67	PF-67
1993W, Bill of Rights silver half dollar	173,224	$10.	
1993S, Same type, S mint, Proof	(559,758)		$9.
1993D, Bill of Rights silver dollar	92,415	10.	
1993S, Same type, S mint, Proof	(515,038)		11.
1993W, Bill of Rights gold $5	(79,422) 22,897	120.	110.

(1993 [1994]) Thomas Jefferson

	Mintage	MS-67	PF-67
1993P, (1994) Thomas Jefferson silver dollar	266,927	$13.	
1993S, (1994) Same type, S mint, Proof	(332,891)		$16.

COMMEMORATIVES

(1994) U.S. Capitol Bicentennial

	Mintage	MS-67	PF-67
1994D, U.S. Capitol Bicentennial silver dollar	68,352	$13.	
1994S, Same type, S mint, Proof . . . . (279,416)			$16.

(1994) U.S. Prisoner of War Memorial

	Mintage	MS-67	PF-67
1994W, U.S. POW Memorial silver dollar	54,790	$45.	
1994P, Same type, P mint, Proof . . . . (220,100)			$37.

(1994) Vietnam Veterans Memorial

	Mintage	MS-67	PF-67
1994W, Vietnam Veterans Memorial silver dollar	57,317	$45.	
1994P, Same type, P mint, Proof . . . . (226,262)			$50.

(1994) Women in Military Service Memorial

	Mintage	MS-67	PF-67
1994W, Women Veterans Memorial silver dollar	53,054	$30.	
1994P, Same type, P mint, Proof	(213,201)		$33.

(1994) World Cup Tournament

	Mintage	MS-67	PF-67
1994D, World Cup Tournament clad half dollar	52,836	$6.	
1994P, Same type, P mint, Proof	(122,412)		$6.
1994D, World Cup Tournament silver dollar	81,698	14.	
1994S, Same type, S mint, Proof	(576,978)		16.
1994W, World Cup Tournament gold $5	(89,619) ... 22,464	120.	110.

COMMEMORATIVES

(1995) Centennial Olympic Games

	Mintage	MS-67	PF-67
1995D, Olympic Games, Basketball clad half dollar 171,001		$11.00	
1995S, Same type, S mint, Proof. . . . . (169,655).			$9.00
1995D, Olympic Games, Baseball clad half dollar. 164,605		11.00	
1995S, Same type, S mint, Proof. . . . . (118,087).			8.50
1996D, Olympic Games, Swimming clad half dollar. 49,533		70.00	
1996S, Same type, S mint, Proof. . . . . (114,315).			18.00
1996D, Olympic Games, Soccer clad half dollar. 52,836		35.00	
1996S, Same type, S mint, Proof. . . . . (112,412).			50.00
1995D, Olympic Games, Gymnastics silver dollar 42,497		45.00	
1995P, Same type, P mint, Proof. . . . . (182,676).			30.00
1995D, Olympic Games, Paralympics silver dollar 28,649		42.00	
1995P, Same type, P mint, Proof. . . . . (138,337).			30.00
1995D, Olympic Games, Track and Field silver dollar. 24,796		41.00	
1995P, Same type, P mint, Proof. . . . . (136,935).			25.00
1995D, Olympic Games, Cycling silver dollar. 19,662		70.00	
1995P, Same type, P mint, Proof. . . . . (118,795).			21.00
1996D, Olympic Games, Tennis silver dollar 15,983		125.00	
1996P, Same type, P mint, Proof. . . . . (92,016).			40.00
1996D, Olympic Games, Paralympics silver dollar 14,497		190.00	
1996P, Same type, P mint, Proof. . . . . (84,280).			40.00
1996D, Olympic Games, Rowing silver dollar. 16,258		175.00	
1996P, Same type, P mint, Proof. . . . . (151,890).			35.00

Chart continues on next page.

	Mintage	MS-67	PF-67
1996D, Olympic Games, High Jump silver dollar	15,697	$180.	
1996P, Same type, P mint, Proof	(124,502)		$30.
1995W, Olympic Games, Torch Runner gold $5	14,675	175.	
1995W, Same type, W mint, Proof	(57,442)		125.
1995W, Olympic Games, Stadium gold $5	10,579	185.	
1995W, Same type, W mint, Proof	(43,124)		140.
1996W, Olympic Games, Flag Bearer gold $5	9,174	210.	
1996W, Same type, W mint, Proof	(32,886)		175.
1996W, Olympic Games, Cauldron gold $5	9,210	220.	
1996W, Same type, W mint, Proof	(38,555)		180.

(1995) Civil War Battlefields

	Mintage	MS-67	PF-67
1995S, Civil War Battlefields clad half dollar	119,510	$22.	
1995S, Same type, S mint, Proof	(330,099)		$22.
1995P, Civil War Battlefields silver dollar	45,866	35.	
1995S, Same type, S mint, Proof	(55,246)		45.
1995W, Civil War Battlefields gold $5	12,735	275.	
1995W, Same type, W mint, Proof	(55,246)		225.

(1995) Special Olympics Games

	Mintage	MS-67	PF-67
1995W, Special Olympics Games silver dollar	89,301	$11.	
1995P, Same type, P mint, Proof	(351,764)		$12.

(1991–1995) 50th Anniversary of World War II

	Mintage	MS-67	PF-67
(1993) 1991–1995P, World War II clad half dollar	(290,3430) . . .	192,968	$20.	$24.
(1993) 1991–1995D, World War II silver dollar	94,700	16.	
(1993) Same type, W mint, Proof	(322,422)		25.
(1993) 1991–1995W, World War II gold $5	(65,461)	23,089	120.	110.

(1996) National Community Service

	Mintage	MS-67	PF-67
1996S, National Community Service silver dollar	23,468	$140.	
1996S, Same type, S mint, Proof	(100,787)		$50.

(1996) Smithsonian Institution 150th Anniversary

	Mintage	MS-67	PF-67
1996D, Smithsonian Institution 150th Anniv silver dollar	30,593	$70.	
1996P, Same type, P mint, Proof	(126,616)		$30.
1996W, Smithsonian Institution gold $5	21,840	200.	
1996W, Same type, W mint, Proof	(8,948)		350.

(1997) Botanic Garden

	Mintage	MS-67	PF-67
1997P, Botanic Garden silver dollar	57,272	$20.	
1997P, Same type, P mint, Proof	(264,528)		$20.

(1997) Franklin D. Roosevelt

	Mintage	MS-67	PF-67
1997W, Franklin D. Roosevelt gold $5	11,805	$160.	
1997W, Same type, W mint, Proof	(29,233)		$140.

(1997) Jackie Robinson

	Mintage	MS-67	PF-67
1997S, Jackie Robinson silver dollar	30,180	$50.	
1997S, Same type, S mint, Proof	(110,002)		$40.
1997W, Jackie Robinson gold $5	5,174	1,500.	
1997W, Same type, W mint, Proof	(24,072)		250.

(1997) National Law Enforcement Officers Memorial

	Mintage	MS-67	PF-67
1997P, National Law Enforcement Memorial silver dollar	28,575	$75.	
1997P, Same type, P mint, Proof	(110,428)		$60.

(1998) Black Revolutionary War Patriots

	Mintage	MS-67	PF-67
1998S, Black Revolutionary War Patriots silver dollar 37,210		$65.	
1998S, Same type, S mint, Proof....................... (75,070)..........			$55.

(1998) Robert F. Kennedy

	Mintage	MS-67	PF-67
1998S, Robert F. Kennedy silver dollar............................ 106,422		$16.	
1998S, Same type, S mint, Proof....................... (99,020)..........			$21.

(1999) Dolley Madison Commemorative

	Mintage	MS-67	PF-67
1999P, Dolley Madison silver dollar 89,100		$25.	
1999P, Same type, P mint, Proof....................... (224,400)..........			$30.

(1999) George Washington Death Bicentennial

	Mintage	MS-67	PF-67
1999W, George Washington gold $5 22,511		$160.	
1999W, Same type, W mint, Proof..................... (41,693).........			$165.

(1999) Yellowstone National Park

	Mintage	MS-67	PF-67
1999P, Yellowstone National Park silver dollar....................... 62,000		$16.	
1999P, Same type, S mint, Proof..................... (144,900).........			$21.

(2000) Leif Ericson Millennium

	Mintage	MS-67	PF-67
2000P, Leif Ericson Millennium silver dollar....................... 28,100		$50.	
2000P, Same type, P mint, Proof..................... (142,900).........			$40.

(2000) Library of Congress Bicentennial

	Mintage	MS-67	PF-67
2000P, Library of Congress Bicentennial silver dollar		$20.	
2000P, Same type, P mint, Proof			$20.
2000W, Library of Congress Bicentennial bimetallic $10.		700.	
2000W, Same type, W mint, Proof			350.

(2001) American Buffalo Commemorative

	Mintage	MS-67	PF-67
2001D, American Buffalo silver dollar	227,131	$90.	
2001P, Same type, P mint, Proof	(272,869).		$90.

(2001) Capitol Visitor Center

COMMEMORATIVES

(2001) Capitol Visitor Center

	Mintage	MS-67	PF-67
2001P, Capitol Visitor Center clad half dollar	99,157	$6.	
2001P, Same type, P mint, Proof	(77,962)		$8.
2001P, Capitol silver dollar	35,380	21.	
2001P, Same type, P mint, Proof	(143,793)		24.
2001P, Capitol gold $5	6,761	350.	
2001P, Same type, P mint, Proof	(27,652)		160.

(2002) Salt Lake City Olympic Games

	Mintage	MS-67	PF-67
2002P, Salt Lake Olympics silver dollar	35,287	$18.	
2002P, Same type, P mint, Proof	(142,813)		$20.
2002W, Salt Lake Olympics gold $5	5,727	170.	
2002W, Same type, W mint, Proof	(8,882)		150.

(2002) West Point Bicentennial

	Mintage	MS-67	PF-67
2002W, West Point silver dollar	101,236	$18.	
2002W, Same type, W mint, Proof	(282,743)		$19.

(2003) First Flight Centennial

	Mintage	MS-67	PF-67
2003P, First Flight Centennial clad half dollar		$6.	
2003P, Same type, P mint, Proof			$8.
2003P, First Flight Centennial silver dollar		15.	
2003P, Same type, P mint, Proof			20.
2003W, First Flight Centennial gold $10		275.	
2003W, Same type, W mint, Proof			280.

(2004) Lewis and Clark Bicentennial

	Mintage	MS-67	PF-67
2004P, Lewis and Clark Bicentennial silver dollar		$18.	
2004P, Same type, P mint, Proof.......................................			$20.

(2004) Thomas Alva Edison

	Mintage	MS-67	PF-67
2004P, Thomas Alva Edison silver dollar................................		$13.	
2004P, Same type, P mint, Proof.......................................			$14.

(2005) Chief Justice John Marshall

	Mintage	MS-67	PF-67
2005P, Chief Justice John Marshall silver dollar		$18.	
2005P, Same type, P mint, Proof.......................................			$20.

	Mintage	MS-67	PF-67
2005P, U.S. Marines silver dollar		$18.	
2005P, Same type, P mint, Proof			$20.

GOVERNMENT COMMEMORATIVE SETS

Values are for commemorative coins and sets in their original packaging.

(1983–1984) Olympics

	Price
1983 and 1984 Proof dollars	$15.
1983 and 1984 6-coin set. One each of 1983 and 1984 dollars, both Proof and Uncirculated gold $10 **(a)**	300.
1983 3-piece collector set. 1983 P, D, and S Uncirculated dollars	17.
1984 3-piece collector set. 1984 P, D, and S Uncirculated dollars	24.
1983 and 1984 gold and silver Uncirculated set. One each of 1983 and 1984 Uncirculated dollar and one 1984 Uncirculated gold $10	150.
1983 and 1984 gold and silver Proof set. One each of 1983 and 1984 Proof dollars and one 1984 Proof gold $10	150.

(1986) Statue of Liberty

	Price
2-coin set. Proof silver dollar and clad half dollar	$12.
3-coin set. Proof silver dollar, clad half dollar, and gold $5	120.
2-coin set. Uncirculated silver dollar and clad half dollar	12.
2-coin set. Uncirculated and Proof gold $5	120.
3-coin set. Uncirculated silver dollar, clad half dollar, and gold $5	120.
6-coin set. One each of Proof and Uncirculated half dollar, silver dollar, and gold $5 **(a)**	250.

(1987) Constitution

	Price
2-coin set. Uncirculated silver dollar and gold $5	$120.
2-coin set. Proof silver dollar and gold $5	120.
4-coin set. One each of Proof and Uncirculated silver dollar and gold $5 **(a)**	240.

(1988) Olympiad

	Price
2-coin set. Uncirculated silver dollar and gold $5	$110.
2-coin set. Proof silver dollar and gold $5	110.
4-coin set. One each of Proof and Uncirculated silver dollar and gold $5 **(a)**	225.

(1989) Congress

	Price
2-coin set. Proof clad half dollar and silver dollar	$15.
3-coin set. Proof clad half dollar, silver dollar, and gold $5	120.
2-coin set. Uncirculated clad half dollar and silver dollar	15.
3-coin set. Uncirculated clad half dollar, silver dollar, and gold $5	120.
6-coin set. One each of Proof and Uncirculated clad half dollar, silver dollar, and gold $5 **(a)**	250.

(1991) Mount Rushmore

	Price
2-coin set. Uncirculated clad half dollar and silver dollar	$25.
2-coin set. Proof clad half dollar and silver dollar	30.
3-coin set. Uncirculated clad half dollar, silver dollar, and gold $5	230.
3 coin set. Proof half dollar, silver dollar, and gold $5	230.
6-coin set. One each of Proof and Uncirculated clad half dollar, silver dollar, and gold $5 **(a)**	460.

a. Packaged in cherrywood box.

(1992) XXV Olympiad

	Price
2-coin set. Uncirculated clad half dollar and silver dollar	$17.
2-coin set. Proof clad half dollar and silver dollar	18.
3-coin set. Uncirculated clad half dollar, silver dollar, and gold $5	110.
3-coin set. Proof clad half dollar, silver dollar, and gold $5	110.
6-coin set. One each of Proof and Uncirculated clad half dollar, silver dollar, and gold $5 **(a)**	225.

(1992) Columbus

	Price
2-coin set. Uncirculated clad half dollar and silver dollar	$20.
2-coin set. Proof clad half dollar and silver dollar	25.
3-coin set. Uncirculated clad half dollar, silver dollar, and gold $5	130.
3-coin set. Proof half dollar, silver dollar, and gold $5.	120.
6-coin set. One each of Proof and Uncirculated clad half dollar, silver dollar, and gold $5 **(a)**	250.

(1993) Bill of Rights

	Price
2-coin set. Uncirculated silver half dollar and silver dollar	$17.
2-coin set. Proof silver half dollar and silver dollar	18.
3-coin set. Uncirculated silver half dollar, silver dollar, and gold $5	135.
3-coin set. Proof half dollar, silver dollar, and gold $5.	125.
6-coin set. One each of Proof and Uncirculated silver half dollar, silver dollar, and gold $5 **(a)**	260.
"Young Collector" set. Silver half dollar.	12.
"Educational" set. Silver half dollar and James Madison medal	10.
Proof silver half dollar and twenty-five-cent stamp	10.

(1993) Thomas Jefferson

	Price
3-piece set (issued in 1994). Silver dollar, Jefferson nickel, and $2 note	$45.

(1993) World War II

	Price
2-coin set. Uncirculated clad half dollar and silver dollar	$17.
2-coin set. Proof clad half dollar and silver dollar	19.
3-coin set. Uncirculated clad half dollar, silver dollar, and gold $5	140.
3-coin set. Proof clad half dollar, silver dollar, and gold $5.	135.
6-coin set. One each of Proof and Uncirculated clad half dollar, silver dollar, and gold $5 **(a)**	280.
"Young Collector" set. Clad half dollar.	12.
"Victory" set. Silver dollar and French franc	10.
Victory Medal set. Uncirculated clad half dollar and reproduction medal	10.

(1994) U.S. Veterans

	Price
3-coin set. Uncirculated POW, Vietnam, and Women in Military Service silver dollars	$125.
3-coin set. Proof POW, Vietnam, and Women in Military Service silver dollars	100.

(1994) World Cup Soccer

	Price
2-coin set. Uncirculated clad half dollar and silver dollar	$17.
2-coin set. Proof clad half dollar and silver dollar	19.
3-coin set. Uncirculated clad half dollar, silver dollar, and gold $5	125.
3-coin set. Proof clad half dollar, silver dollar, and gold $5	125.
6-coin set. One each of Proof and Uncirculated clad half dollar, silver dollar, and gold $5	250.
"Young Collector" set. Uncirculated clad half dollar.	10.
"Special Edition" set. Proof clad half dollar and silver dollar	20.

a. Packaged in cherrywood box.

(1995) Civil War Battlefield Preservation

	Price
2-coin set. Uncirculated clad half dollar and silver dollar	$40.
2-coin set. Proof clad half dollar and silver dollar	50.
3-coin set. Uncirculated clad half dollar, silver dollar, and gold $5	325.
3-coin set. Proof clad half dollar, silver dollar, and gold $5	275.
6-coin set. One each of Proof and Uncirculated clad half dollar, silver dollar, and gold $5 (a)	600.
"Young Collector" set. Uncirculated clad half dollar	12.
2-coin "Union" Set. Clad half dollar and silver dollar	25.
3-coin "Union" Set. Clad half dollar, silver dollar, and gold $5	175.

(1995) Special Olympics

	Price
2-coin set. Proof Special Olympics silver dollar, 1995S Kennedy half dollar	$50.

(1995–1996) Centennial Olympic Games

	Price
4-coin set #1. Uncirculated half dollar (Basketball), dollars (Gymnast, Paralympics), gold $5 (Torch Bearer)	$225.
4-coin set #2. Proof half dollar (Basketball), dollars (Gymnast, Paralympics), gold $5 (Torch Bearer)	150.
2-coin set #1. Proof silver dollars (Gymnast, Paralympics)	45.
"Young Collector" set. Uncirculated Basketball, Swimming, or Soccer half dollar	10.
1995–1996 16-coin Uncirculated set. One each of all Uncirculated coins (a)	800.
1995–1996 16-coin Proof set. One each of all Proof coins (a)	800.
1995–1996 32-coin set. One each of all Uncirculated and Proof coins (a)	2,750.

(1996) National Community Service

	Price
Proof silver dollar and Saint-Gaudens stamp	$40.

(1996) Smithsonian Institution 150th Anniversary

	Price
2-coin set. Proof silver dollar and $5 gold	$180.
4-coin set. One each of Proof and Uncirculated silver dollar and $5 gold (a)	565.
"Young Collector" set. Proof silver dollar	25.

(1997) Botanic Garden

	Price
Silver dollar, Jefferson nickel, and $1 note	$110.

(1997) Jackie Robinson

	Price
2-coin set. Proof silver dollar and gold $5	$300.
4-coin set. One each of Proof and Uncirculated silver dollar and gold $5 (a)	1,850.
3-piece "Legacy" set. Baseball card, pin, and gold $5	300.

(1997) National Law Enforcement Officers Memorial

	Price
Insignia set. Silver dollar, lapel pin, and patch	$90.

a. Packaged in cherrywood box.

(1998) Black Revolutionary War Patriots

	Price
2-coin set. Uncirculated and Proof silver dollars	$120.
"Young Collector" set. Uncirculated silver dollar	70.
Black Revolutionary War Patriots set. Silver dollar and four stamps	70.

(1998) Robert F. Kennedy

	Price
2-coin set. RFK silver dollar and JFK silver half dollar	$240.
2-coin set. RFK silver dollar, Proof and Uncirculated	50.

(1999) Dolley Madison Commemorative

	Price
2-coin set. Proof and Uncirculated silver dollars	$50.

(1999) George Washington

	Price
2-coin set. One each of Proof and Uncirculated gold $5	$350.

(1999) Yellowstone National Park

	Price
2-coin set. One each of Proof and Uncirculated silver dollars	$45.

(2000) Leif Ericson Millennium

	Price
2-coin set. Proof silver dollar and Icelandic 1,000 kronur	$55.

(2001) American Buffalo

	Price
2-coin set. One each of Proof and Uncirculated silver dollars	$180.
"Coinage and Currency" set. Uncirculated silver dollar, two 2005 nickels, replica medal, replica $10 Bison note, and three stamps	100.

(2001) Capitol Visitor Center

	Price
3-coin set. Proof clad half dollar, silver dollar, and gold $5	$180.

(2002) Salt Lake Olympic Games

	Price
2-coin set. Proof silver dollar and gold $5	$160.
4-coin set. One each of Proof and Uncirculated silver dollar and gold $5	350.

(2004) Lewis and Clark

	Price
Pouch set. Proof silver dollar and beaded pouch	$120.
"Coinage and Currency" set. Uncirculated silver dollar, two 2005 nickels, replica medal, replica $10 Bison note, three stamps	45.
Western Journey nickel set. Proof silver dollar, two 2005 Proof nickels, silver-plated Peace Medal	11.

(2004) Thomas Alva Edison

	Price
Edison set. Uncirculated silver dollar and light bulb	$25.

PROOF COINS AND SETS

Proof coins can usually be distinguished by their sharpness of detail, high wire edge, and extremely brilliant, mirrorlike surface. All proofs are originally sold by the mint at a premium.

Proof coins were not struck during 1943–1949 or 1965–1967. Sets from 1936 through 1972 include the cent, nickel, dime, quarter, and half dollar; from 1973 through 1981 the dollar was also included. Proof sets may be ordered during the year of issue from the U.S. Mint, Customer Care Center, 801 9th Street NW, Washington, DC, 20220.
Values shown are for original unblemished sets.
Figures in parentheses represent the total number of full sets minted.

Year	Mintage	Issue Price	Current Value
1936	(3,837)	$1.89	$3,700.00
1937	(5,542)	1.89	1,900.00
1938	(8,045)	1.89	950.00
1939	(8,795)	1.89	750.00
1940	(11,246)	1.89	650.00
1941	(15,287)	1.89	625.00
1942, Both nickels	(21,120)	1.89	675.00
1942, One nickel	*	1.89	550.00
1950	(51,386)	2.10	375.00
1951	(57,500)	2.10	350.00
1952	(81,980)	2.10	200.00
1953	(128,800)	2.10	200.00
1954	(233,300)	2.10	95.00
1955, Box pack	(378,200)	2.10	65.00
1955, Flat pack	*	2.10	85.00
1956	(669,384)	2.10	30.00
1957	(1,247,952)	2.10	14.50
1958	(875,652)	2.10	30.00
1959	(1,149,291)	2.10	14.50
1960, With Large Date cent	(1,691,602)	2.10	10.00
1960, With Small Date cent	*	2.10	22.00
1961	(3,028,244)	2.10	6.00
1962	(3,218,019)	2.10	6.00
1963	(3,075,645)	2.10	7.00
1964	(3,950,762)	2.10	6.50
1968S	(3,041,506)	5.00	3.75
1969S	(2,934,631)	5.00	3.75
1970S	(2,632,810)	5.00	7.00
1970S, With Small Date cent	*	5.00	47.00
1971S	(3,220,733)	5.00	3.00
1972S	(3,260,996)	5.00	2.50
1973S	(2,760,339)	7.00	7.00
1974S	(2,612,568)	7.00	6.00
1975S, With 1976 quarter, half, and dollar	(2,845,450)	7.00	8.50
1976S	(4,149,730)	7.00	4.00
1976S, 3-piece set	(3,998,621)	15.00	8.50
1977S	(3,251,152)	9.00	5.00
1978S	(3,127,781)	9.00	5.50
1979S, Filled S	(3,677,175)	9.00	6.00
1979S, Clear S	*	9.00	55.00
1980S	(3,554,806)	10.00	5.00
1981S, Filled S	(4,063,083)	11.00	4.50
1982S	(3,857,479)	11.00	2.50
1983S	(3,138,765)	11.00	3.50
1983S, Prestige Set (Olympic dollar)	(140,361)	59.00	37.00
1984S	(2,748,430)	11.00	6.00
1984S, Prestige Set (Olympic dollar)	(316,680)	59.00	10.00
1985S	(3,362,821)	11.00	3.00
1986S	(2,411,180)	11.00	10.00
1986S, Prestige Set (Statue of Liberty half, dollar)	(599,317)	48.50	19.00

* Included in number above.

PROOF AND MINT SETS

Year	Mintage	Issue Price	Current Value
1987S	(3,792,233)	$11.00	$3.00
1987S, Prestige Set (Constitution dollar)	(435,495)	45.00	12.00
1988S	(3,031,287)	11.00	6.00
1988S, Prestige Set (Olympic dollar)	(231,661)	45.00	15.00
1989S	(3,009,107)	11.00	4.50
1989S, Prestige Set (Congressional half, dollar)	(211,807)	45.00	18.00
1990S	(2,793,433)	11.00	5.00
1990S, With No S cent	(3,555)	11.00	5,000.00
1990S, With No S cent (Prestige set)		45.00	5,500.00
1990S, Prestige Set (Eisenhower dollar)	(506,126)	45.00	24.00
1991S	(2,610,833)	11.00	8.00
1991S, Prestige Set (Mt. Rushmore half, dollar)	(256,954)	59.00	35.00
1992S	(26,756,118)	11.00	6.00
1992S, Prestige Set (Olympic half, dollar)	(183,285)	56.00	20.00
1992S, Silver	(1,009,586)	21.00	9.00
1992S, Silver Premier Set	(308,055)	37.00	9.00
1993S	(2,409,394)	12.50	8.00
1993S, Prestige Set (Madison half, dollar)	(232,063)	57.00	22.00
1993S, Silver	(570,213)	21.00	17.00
1993S, Silver Premier Set	(191,140)	37.50	18.00
1994S	(2,308,701)	12.50	9.00
1994S, Prestige Set (World Cup half, dollar)	(175,893)	57.00	25.00
1994S, Silver	(636,009)	21.00	17.00
1994S, Silver Premier Set	(149,320)	37.50	20.00
1995S	(2,010,384)	12.50	30.00
1995S, Prestige Set (Civil War half, dollar)	(105,845)	57.00	100.00
1995S, Silver	(549,878)	21.00	50.00
1995S, Silver Premier Set	(130,107)	37.50	55.00
1996S	(2,085,285)	12.50	8.00
1996S, Prestige Set (Olympic half, dollar)	(59,886)	57.00	225.00
1996S, Silver	(623,655)	21.00	28.00
1996S, Silver Premier Set	(151,366)	37.50	28.00
1997S	(1,975,000)	12.50	28.00
1997S, Prestige Set (Botanic dollar)	(80,000)	48.00	90.00
1997S, Silver	(605,473)	21.00	45.00
1997S, Silver Premier Set	(136,205)	37.50	45.00
1998S	(2,086,507)	12.50	20.00
1998S, Silver	(638,134)	21.00	22.00
1998S, Silver Premier Set	(240,658)	37.50	22.00
1999S, 9-piece set	(2,543,401)	19.95	45.00
1999S, 5-piece quarter set	(1,169,958)	13.95	30.00
1999S, Silver 9-piece set	(804,565)	31.95	125.00
2000S, 10-piece set	(3,082,483)	19.95	12.00
2000S, 5-piece quarter set	(937,600)	13.95	10.00
2000S, Silver 10-piece set	(965,421)	31.95	22.00
2001S, 10-piece set	(2,294,043)	19.95	35.00
2001S, 5-piece quarter set	(799,231)	13.95	16.00
2001S, Silver 10-piece set	(889,697)	31.95	48.00
2002S, 10-piece set	(2,319,766)	19.95	25.00
2002S, 5-piece quarter set	(764,479)	13.95	14.00
2002S, Silver 10-piece set	(892,229)	31.95	34.00
2003S, 10-piece set		19.95	23.00
2003S, 5-piece quarter set		13.95	13.00
2003S, Silver 10-piece set		31.95	26.00
2004S, 11-piece set		22.95	45.00
2004S, 5-piece quarter set		15.95	20.00
2004S, Silver 11-piece set		37.95	35.00
2004S, Silver 5-piece quarter set		23.95	21.00
2005S, 11-piece set		22.95	18.00
2005S, 5-piece quarter set		15.95	13.00
2005S, Silver 11-piece set		37.95	19.00
2005S, Silver 5-piece quarter set		23.95	14.00

* Included in number above.

UNCIRCULATED MINT SETS

Official Mint Sets are specially packaged by the government for sale to collectors. They contain uncirculated specimens of each year's coins for every denomination issued from each mint. Sets from 1947 through 1958 contain two examples of each regular-issue coin. No official sets were produced in 1950, 1982, or 1983. Privately assembled sets are valued according to individual coin prices. Only official sets are included in the following list. Unlike the Proof sets, these are normal coins intended for circulation and are not minted with any special consideration for quality.

Year	Mintage	Issue Price	Current Value	Year	Mintage	Issue Price	Current Value
1947 P-D-S	5,000	$4.87	$650.00	1976 P-D	1,892,513	$6.00	$5.00
1948 P-D-S	6,000	4.92	325.00	1977 P-D	2,006,869	7.00	4.50
1949 P-D-S	5,000	5.45	450.00	1978 P-D	2,162,609	7.00	5.00
1951 P-D-S	8,654	6.75	480.00	1979 P-D	2,526,000	8.00	4.00
1952 P-D-S	11,499	6.14	400.00	1980 P-D-S	2,815,066	9.00	4.00
1953 P-D-S	15,538	6.14	300.00	1981 P-D-S	2,908,145	11.00	9.00
1954 P-D-S	25,599	6.19	150.00	1984 P-D	1,832,857	7.00	3.50
1955 P-D-S	49,656	3.57	95.00	1985 P-D	1,710,571	7.00	4.00
1956 P-D	45,475	3.34	85.00	1986 P-D	1,153,536	7.00	13.00
1957 P-D	34,324	4.40	140.00	1987 P-D	2,890,758	7.00	4.00
1958 P-D	50,314	4.43	95.00	1988 P-D	1,646,204	7.00	4.00
1959 P-D	187,000	2.40	25.00	1989 P-D	1,987,915	7.00	4.00
1960 P-D	260,485	2.40	15.00	1990 P-D	1,809,184	7.00	4.00
1961 P-D	223,704	2.40	24.00	1991 P-D	1,352,101	7.00	6.50
1962 P-D	385,285	2.40	10.00	1992 P-D	1,500,143	7.00	4.00
1963 P-D	606,612	2.40	8.00	1993 P-D	1,297,431	8.00	6.00
1964 P-D	1,008,108	2.40	7.50	1994 P-D	1,234,813	8.00	5.00
1965 *	2,360,000	4.00	7.00	1995 P-D	1,038,787	8.00	14.00
1966 *	2,261,583	4.00	8.00	1996 P-D, Plus			
1967 *	1,863,344	4.00	11.00	1996-W dime	1,457,949	8.00	15.00
1968 P-D-S	2,105,128	2.50	2.25	1997 P-D	950,473	8.00	20.00
1969 P-D-S	1,817,392	2.50	3.50	1998 P-D	1,187,325	8.00	9.00
1970 P-D-S	2,038,134	2.50	13.00	1999 P-D (18 pieces)	1,243,867	14.95	18.00
1971 P-D-S	2,193,396	3.50	3.00	2000 P-D (20 pieces)	1,416,000	14.95	9.00
1972 P-D-S	2,750,000	3.50	3.00	2001 P-D (20 pieces)	1,113,623	14.95	10.00
1973 P-D-S	1,767,691	6.00	12.00	2002 P-D (20 pieces)	1,139,388	14.95	9.00
1974 P-D-S	1,975,981	6.00	4.00	2003 P-D (20 pieces)	1,002,555	14.95	12.00
1975 P-D	1,921,488	6.00	6.00	2004 P-D (22 pieces)		16.95	25.00
1776–1976 (3 pieces)	4,908,319	9.00	9.00	2005 P-D (22 pieces)		16.95	10.00

* Special Mint Set.
Note: From 2005 onward, all Mint sets have satin (rather than Uncirculated) finish.

SILVER BULLION

SILVER EAGLES

	Mintage	Unc.	PF
$1 1986	5,393,005	$11.	
$1 1986S	(1,446,778)		$22.
$1 1987	11,442,335	8.	
$1 1987S	(904,732)		22.
$1 1988	5,004,646	8.	
$1 1988S	(557,370)		50.
$1 1989	5,203,327	8.	
$1 1989S	(617,694)		30.
$1 1990	5,840,210	8.	
$1 1990S	(695,510)		27.
$1 1991	7,191,066	8.	
$1 1991S	(511,925)		35.
$1 1992	5,540,068	8.	
$1 1992S	(498,654)		32.
$1 1993	6,763,762	8.	
$1 1993P	(403,625)		110.
$1 1994	4,227,319	8.	
$1 1994P	(372,168)		120.
$1 1995	4,762,051	8.	
$1 1995P	(395,400)		100.
$1 1995W	(30,125)		1,800.
$1 1996	3,603,386	20.	
$1 1996P	(473,021)		32.
$1 1997	4,295,004	8.	
$1 1997P	(429,682)		50.
$1 1998	4,847,549	8.	
$1 1998P	(452,319)		35.
$1 1999	7,408,640	8.	
$1 1999P	(549,769)		50.
$1 2000(W)	9,239,132	8.	
$1 2000P			25.
$1 2001(W)	9,001,711	8.	
$1 2001W			25.
$1 2002(W)	10,539,026	8.	
$1 2002(P)			25.
$1 2003(W)	8,495,008	8.	
$1 2003P			25.
$1 2004(W)	8,882,754	8.	
$1 2004P			25.
$1 2005(W)		8.	
$1 2005P			25.

AMERICAN EAGLE GOLD COINS

Bullion values are based on spot gold at $425.00 per ounce, and silver at $7.00 per ounce.

Tenth-Ounce Gold

	Mintage	Unc.	PF
$5 MCMLXXXVI (1986)	912,609	$42.	
$5 MCMLXXXVII (1987)	580,266	42.	
$5 MCMLXXXVIII (1988)	159,500	100.	
$5 MCMLXXXVIII (1988)P	(143,881)		$50.
$5 MCMLXXXIX (1989)	264,790	50.	
$5 MCMLXXXIX (1989)P	(84,924)		50.
$5 MCMXC (1990)	210,210	45.	
$5 MCMXC (1990)P	(99,349)		50.
$5 MCMXCI (1991)	165,200	60.	
$5 MCMXCI (1991)P	(70,334)		50.
$5 1992	209,300	42.	
$5 1992P	(64,902)		60.
$5 1993	210,709	45.	
$5 1993P	(58,649)		50.
$5 1994	206,380	42.	
$5 1994W	(62,100)		50.
$5 1995	223,025	42.	
$5 1995W	(48,675)		50.
$5 1996	401,964	42.	
$5 1996W	(57,449)		60.
$5 1997	528,266	42.	
$5 1997W	(35,164)		65.
$5 1998	1,344,520	42.	
$5 1998W	(39,706)		50.
$5 1999	2,750,338	42.	
$5 1999W	(19,919)		50.
$5 2000	569,153	42.	
$5 2000W			50.
$5 2001	269,147	42.	
$5 2001W			50.
$5 2002	230,027	42.	
$5 2002W			50.
$5 2003	245,029	42.	
$5 2003W			50.
$5 2004	250,016	42.	
$5 2004W			50.
$5 2005		42.	
$5 2005W			50.

Quarter-Ounce Gold

	Mintage	Unc.	PF
$10 MCMLXXXVI (1986)	726,031	$110.	
$10 MCMLXXXVII (1987)	269,255	110.	
$10 MCMLXXXVIII (1988)	49,000	110.	
$10 MCMLXXXVIII (1988)P	(98,028)		$120.
$10 MCMLXXXIX (1989)	81,789	110.	
$10 MCMLXXXIX (1989)P	(53,593)		120.
$10 MCMXC (1990)	41,000	110.	
$10 MCMXC (1990)P	(62,674)		120.
$10 MCMXCI (1991)	36,100	200.	
$10 MCMXCI (1991)P	(50,480)		120.
$10 1992	59,546	110.	
$10 1992P	(42,290)		120.
$10 1993	71,864	110.	
$10 1993P	(46,271)		120.
$10 1994	72,650	110.	
$10 1994W	(47,600)		120.
$10 1995	83,752	110.	
$10 1995W	(46,825)		120.
$10 1996	60,318	110.	
$10 1996W	(37,755)		120.
$10 1997	108,805	110.	
$10 1997W	(29,984)		120.
$10 1998	309,829	110.	
$10 1998W	(29,731)		120.
$10 1999	564,232	110.	
$10 1999W	(34,410)		120.
$10 2000	128,964	110.	
$10 2000W			130.
$10 2001	71,280	110.	
$10 2001W			130.
$10 2002	62,027	110.	
$10 2002W			120.
$10 2003	74,029	110.	
$10 2003W			120.
$10 2004	72,014	110.	
$10 2004W			120.
$10 2005		110.	
$10 2005W			120.

Half-Ounce Gold

	Mintage	Unc.	PF		Mintage	Unc.	PF
$25 MCMLXXXVI (1986)	599,566	$275.		$25 MCMXC (1990)	31,000	$375.	
$25 MCMLXXXVII (1987)	131,255	225.		$25 MCMXC (1990)P	(51,636)		$260.
$25 MCMLXXXVII (1987)P	(143,398)		$260.	$25 MCMXCI (1991)	24,100	425.	
$25 MCMLXXXVIII (1988)	45,000	275.		$25 MCMXCI (1991)P	(53,125)		260.
$25 MCMLXXXVIII (1988)P	(76,528)		260.	$25 1992	54,404	275.	
				$25 1992P	(40,982)		260.
$25 MCMLXXXIX (1989)	44,829	350.		$25 1993	73,324	215.	
$25 MCMLXXXIX (1989)P	(44,264)		260.	$25 1993P	(43,319)		260.
				$25 1994	62,400	215.	
				$25 1994W	(44,100)		260.
				$25 1995	53,474	225.	
				$25 1995W	(46,200)		260.

	Mintage	Unc.	PF		Mintage	Unc.	PF
$25 1996	39,287	$360.		$25 2001	48,047	$275.	
$25 1996W	(34,769)		$260.	$25 2001W			$260.
$25 1997	79,605	215.		$25 2002	70,027	215.	
$25 1997W	(26,801)		260.	$25 2002W			260.
$25 1998	169,029	215.		$25 2003	79,029	215.	
$25 1998W	(25,550)		260.	$25 2003W			260.
$25 1999	263,013	215.		$25 2004	98,040	215.	
$25 1999W	(30,452)		260.	$25 2004W			260.
$25 2000	79,287	215.		$25 2005		215.	
$25 2000W			260.	$25 2005W			260.

One-Ounce Gold

	Mintage	Unc.	PF		Mintage	Unc.	PF
$50 MCMLXXXVI (1986)	1,362,650	$425.		$50 1993	480,192	$425.	
				$50 1993W	(34,389)		$475.
$50 MCMLXXXVI (1986)W	(446,290)		$475.	$50 1994	221,633	425.	
				$50 1994W	(46,300)		475.
$50 MCMLXXXVII (1987)	1,045,500	425.		$50 1995	200,636	425.	
				$50 1995W	(48,075)		475.
$50 MCMLXXXVII (1987)W	(147,498)		475.	$50 1996	189,148	425.	
				$50 1996W	(36,086)		475.
$50 MCMLXXXVIII (1988)	465,000	425.		$50 1997	664,508	425.	
				$50 1997W	(27,803)		475.
$50 MCMLXXXVIII (1988)W	(87,133)		475.	$50 1998	1,468,530	425.	
				$50 1998W	(26,047)		475.
$50 MCMLXXXIX (1989)	415,790	425.		$50 1999	1,505,026	425.	
				$50 1999W	(31,446)		475.
$50 MCMLXXXIX (1989)W	(53,960)		475.	$50 2000	433,319	425.	
				$50 2000W			475.
$50 MCMXC (1990)	373,210	425.		$50 2001	143,605	425.	
				$50 2001W			475.
$50 MCMXC (1990)W	(62,401)		475.	$50 2002	222,029	425.	
				$50 2002W			475.
$50 MCMXCI (1991)	243,100	425.		$50 2003	416,032	425.	
				$50 2003W			475.
$50 MCMXCI (1991)W	(50,411)		475.	$50 2004	417,019	425.	
				$50 2004W			475.
$50 1992	275,000	425.		$50 2005		425.	
$50 1992W	(44,835)		475.	$50 2005W			475.

Gold Bullion Sets

	PF		PF
1987 Gold Set. $50, 25	$700.	1996 Gold Set. $50, 25, 10, 5	$900.
1988 Gold Set. $50, 25, 10, 5	900.	1997 Gold Set. $50, 25, 10, 5	900.
1989 Gold Set. $50, 25, 10, 5	900.	1997 Impressions of Liberty Set.	
1990 Gold Set. $50, 25, 10, 5	900.	$100 platinum, $50 gold, $1 silver	1,400.
1991 Gold Set. $50, 25, 10, 5	900.	1998 Gold Set. $50, 25, 10, 5	900.
1992 Gold Set. $50, 25, 10, 5	900.	1999 Gold Set. $50, 25, 10, 5	900.
1993 Gold Set. $50, 25, 10, 5	900.	2000 Gold Set. $50, 25, 10, 5	1,000.
1993 Bicentennial Gold Set. $25, 10, 5,		2001 Gold Set. $50, 25, 10, 5	900.
$1 Silver Eagle, and medal	500.	2002 Gold Set. $50, 25, 10, 5	900.
1994 Gold Set. $50, 25, 10, 5	900.	2003 Gold Set. $50, 25, 10, 5	900.
1995 Gold Set. $50, 25, 10, 5	900.	2004 Gold Set. $50, 25, 10, 5	900.
1995 Anniversary Gold Set. $50, 25, 10,		2005 Gold Set. $50, 25, 10, 5	900.
5, and $1 Silver Eagle	2,800.		

PLATINUM BULLION

AMERICAN EAGLE PLATINUM COINS

The one-ounce American Eagle platinum coin is designated $100.00 and contains one ounce of pure platinum. Fractional denominations containing 1/2 ounce, 1/4 ounce, or 1/10 ounce are called $50, $25, and $10, respectively.

Obverse for Bullion and Proof, All Years

Reverse for Bullion, All Years; for Proof in 1997

Vistas of Liberty Reverse Designs

1998, Eagle Over New England

1999, Eagle Above Southeastern Wetlands

2000, Eagle Above America's Heartland

2001, Eagle Above America's Southwest

2002, Eagle Fishing in America's Northwest

2003, Proof Reverse
See next page for chart.

2004, Proof Reverse

2005, Proof Reverse

Tenth-Ounce Platinum

	Mintage	Unc.	PF		Mintage	Unc.	PF
1997	70,250	$85.		2001W			$100.
1997W	(37,260)		$100.	2002	23,005	$85.	
1998	39,525	100.		2002W			100.
1998W	(19,919)		100.	2003	22,007	85.	
1999	55,955	85.		2003W			120.
1999W	(19,123)		100.	2004	15,010	85.	
2000	34,027	85.		2004W			120.
2000W			100.	2005		85.	
2001	52,017	85.		2005W			100.

Quarter-Ounce Platinum

	Mintage	Unc.	PF		Mintage	Unc.	PF
1997	27,100	$220.		2001W			$230.
1997W	(18,726)		$230.	2002	27,405	$230.	
1998	38,887	220.		2002W			240.
1998W	(14,203)		230.	2003	25,207	220.	
1999	39,734	220.		2003W			250.
1999W	(13,524)		230.	2004	18,010	220.	
2000	20,054	220.		2004W			250.
2000W			230.	2005		220.	
2001	21,815	230.		2005W			240.

Half-Ounce Platinum

	Mintage	Unc.	PF		Mintage	Unc.	PF
1997	20,500	$410.		2001W			$420.
1997W	(14,637)		$420.	2002	24,005	$410.	
1998	32,419	410.		2002W			420.
1998W	(13,919)		420.	2003	17,409	410.	
1999	32,309	410.		2003W			420.
1999W	(11,098)		420.	2004	13,236	410.	
2000	18,892	410.		2004W			420.
2000W			420.	2005		410.	
2001	12,815	410.		2005W			420.

One-Ounce Platinum

	Mintage	Unc.	PF		Mintage	Unc.	PF
1997	56,000	$820.		2001W			$830.
1997W	(16,000)		$830.	2002	11,502	$820.	
1998	133,002	820.		2002W			830.
1998W	(26,047)		830.	2003	8,007	820.	
1999	56,707	820.		2003W			830.
1999W	(12,351)		830.	2004	7,009	820.	
2000	10,003	820.		2004W			830.
2000W			830.	2005		820.	
2001	14,070	820.		2005W			

Platinum Bullion Sets

	PF		PF
1997 Platinum Set. $100, 50, 25, 10	$1,500.	2002 Platinum Set. $100, 50, 25, 10	$1,500.
1998 Platinum Set. $100, 50, 25, 10	1,500.	2003 Platinum Set. $100, 50, 25, 10	1,500.
1999 Platinum Set. $100, 50, 25, 10	1,500.	2004 Platinum Set. $100, 50, 25, 10	1,500.
2000 Platinum Set. $100, 50, 25, 10	1,500.	2005 Platinum Set. $100, 50, 25, 10	1,500.
2001 Platinum Set. $100, 50, 25, 10	1,550.		

Private coins were circulated in most instances because of a shortage of regular coinage. Some numismatists use the general term *private gold* to refer to coins struck outside of the United States Mint. In the sense that no state or territory had authority to coin money, *private gold* simply refers to those interesting necessity pieces of various shapes, denominations, and degrees of intrinsic worth which were circulated in isolated areas of our country by individuals, assayers, bankers, etc. Some will use the words "Territorial" and "State" to cover certain issues because they were coined and circulated in a territory or state. While the state of California properly sanctioned the ingots stamped by F.D. Kohler as state assayer, in no instance were any of the gold pieces struck by authority of any of the territorial governments.

The stamped ingots put out by Augustus Humbert, the United States assayer of gold, were not recognized at the United States Mint as an official issue of coins, but simply as ingots, though Humbert placed the value and fineness on the pieces as an official agent of the federal government.

TEMPLETON REID
Georgia Gold 1830

The first private gold coinage under the Constitution was struck by Templeton Reid, a jeweler and gunsmith, in Milledgeville, Georgia in July 1830. To be closer to the mines, he moved to Gainesville, where most of his coins were made. Although weights were accurate, Reid's assays were not, and his coins were slightly short of claimed value. Accordingly, he was severely attacked in the newspapers and soon lost the public's confidence.

	VG	VF
1830, $2.50		$30,000.
1830, $5		65,000.
1830, TEN DOLLARS	$65,000.	
(No Date), TEN DOLLARS	55,000.	

California Gold 1849

1849, TEN DOLLAR CALIFORNIA GOLD (Smithsonian Collection) *(unique)*. . . . .

THE BECHTLERS
RUTHERFORD COUNTY, NC, 1830–1852

Two skilled German metallurgists, Christopher Bechtler and his son August, and later Christopher Bechtler, Junior, a nephew of Christopher the elder, operated a private mint at Rutherfordton, North Carolina. Rutherford County, in which Rutherfordton is located, was the principal source of the nation's gold supply from 1790 to 1848.

Christopher Bechtler

	VF	EF	AU	Unc.
ONE DOLLAR CAROLINA, 28 G, N Reversed	$900.	$1,600.	$2,100.	$4,250.
ONE GOLD DOLLAR N. CAROLINA, 28.G, No Star.	1,450.	2,750.	4,000.	6,500.
ONE GOLD DOLLAR N. CAROLINA, 30.G.	925.	1,650.	2,100.	3,700.
2.50 CAROLINA, 67.G., 21 CARATS.	2,100.	3,200.	4,200.	6,500.
2.50 CAROLINA, 70.G., 20 CARATS	2,100.	3,400.	4,200.	6,750.
2.50 GEORGIA, 64.G, 22 CARATS	2,200.	3,600.	4,500.	7,000.
2.50 NORTH CAROLINA, 75.G., 20 CARATS.				
RUTHERFORD in a Circle. Border of Large Beads	4,500.	6,500.	8,000.	13,000.
2.50 NORTH CAROLINA, Without 75.G.	4,500.	6,500.	8,000.	13,000.

Without 150.G.

	VF	EF	AU	Unc.
5 DOLLARS CAROLINA, RUTHERFORD, 140.G., 20 CARATS. AUGUST 1, 1834,				
Plain Edge	$2,400.	$4,000.	$5,750.	$7,500.
Reeded Edge	3,000.	4,250.	6,000.	8,000.
5 DOLLARS BECHTLER, Without Star and C	—			
5 DOLLARS CAROLINA GOLD, 134.G., 21 CARATS,	2,200.	3,400.	5,200.	6,750.
With Star (Obverse of A.BECHTLER as Shown)				
5 DOLLARS GEORGIA GOLD, RUTHERFORD, 128.G., 22 CARATS	2,400.	3,600.	5,100.	7,750.
5 DOLLARS GEORGIA GOLD, RUTHERF., 128.G., 22 CARATS	2,400.	3,600.	5,100.	7,750.
5 DOLLARS CAROLINA GOLD, RUTHERF., 140.G., 20 CARATS, AUGUST 1, 1834	2,800.	4,500.	5,500.	7,750.
Similar, But "20" Distant From Carats	3,750.	5,200.	7,500.	—
5 DOLLARS NORTH CAROLINA GOLD, 150.G., 20 CARATS	4,500.	7,000.	9,000.	16,000.
Similar, Without 150.G.	5,000.	7,500.	11,000.	17,500.

August Bechtler

	VF	EF	AU	Unc.
1 DOL:, CAROLINA GOLD, 27.G., 21.C.	$550.	$900.	$1,200.	$2,000.
5 DOLLARS, CAROLINA GOLD, 134.G., 21 CARATS	1,900.	3,400.	4,500.	7,000.

	VF	EF	AU	Unc.
5 DOLLARS, CAROLINA GOLD, 134.G.; 21 CARATS	$3,700.	$4,750.	$6,100.	$9,500.
5 DOLLARS, CAROLINA GOLD, 128.G., 22 CARATS	3,700.	4,750.	6,100.	9,500.

NORRIS, GREGG & NORRIS
SAN FRANCISCO 1849

These pieces are considered the first of the California private gold coins. A newspaper account dated May 31, 1849, described a five-dollar gold coin struck at Benicia City, though with the imprint San Francisco, and the private stamp of Norris, Gregg & Norris.

	F	VF	EF	AU	Unc.
1849, HALF EAGLE, Plain Edge	$1,900.	$2,750.	$4,500.	$7,500.	$13,000.
1849, HALF EAGLE, Reeded Edge	1,900.	2,750.	4,500.	7,500.	13,000.
1850, HALF EAGLE, With STOCKTON Beneath Date *(unique)*					

MOFFAT & CO.
SAN FRANCISCO 1849–1853

The firm of Moffat & Company was perhaps the most important of the California private coiners. The assay office they conducted was semi-official in character, and successors to this firm later sold its facilities to the Treasury Department, which used them to create the San Francisco Mint.

In June or July, 1849, Moffat & Co. began to issue small rectangular pieces of gold in values from $9.43 to $264. The $9.43, $14.25, and $16.00 varieties are the only types known today.

	EF
$9.43 Ingot *(unique)*...	—
$14.25 Ingot *(unique)*...	—
$16.00 Ingot	$17,000.

The dies for the $10 piece were cut by Albert Kuner. The words MOFFAT & CO. appear on Liberty's coronet instead of the word LIBERTY as in regular United States issues.

	F	VF	EF	AU	Unc.
1849, FIVE DOL. *(all varieties)*	$700.	$950.	$1,600.	$2,700.	$4,600.
1850, FIVE DOL. *(all varieties)*	700.	950.	1,600.	2,700.	4,600.
1849, TEN DOL.	1,200.	1,650.	3,200.	5,500.	8,500.
1849, TEN D.	1,300.	1,700.	3,500.	5,750.	8,000.

UNITED STATES ASSAY OFFICE
Augustus Humbert
United States Assayer of Gold, 1851

When Augustus Humbert was appointed United States Assayer, he placed his name and the government imprint on the ingots of gold issued by Moffat & Co. The assay office, a provisional government mint, was a temporary expedient to accommodate the Californians until the establishment of a permanent branch mint. The $50 gold piece was accepted as legal tender on a par with standard U.S. gold coins.

Lettered Edge Varieties

	F	VF	EF	AU	Unc.
1851, 50 D C 880 THOUS., No 50 on Reverse. Sunk in Edge: AUGUSTUS HUMBERT UNITED STATES ASSAYER OF GOLD CALIFORNIA 1851	$4,500.	$6,000.	$10,000.	$17,000.	—

50 on Reverse

	F	VF	EF	AU	Unc.
1851, 50 D C, Similar to Last Variety, but 50 on Reverse	$5,000.	$6,000.	$10,000.	$18,000.	—
1851, 50 D C, 887 THOUS., With 50 on Reverse	5,000.	6,000.	10,000.	17,500.	—

Reeded Edge Varieties

	F	VF	EF	AU	Unc.
1851, FIFTY DOLLS, 880 THOUS., "Target" Reverse	$3,500.	$4,500.	$6,500.	$10,000.	$16,000.
1851, FIFTY DOLLS, 887 THOUS., "Target" Reverse	3,500.	4,500.	6,500.	10,000.	16,000.
1852, FIFTY DOLLS, 887 THOUS.	3,500.	4,500.	6,500.	10,000.	17,000.

Moffat & Co. proceeded in January, 1852 to issue a new ten-dollar piece bearing the stamp MOFFAT & CO.

	F	VF	EF	AU	Unc.
1852, TEN D. MOFFAT & CO	$1,000.	$2,000.	$3,300.	$8,500.	—

	F	VF	EF	AU	Unc.
1852, TEN DOLS., 1852, 2 Over 1	$700.	$1,300.	$2,400.	$4,000.	—
1852, TEN DOLS.	650.	1,100.	1,800.	3,000.	$5,500.

	F	VF	EF	AU	Unc.
1852, TWENTY DOLS., 1852, 2 Over 1	$1,700.	$2,400.	$4,000.	$8,500.	—

United States Assay Office of Gold – 1852

The firm of Moffat & Co. was reorganized as Curtis, Perry & Ward, which assumed the government contract to conduct the United States Assay Office of Gold.

	F	VF	EF	AU	Unc.
1852, FIFTY DOLLS., 887 THOUS.	$4,000.	$4,500.	$6,500.	$9,500.	$17,000.
1852, FIFTY DOLLS., 900 THOUS.	4,000.	4,500.	6,750.	9,800.	22,000.

	F	VF	EF	AU	Unc.
1852, TEN DOLS., 884 THOUS.	$650.	$1,000.	$1,500.	$2,500.	$5,500.
1853, TEN D., 884 THOUS.	1,650.	2,600.	5,750.	9,000.	—
1853, TEN D., 900 THOUS.	1,300.	1,900.	3,200.	4,400.	—
1853, TWENTY D., 884 THOUS.	2,000.	4,000.	6,000.	10,000.	—
1853, TWENTY D., 900 THOUS.	800.	1,200.	1,500.	2,300.	4,000.

United States Assay Office of Gold – Moffat

The last Moffat issue was an 1853 $20 piece that is very similar to the U.S. double eagle of that period. It was struck after the retirement of John L. Moffat from Moffat & Company.

	F	VF	EF	AU	Unc.
1853, TWENTY D.	$1,300.	$1,750.	$2,500.	$3,750.	$6,500.

CINCINNATI MINING & TRADING CO. (1849)

The origin and location of this company are unknown. It might have been organized in Ohio, and conducted business in California.

	EF	Unc.
1849, FIVE DOLLARS	—	—
1849, TEN DOLLARS	—	—

MASSACHUSETTS AND CALIFORNIA COMPANY

This company was believed to have been organized in Northampton, Massachusetts, in May 1849.

	F	VF	EF
1849, FIVE D.	$35,000	$50,000	$80,000

MINERS' BANK
SAN FRANCISCO 1849

The institution of Wright & Co., exchange brokers located in Portsmouth Square, San Francisco, was known as the Miners' Bank.

A $10 piece was issued in the autumn of 1849, but the coins were not readily accepted because they were worth less than face value.

	VF	EF	AU	Unc.
(1849) TEN. D.	$4,250	$8,000	$12,000	$25,000

J.S. ORMSBY
SACRAMENTO 1849

The initials J.S.O., which appear on certain issues of California privately coined gold pieces, represent the firm of J.S. Ormsby & Co. The firm struck both $5 and $10 denominations, all undated.

	VF
(1849) 5 DOLLS *(unique)*.	—
(1849) 10 DOLLS *(4 known)*	—

PACIFIC COMPANY, SAN FRANCISCO 1849

The origin of the Pacific Company is uncertain. All data regarding the firm are based on conjecture.

Edgar H. Adams wrote that he believed that the coins bearing the stamp of the Pacific Company were produced by the coining firm of Broderick and Kohler. The coins were probably hand struck with the aid of a sledgehammer.

	EF
1849, 1 DOLLAR *(2 known)*	—
1849, 5 DOLLARS.	$75,000.
1849, 10 DOLLARS.	$100,000.

F.D. KOHLER
CALIFORNIA STATE ASSAYER 1850

The State Assay Office was authorized on April 12, 1850. That year, Governor Burnett appointed F.D. Kohler, who thereupon sold his assaying business to Baldwin & Co. Kohler served at both the San Francisco and Sacramento offices. The State Assay Offices were discontinued when the U.S. Assay Office was established, on February 1, 1851.

	EF
$36.55 Sacramento	—
$37.31 San Francisco	—
$40.07 San Francisco	—
$45.34 San Francisco	—
$50.00 San Francisco	—
$54.09 San Francisco	—

DUBOSQ & COMPANY
SAN FRANCISCO 1850

Theodore Dubosq, a Philadelphia jeweler, took melting and coining machinery to San Francisco in 1849.

	VF
1850, FIVE D.	$25,000.
1850, TEN D.	30,000.

BALDWIN & CO.
SAN FRANCISCO 1850

George C. Baldwin and Thomas S. Holman were in the jewelry business in San Francisco and were known as Baldwin & Co. They were the successors to F.D. Kohler & Co., taking over its machinery and other equipment in May 1850.

	F	VF	EF	AU	Unc.
1850, FIVE DOL.	$2,500.	$3,500.	$6,500.	$8,000.	$12,000.
1850, TEN DOLLARS, Horseman type	13,000.	25,000.	35,000.	45,000.	55,000.

	F	VF	EF	AU	Unc.
1851, TEN D.	$3,500.	$5,250.	$12,000.	$15,000.	—

		VF	EF	AU	Unc.
1851, TWENTY D.		$40,000	$80,000	—	—

SHULTZ & COMPANY
SAN FRANCISCO 1851

The firm, located in back of Baldwin's establishment, operated a brass foundry beginning in 1851. Judge G.W. Shultz and William T. Garratt were partners in the enterprise.

	F	VF
1851, FIVE D.	$12,000	$22,000

DUNBAR & COMPANY
SAN FRANCISCO 1851

Edward E. Dunbar operated the California Bank in San Francisco. Dunbar later returned to New York and organized the famous Continental Bank Note Co.

	EF
1851, FIVE D.	$60,000.

WASS, MOLITOR & CO.
SAN FRANCISCO 1852–1855

The gold-smelting and assaying plant of Wass, Molitor & Co. was operated by two Hungarian patriots, Count S.C. Wass and A.P. Molitor. They maintained an excellent laboratory and complete apparatus for analysis and coinage of gold.

	F	VF	EF	AU	Unc.
1852, FIVE DOLLARS	$1,600.	$2,500.	$4,700.	$7,500.	$15,000.

Large Head   **Small Head**

	F	VF	EF	AU	Unc.
1852, TEN D., Large Head.	$950.	$1,600.	$2,750.	$3,750.	$5,500.
1852, TEN D., Small Head.	1,700.	3,000.	5,500.	8,500.	—
1855, TEN D.	4,500.	7,500.	8,700.	13,000.	—

Large Head   **Small Head**

	F	VF	EF	AU	Unc.
1855, TWENTY DOL., Large Head.	—	—	—	—	—
1855, TWENTY DOL., Small Head.	$4,500.	$7,500.	$14,000.	$30,000.	$50,000.

	F	VF	EF	AU	Unc.
1855, 50 DOLLARS	$9,000.	$14,000.	$20,000.	$35,000.	$80,000.

KELLOGG & CO.
SAN FRANCISCO 1854–1855

When the U.S. Assay Office ceased operations, a period ensued during which no private firm was striking gold. The new San Francisco branch mint did not produce coins for some months after Curtis & Perry took the government contract. The lack of coin was again keenly felt by businessmen, who petitioned Kellogg & Richter to "supply the vacuum" by issuing private coin. Their plea was soon answered, for on February 9, 1854, Kellogg & Co. placed their first $20 piece in circulation.

	F	VF	EF	AU	Unc.	PF
1854, TWENTY D.	$900.	$1,400.	$2,000.	$3,500.	$8,000.	
1855, TWENTY D.	900.	1,500.	2,100.	3,750.	9,000.	
1855, FIFTY DOLLS.						—

OREGON EXCHANGE COMPANY
OREGON CITY 1849
The Beaver Coins of Oregon

On February 16, 1849, the legislature passed an act providing for a mint and specified $5 and $10 gold coins without alloy. Oregon City, the largest city in the territory with a population of about 1,000, was designated as the location for the mint. At the time this act was passed, Oregon had been brought into the United States as a territory by act of Congress. When the new governor arrived on March 2, he declared the coinage act unconstitutional.

	F	VF	EF	AU	Unc.
1849, 5 D.	$8,500.	$15,000.	$20,000.	$40,000.	—
1849, TEN.D	18,000.	36,000.	50,000.	90,000.	—

MORMON GOLD PIECES
SALT LAKE CITY, UTAH, 1849–1860

Brigham Young was the instigator of the coinage system and personally supervised the mint, which was housed in a little adobe building in Salt Lake City. The mint was inaugurated in 1849 as a public convenience.

	F	VF	EF	AU	Unc.
1849, TWO.AND.HALF.DO.	$3,500.	$6,000.	$8,500.	$15,000.	—
1849, FIVE.DOLLARS	3,200.	5,000.	6,000.	10,000.	$19,000.

	F	VF	EF
1849, TEN.DOLLARS	$65,000.	$85,000.	$120,000.
1849, TWENTY.DOLLARS	26,000.	45,000.	70,000.

	F	VF	EF	AU	Unc.
1850, FIVE DOLLARS	$3,500.	$5,500.	$6,500.	$13,000.	$25,000.
1860, 5.D.	5,500.	9,500.	15,000.	24,000.	35,000.

COLORADO GOLD PIECES
Clark, Gruber & Co.
Denver 1860–1861

Clark, Gruber & Co. was a well-known private minting firm in Denver, Colorado, in the early 1860s.

 (within)

	F	VF	EF	AU	Unc.
1860, 2 1/2 D.	$750.	$1,100.	$1,750.	$3,000.	$6,000.
1860, FIVE D.	850.	1,500.	1,800.	3,500.	6,500.

	F	VF	EF	AU	Unc.
1860, TEN D.	$3,500.	$4,500.	$6,500.	$10,000.	$18,000.
1860, TWENTY D.	18,000.	35,000.	60,000.	80,000.	—

	F	VF	EF	AU	Unc.
1861, 2 1/2 D.	$800.	$1,200.	$1,600.	$3,000.	$8,000.
1861, FIVE D.	1,000.	1,500.	2,500.	4,000.	16,000.
1861, TEN D.	1,000.	1,600.	2,750.	4,000.	15,000.

	F	VF	EF	AU
1861, TWENTY D	$3,500.	$7,000.	$14,000.	$27,000.

John Parsons & Company
Tarryall Mines – Colorado, 1861

Very little is known regarding the mint of John Parsons and Co., although it is reasonably certain that it operated in the South Park section of Park County, Colorado, near the original town of Tarryall, in the summer of 1861.

	VF
(1861) Undated 2 1/2 D.	$75,000
(1861) Undated FIVE D.	90,000

J.J. Conway & Co.
Georgia Gulch, Colorado, 1861

Records show that the Conway mint operated for a short while in 1861. As in all gold mining areas, the value of gold dust caused disagreement among the merchants and the miners. The firm of J.J. Conway & Co. solved this difficulty by bringing out its gold pieces in August 1861.

	VF
(1861) Undated 2 1/2 DOLL'S	$50,000
(1861) Undated FIVE DOLLARS	75,000
(1861) Undated TEN DOLLARS	—

CALIFORNIA SMALL-DENOMINATION GOLD

There was a scarcity of small coins during the California Gold Rush and, starting in 1852, quarter, half, and dollar pieces were privately minted from native gold to alleviate the shortage. The need and acceptability of these pieces declined after 1856 and they then became popular as souvenirs. Authentic pieces all have CENTS, DOLLAR, or an abbreviation thereof on the reverse. The tokens are much less valuable. Modern restrikes and replicas have no numismatic value.

The values in the following charts are only for coins made before 1883 with the denomination on the reverse expressed as CENTS, DOL., DOLL., or DOLLAR.

Quarter Dollar – Octagonal

	EF-40	AU-50	MS-60
Liberty Head	$55.	$75.	$115.
Indian Head	65.	85.	125.
Washington Head	275.	400.	450.

Quarter Dollar – Round

	EF-40	AU-50	MS-60
Liberty Head	$55.	$75.	$115.
Indian Head	75.	100.	150.
Washington Head	325.	450.	550.

Half Dollar – Octagonal

	EF-40	AU-50	MS-60
Liberty Head	$75.	$110.	$135.
Liberty Head/Eagle	400.	600.	900.
Indian Head	125.	140.	200.

Half Dollar – Round

	EF-40	AU-50	MS-60
Liberty Head	$75.	$120.	$150.
Indian Head	100.	125.	150.

Dollar – Octagonal

	EF-40	AU-50	MS-60
Liberty Head	$200.	$250.	$300.
Liberty Head/Eagle	700.	1,200.	1,700.
Indian Head	250.	350.	525.

Dollar – Round

	EF-40	AU-50	MS-60
Liberty Head	$700.	$850.	$1,250.
Indian Head	700.	800.	1,450.

HARD TIMES TOKENS (1832–1844)

During the financial crises of 1832 to 1844 many government coins were hoarded, and privately made tokens were used out of necessity. The so-called Hard Times tokens of this period were slightly smaller and lighter than normal large cents. They were made of copper or brass and are of two general groups: political tokens whose theme centered on President Jackson's fight against the United States Bank, and tradesmen's cards, issued by merchants. Many different designs and varieties exist.

	VF	EF
Hard Times Tokens, 1832–1844, most common pieces	$4.	$15.

CIVIL WAR TOKENS (1860s)

Civil War tokens are generally divided into two groups: tradesmen's tokens, and anonymously issued pieces with political or patriotic themes. They came into existence only because of the scarcity of government coins and disappeared as soon as the bronze coins of 1864 met the public demand for small copper change.

These tokens vary greatly in composition and design. A number were more or less faithful imitations of the copper-nickel cent. A few of this type have the word "not" in very small letters above the words ONE CENT.

	F	VF	EF	Unc.
Copper or Brass Tokens	$5.	$6.	$10.	$20.
Nickel or German Silver Tokens	12.	20.	30.	60.
White Metal Tokens	14.	23.	35.	65.
Copper-Nickel Tokens	25.	35.	45.	90.
Silver Tokens	60.	90.	140.	225.

Common-date silver coins are valued according to the price of silver bullion. In recent years the price of silver bullion has been subject to extreme fluctuation. Therefore, when you read this it is highly probable that the current bullion price may differ from the prevailing market price used in tabulating valuations of many 19th- and 20th-century silver coins (priced in italics) listed in this edition. The following chart will help to determine the approximate bullion value of these coins at various price levels. Or, the approximate value may be calculated by multiplying the current spot price of silver times the content for each coin as indicated below. Dealers generally purchase common silver coins at 15% below bullion value, and sell them at 15% above bullion value.

Bullion Values of Silver Coins

Silver Price Per Ounce	Wartime Nickel .05626 oz.	Dime .07234 oz.	Quarter .18084 oz.	Half Dollar .36169 oz.	Silver Clad Half Dollar .14792 oz.	Silver Dollar .77344 oz.
$5.00	$.28	$.36	$.90	$1.81	$.74	$3.87
5.50	.31	.40	1.00	1.99	.81	4.26
6.00	.34	.44	1.09	2.17	.89	4.64
6.50	.36	.47	1.18	2.35	.96	5.03
7.00	.40	.51	1.27	2.53	1.04	5.42
7.50	.42	.55	1.36	2.72	1.11	5.80
8.00	.45	.58	1.45	2.90	1.19	6.19

The value of common-date gold coins listed in this book may be affected by the rise or fall in the price of gold bullion. Nearly all U.S. gold coins have an additional premium value beyond their bullion content, and thus are not subject to the minor variations described for silver coins. The premium amount is not necessarily tied to the bullion price of gold, but is usually determined by supply and demand levels for actual gold coins occurring in the numismatic marketplace. Because these factors can vary significantly, there is no reliable formula for calculating "percentage above bullion" prices that would remain accurate over time. For this reason the chart below lists bullion values based on gold content only. Consult your nearest coin dealer to ascertain current premium prices.

Bullion Values of Gold Coins

Gold Price Per Ounce	$5.00 Liberty Head 1839–1908 Indian Head 1908–1929 .24187 oz.	$10.00 Liberty Head 1838–1907 Indian Head 1907–1933 .48375 oz.	$20.00 1849–1933 .96750 oz.
$275.00	$66.50	$133.03	$266.07
300.00	72.56	145.13	290.25
325.00	78.60	157.22	314.44
350.00	84.65	169.31	338.63
375.00	90.70	181.40	362.81
400.00	96.75	193.50	387.00
425.00	102.80	205.60	411.19
450.00	108.84	217.69	435.38
475.00	114.89	229.78	459.56

Note: The U.S. bullion coins first issued in 1986 are unlike the older regular issues. They contain the following amounts of pure metal: silver $1, 1 oz.; gold $50, 1 oz.; gold $25, 1/2 oz.; gold $10, 1/4 oz.; gold $5, 1/10 oz.

INDEX